Ayşe Gülnev Osmanoğlu is a member of the Ottoman Imperial family, being descended from Sultan Murad V through her grandfather, and from Sultan Mehmed V (Mehmed Reşad) through her grandmother. After reading History and Politics at the University of Exeter, she obtained an M.A. in Turkish Studies from SOAS, University of London, where she specialised in Ottoman History. She lives in the UK with her husband and five children.

THE GILDED CAGE ON THE BOSPHORUS

THE OTTOMANS : THE STORY OF A FAMILY

Ayşe Gülnev Osmanoğlu

HANEDAN PRESS

The Gilded Cage on the Bosphorus
The Ottomans: The Story of a Family

Copyright © Ayşe Osmanoğlu, 2020

ISBN 978-1-9163614-0-9

First published in 2020 by
HANEDAN PRESS
hanedanpress@gmail.com

Edited by John Shakespeare Dyson
Cover Design by Aimee Coveney, Bookollective
Typeset by Geoff Fisher in Times New Roman
Cover photograph of the Çırağan Palace from the Pera Museum;
reproduced by kind permission of the Suna and
İnan Kıraç Foundation

*In memory of all those who once lived as prisoners in the
Çırağan Palace – in particular, His Imperial Majesty
Sultan Murad V. You will never be forgotten, ghosts
and shadows: your memory lives on in the hearts
and souls of your descendants ...*

CONTENTS

ix

FOREWORD

by
His Imperial Highness Prince Osman Selahaddin Osmanoğlu

The Ottoman Dynasty is an exceptional family in that it ruled uninterruptedly for 625 years, from the thirteenth century until the twentieth, each new sultan being descended from a previous one through the male line. For over 400 years the Ottoman sultans also held the office of Caliph of Islam. During most of that time the Ottoman Empire spanned three continents; at its apogee, it covered a vast expanse of territory which is currently occupied wholly or partially by thirty-seven independent nations.

This book covers the early years of the twentieth century and is specifically about the family of Sultan Murad V, who was the thirty-third sovereign of the Ottoman Dynasty. His reign of only three months was the shortest among those of the thirty-six sultans of the dynasty. In August 1876 his brother Sultan Abdülhamid II replaced him as Sultan, and thereafter kept him and his entire family confined within the walls of the Çırağan Palace for twenty-eight years – until the death of the former Sultan Murad in 1904. The Çırağan Palace was therefore the home of many of the members of my family who were alive in those times, and it was here that both my grandfather and my father were born. During the nineteenth, twentieth and twenty-first centuries, descendants of Sultan Murad have also held numerous weddings and other ceremonies and celebrations there.

It is with great pride that I write these lines as a Foreword to my daughter Ayşe Gülnev's first book. She has always been interested in history in general, and in Ottoman history in particular. During her childhood, she enjoyed being in the company of her grandparents and soaking up first-hand information from them – both at our home in England and on her visits to them in Egypt and Turkey. Later on, she read History and Politics at university, going on to do postgraduate studies in Ottoman History. I would like to assure the reader that the characters in this book are real people, that the dates mentioned are accurate, and that the historical events described are genuine occurrences.

Ayşe is a devoted and loving mother to five wonderful children, and I am therefore all the more delighted that she has been able to apply herself to the task of recording the lives of our immediate forebears and the times through which they lived – a task which involved a great deal of detailed research.

Thanks to this exhaustive and thorough research, as well as to her unique position as a member of the Ottoman family, I think my daughter has presented as accurate a picture of the Ottomans in the first decade of the twentieth century as you are ever likely to find. I am particularly grateful to her for bringing home to the reader the fact that these people – our ancestors – were not just names in a history book, but living, breathing human beings who experienced real tragedy in their lives, and did their best to rise above it.

Osman Selahaddin Osmanoğlu
May 2020

PREFACE

Many books have been written about the twilight years of the Ottoman Empire, but few tell the intimate story of the members of the Imperial family. Prompted by a desire to keep their memory alive and to light a spark of interest in the hearts of my five children – a spark which I hope will one day develop into a flame of pride in their ancestry – I began to write this account of Sultan Murad V and his descendants, who for many long years were held captive in the Çırağan Palace by the shores of the Bosphorus.

I wrote the first word of this book on 13th October 2016, the 113th anniversary of my grandfather's birth. It was as though he took me by the hand, led me to my desk and opened my laptop for me – before whispering into my ear the words I was to type. During the months I spent working on this narrative, I could sense the constant presence of my beloved *Dede* as he helped me explore the realities of his life and times so that these could be recorded for his great-grandchildren.

The result is neither an historical novel, nor an academic study – it seems to me to sit somewhere in between! I am fully aware that I have only lightly sketched the characters, as it somehow felt disloyal and disrespectful to even consider embellishing or misrepresenting their true natures; and I certainly do not claim to be a History professor. In addition I make it quite clear where my sympathies lie, and make no apologies for this: I would ask the reader to remember that I am writing about my own family, and essentially for my own family, so I trust that a little bias will be thought permissible!

There are three people I would like to thank for giving me their love and support while I was writing this book. My father was extremely generous with both his time and his advice, never tiring when I turned to him with a question; his help and his knowledge were invaluable. I am also grateful to my mother, who kindly undertook the laborious task of proofreading the initial draft, and to my husband for the enthusiasm he expressed for this project; without his encouragement, I would certainly never have begun it!

In addition, I would like to extend my sincere thanks to Ekrem Ekinci, my learned and endlessly knowledgeable *hodja*; his willingness to share with me his expertise in the matter of my family's history has allowed me to paint a far more accurate picture of the people and events in this story than I had ever hoped. I am likewise indebted to Hüseyin Birol, my father's friend and now mine, whose remarkable familiarity with the various palaces and mansions in which members of my family lived – a familiarity that extends even to the details of their exteriors and interiors – has enabled me to describe them with a faithfulness that I would never have thought possible. My beautiful cousin Leïla Samy Beggin proofread the penultimate draft, and her helpful advice and suggestions are much appreciated. As a teenager, I always looked up to her, and that admiration has not diminished: she continues to inspire me.Lastly, of course, my thanks must go to John Shakespeare Dyson, my diligent, meticulous and extremely thorough editor; not only did his patient attention to detail and his ability to use the English language in an impeccable manner enhance my writing, but he also pushed me to look more deeply into the hearts and minds of my characters, encouraging me to be more imaginative in my treatment of their psychology.

My greatest debt of gratitude, however, will always be to my grandparents, who shared with me the stories of their unique lives and their memories of a bygone age; it was they who taught me to have pride in being an Ottoman, to love Turkey – my homeland – and to believe in Islam. I love and miss them both.

It is my hope that readers will enjoy this journey back in time to the splendour of Imperial İstanbul, that lost world ruled over by the House of Osman. I hope, too, that during the hours they spend in their company they will feel able to open their hearts a little to the family of Sultan Murad V.

Ayşe Gülnev Osmanoğlu
May 2020

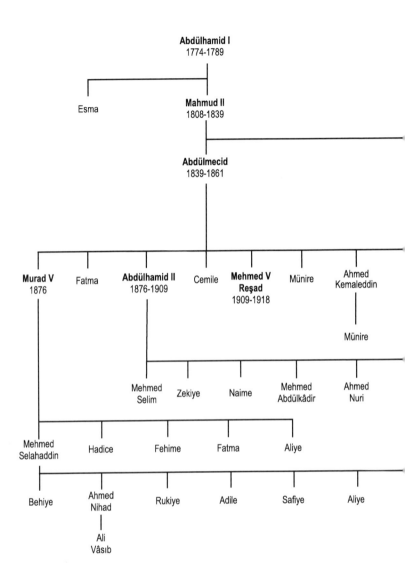

OTTOMAN FAMILY TREE

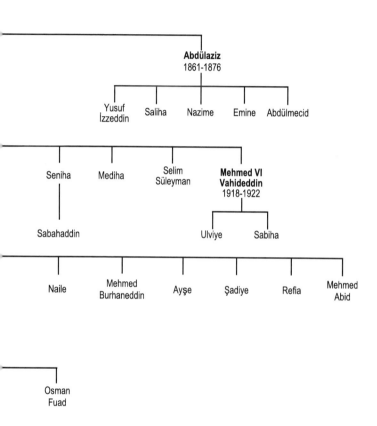

This family tree only shows members of the Imperial Ottoman family who are mentioned in the book, and is not intended to be fully comprehensive.

MURAD V'S FAMILY TREE

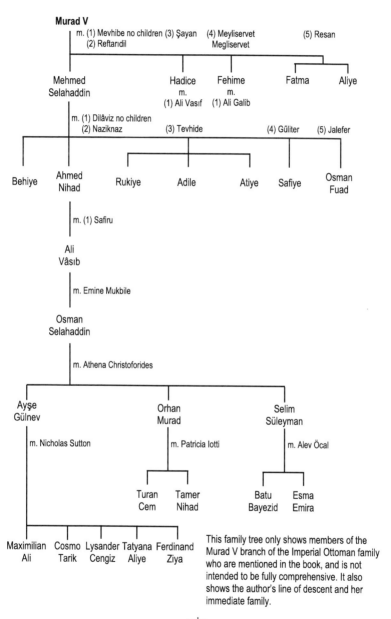

This family tree only shows members of the Murad V branch of the Imperial Ottoman family who are mentioned in the book, and is not intended to be fully comprehensive. It also shows the author's line of descent and her immediate family.

PART I

CHAPTER ONE

Birth of a Prince

Tuesday 13ᵗʰ October 1903

"IT's a boy! It's a healthy baby boy!" announced Hayriye Hanım.

Seconds earlier, at the exact moment of his birth, the midwife had recited the Shahada, the profession of faith: "I bear witness that I will worship no god but Allah, and that Muhammed is His Messenger."

The Lady Safiru fell back against the warm walnut of the birthing chair, oblivious to all the activity surrounding her. Hayriye washed the baby with warm, salty water from a silver bowl held by her apprentice. "May his voice be beautiful," she said as she cut the umbilical cord; then she wrapped it in a white cloth and placed it inside a small box. She knew the family would want to bury it in an appropriate place later.

An embroidered bag containing a miniature Quran was hung at the head of the bed, while an onion and slices of garlic, wrapped in a piece of red muslin covered with blue glass beads, were secured to the lower end. A needle was discreetly slipped under the bottom pillow. The woody aroma of sandalwood and musk filled the room as incense burned in the bronze urn, exquisitely inlaid with eau de nil enamel

1

and set with diamonds, which sat on a nearby table. Every precaution had been taken to ward off the evil eye, and to protect Safiru and her son from the feared 'Mother-Snatcher' and 'Baby-Snatcher' who lurked in corners at such times. Finally, a small silver mirror, symbolising a bright new life, was placed on the table next to the bed. After cleaning Safiru, the attendants gently helped her into her bed; then they offered her some sweet, plump dates to soothe her after her long and difficult labour.

Safiru lay back, her long brown hair strewn wildly across the embroidered silk pillows. A single tear of joy escaped from between her long lashes and trickled slowly down her flushed cheek. She felt exhausted. Her pains had been intense and almost constant for the last few hours before the birth – but now they were over, and she thanked Allah for the safe delivery of her child.

The little prince was dressed in a cream-coloured linen tunic, and his feet and shoulders bound with strips of soft muslin. A miniature crocheted cap, adorned with a silk pearl tassel and a gold coin minted during the short reign of Sultan Murad V, was placed on his head. On hearing that Safiru had gone into labour, Naziknaz Hanımefendi, grandmother of the newborn baby, had written a verse of the Quran on a tiny piece of blue satin, and this was now pinned to the cap. Hayriye then swaddled the baby in a square of blue silk followed by a blanket of embroidered green gauze, and tied a thin red ribbon to one corner of the blanket as yet another precaution against evil spirits. Safiru held out her arms to hold her little prince, and Hayriye gently placed him against her breast.

"Alhamdulillah! He is a beautiful, strong child, Your Highness," said Hayriye. "A perfect Ottoman prince. I pray that Allah may grant him the blessing of growing up with

2

both his parents by his side, and that he may enjoy good health and liberty while on this earth. I trust the Lady Safiru is recovering well?"

Hayriye had arrived at the Çırağan Palace very early that morning, long before the sun had risen and the birds had begun to stir in the gardens of the palace by the shores of the Bosphorus. She had been sent on the orders of Sultan Abdülhamid II as soon as word had reached Yıldız Palace, his secluded – and, he hoped and prayed, secure – residence at the top of the long, wooded hill behind Çırağan, that a midwife was needed in his elder brother's household down below on the waterfront. Hayriye had been a midwife since girlhood, just like her mother and grandmother before her. She had risen to the position of Midwife to the Imperial House, and as such had delivered many Ottoman princes and princesses. Although she was now an old woman, her devotion to the family of the deposed Sultan Murad V remained undiminished. Hayriye had first come to Çırağan over twenty years before to deliver Sultan Murad's third daughter, Princess Fatma, and since then had returned several times to deliver other members of the family – one of whom had been the father of this new baby boy. Over the years her hair had turned grey and wiry, and her face was now etched with deep lines, but her voice and hands were still as soft and gentle as those of a young girl.

Safiru smiled, her pale blue eyes not leaving the face of her newborn child. "Hayriye Hanım, I thank you for your help in bringing my son into the world." She could not take her eyes off the baby boy sleeping in her arms, and felt as if her heart would burst with love for him. Her happiness was now complete.

Safiru had entered the harem of the former Ottoman Sultan Murad V when very young. She remembered little of her old life beyond the walls of the Çırağan Palace. Her family came from a small Moslem village in the foothills of the Caucasus Mountains, on the north-eastern shores of the Black Sea. They had fled from the horrific invasion of the merciless Russian army to the safety of the Ottoman Empire, and had eventually found refuge in the bustling town of Adapazarı, a day's journey to the east of İstanbul. Life there had been a struggle for her parents; and so, desperate to give their two daughters a life in which they would have more security and comfort than they themselves had had, they had taken Safiru and her sister to İstanbul to find a position for them in the harem of one of the members of the Imperial family.

The sisters had initially entered the harem of Sultan Abdülhamid II at Yıldız Palace, but after a short time they had been sent to serve his elder brother at Çırağan. Safiru never knew whether this was because they had displeased someone important, or whether it was simply because they were not needed at Yıldız. Her sister had always said it was because they were not pretty enough to remain at Court! But whatever the reason, Safiru did not mind as she was perfectly happy at Çırağan.

After joining the household of the former Sultan Murad, Safiru had come under the tutelage of a kind, caring *kalfa* – a housemaid who was totally different in character from the much stricter one who had treated her so harshly at Yıldız. She nurtured both girls as if she were their mother, teaching them all they needed to know to become Ottoman gentle-women. Safiru had enjoyed her daily duties, which were many and varied: she had spent her days mending clothes, helping to prepare and serve food, arranging flowers she had picked from the palace gardens, and embroidering linens. In addition, she had obtained a basic education and had learned to read and write. When she became older, she had served as a *kalfa* to Murad's daughters; then, one day, she had caught the eye of Prince Ahmed Nihad Efendi as he passed her in one of the many secluded corridors of the palace. Every young *kalfa* craved the attentions of the dashingly handsome grandson of the former Sultan, and they playfully referred to these corridors as 'Peach Street'. They felt ripe and ready to be plucked by the young prince, but these desires were destined to be continually frustrated, and their honour to remain intact, since he never abandoned his reserve – until, that is, his eye fell on Safiru. For centuries, the piercing blue eyes of Circassian women had attracted the attention of Ottoman princes. Many such women had risen to the elevated status of wife and mother to princes of the Imperial House of Osman, and this is indeed what had become of Safiru.

Safiru had married Nihad on a cold, dark February afternoon the previous year in one of the elegant formal drawing rooms at the Çırağan Palace. She had been a young bride – only fourteen years old at the time; her distinguished bridegroom, meanwhile, had been only eighteen. Nihad's immediate family had been guests at the wedding, but of Safiru's family only her sister had been present. Her sister had left the palace soon afterwards to marry a young cavalry officer, and Safiru had not seen her since. She missed her beloved sister desperately, but at the same time was glad that she had found happiness. Safiru rarely thought of her long-lost parents, but she thought of them that day – as indeed she had done on her wedding day. She wished she could share the joy of becoming a mother with them, yet knew that this would never be possible. It had been so long since she had seen her mother and father that Safiru could no longer remember their names or picture their faces. Any attempt to find them again, after so many years, would be futile. Even her one treasured memory of her mother, singing to her as she brushed her hair, was now so faint that she could not be at all certain that it was real.

At that moment, Safiru vowed that she would never leave her son's side: she would never do to him what her parents had once done to her. She whispered her promise into the tiny pink ear of her baby boy. "I love you with all my heart, my little one. You are never to worry about anything, because whatever happens in your life, I will always be with you to keep you safe. I will never abandon you. Never, until the day I leave this world." Safiru decided she would never again speculate about her parents' fate. Her life was here in İstanbul, and her family was now Nihad, her noble husband, and this precious little boy. A gentle knock on the door interrupted her train of thought.

☽ ☽ ☽ ☽ ☽

Nihad entered the darkened room accompanied by Dilberici-han Kalfa, his senior housemaid, who had hurried to tell him the news that he had become a father. Safiru's bedroom was in a tastefully-decorated suite of rooms that she shared with her husband and Naziknaz, his mother, on the ground floor of the harem building at the Çırağan Palace. It was known as 'Suite Three'. The pink silk damask curtains remained tightly closed, the only light coming from the two gilt gas lamps that hung on the wall, on either side of the imposing bed. The ivory silk gauze draped over the brass four-poster concealed Safiru from her husband. Hayriye lowered her eyes and bowed before Nihad, who stopped to thank the elderly midwife before nervously approaching the bed.

Nihad's fingers hesitantly parted the silk bed curtains. Gazing down on his wife, his serious expression broke into a warm, loving smile. "My dear Safi, I am so proud of you," he said as he gently stroked away a loose strand of hair from her face. Nihad leaned forward and gave her a tender kiss on the forehead before doing the same to his son. Then he sat on a chair next to the bed and took Safiru's delicate hand in his. "I have been told that you are well and that our son is healthy," he continued. Safiru nodded. "*Alhamdulillah* – Praise be to Allah! I could not possibly be any happier than I am today, my love. Thank you for making this the happiest day of my life." Nihad looked at the baby, still sleeping in the arms of his exhausted young wife. "Welcome to the world, my son."

After closing the door of his wife's bedroom behind him, Nihad hurried along the corridor to find his father and grandfather in order to give them the good news. They, too, lived in the harem building, which stood across the gardens from the main palace. His grandfather occupied Suite Five, a large suite of rooms at the end that was furthest away from the Bosphorus. He had initially lived in the Sultan's apartments at the palace; Murad did not have ostentatious tastes, however, so after the death of his mother he chose to move into the harem building, where he would be able to live in more modest surroundings. His consorts, on the other hand, enjoyed the opulence of the main palace, so most of them lived separately from their husband in the splendour that that building afforded. Nihad found his father and grandfather sitting near the open window in Murad's study. They were playing backgammon. As he entered, the two men looked up from their game. The expression on their faces betrayed anxiety: they had been waiting for news all day and had been praying that it would come soon.

Nihad hurried towards them, his habitually calm demeanour

having temporarily deserted him. He kissed his grandfather's hand and raised it to his forehead in the traditional Ottoman manner before greeting his father, Prince Mehmed Selahaddin Efendi, in the same way. "I am so sorry to interrupt your game, but I have happy news. Such very happy news!" The words came tumbling out of his mouth – louder, faster and higher in pitch than was the case with his usual manner of speaking, which was measured and controlled. "Safiru has borne me a son," he blurted out at last. Nihad was breathless with excitement; his chest heaved up and down as he struggled to contain himself.

Murad rose from his chair, took his grandson in his arms and kissed him on both cheeks. "*Mashallah! Mashallah!* It is the will of Allah. I pray that he will have a long and happy life." Murad stared deeply into Nihad's eyes. "I trust all went well?" he asked, suddenly becoming more serious. "I trust that your son is strong and that the Lady Safiru is recovering?"

"Yes, Grandfather. Thank you for your concern, but all is well," Nihad replied as his grandfather tightened his embrace.

"Then we must celebrate," Murad continued, a tone of enthusiasm entering his voice. "We will all dine together this evening to celebrate the birth of the new prince, for this is indeed a most special day. Such days are so rare." Murad summoned the attendant standing outside the door of the study. "Nefidem Kalfa, please ask Aynifer Usta to tell the kitchens to prepare a feast in the large dining room. We are going to celebrate the birth of my great-grandson. And can you also see to it that all the ladies are informed, as I would like the whole family to dine together this evening, and I want everyone to be present? Thank you." The attendant bowed her head and withdrew to find Aynifer Usta, the High Hazinedar, and carry out the other instructions she had been given.

Mistress Aynifer was the highest-ranking person in the palace after the members of the Imperial family, their spouses and the former Sultan's Favourites – the *Gözdes*. Since her position, her duties and her responsibilities were of the highest order, she could almost be said to be the Grand Vizier of the harem. All the other household staff were subordinate to her, and nothing happened without her knowledge. It was she who organised all ceremonies and special functions, and it was she who was consulted on all matters relating to the harem and everyone living in it. Murad and his family trusted her implicitly, and she was privy to many of the family's most closely-guarded secrets. Tradition dictated that only she and other servants who held the rank of *usta* should serve Murad, but many of the strict, unbending rules of protocol that were a time-honoured feature of the Ottoman Court had been abandoned by Murad during the long years of his confinement. Çırağan was, after all, not just a palace: for all it had become a prison, it was essentially a family home, and it was a warm and loving one in which the stiff, formal atmosphere of the Imperial Court was conspicuously absent. This being so, a certain amount of familiarity with the household staff could be considered normal. The very few visitors who were permitted to come to the palace were sometimes surprised to see that the members of the Imperial family, and in particular the deposed Sultan, spoke directly and informally even to the most junior of the servants.

Selahaddin was now embracing his son. "My dear boy, what wonderful news! I am delighted for you. Believe me, a son is truly a gift from Allah. You have been blessed," he said with a smile. "I know you will be a good and loving father, and I am so proud of you." He kissed his son on both cheeks, blinking back tears of joy – and, of course, relief.

At that moment the gilded bronze door handle turned, the door swung open, and Prince Osman Fuad Efendi burst into the room. He was Nihad's eight-year-old brother. "Is it true, Nihad? Am I really an uncle? Tirendaz Kalfa has just told me that Safiru Abla has had a baby boy." Tirendaz was Selahaddin's senior housemaid. She had been a member of his household staff ever since he first established his own entourage as a young prince soon after his father had ascended the throne. Today, she had the challenging task of keeping an eye on Fuad! He was an energetic and fun-loving boy, always on the look-out for adventure – very different in character from his far more serious-minded elder brother. Tirendaz looked rather flustered as she followed the young prince into the study a second or two later.

"Fuad, have you forgotten your manners?" prompted Nihad. The excited boy remembered himself and greeted his grandfather and father in turn before repeating his question.

Murad laughed. "It's true, Fuad! You are no longer the baby of the family. I trust you will take your duties as uncle seriously?"

For a brief moment, Fuad looked solemn. "I will take them most seriously, Grandfather," he replied earnestly. "I will not only be an uncle to my nephew, but also a big brother and a best friend. And I will always love him and protect him. I can't wait to show him all my toys and teach him how to escape from Tirendaz Kalfa!" Everyone laughed. Fuad's passion for life, and the enthusiasm he had for everything, were infectious.

Selahaddin smiled at his young son. How different his boys were, but how he loved them both! There was a big gap in their ages, but the bond between them was strong. Nihad was protective towards Fuad, who in turn looked up to his elder brother and always sought his approval. Selahaddin thought of their mothers. He loved them both equally, but like his sons, his wives were also very different. Nihad's mother, the Lady Naziknaz, was a selfless person – always gentle, thoughtful and kind. She asked for nothing, having devoted her life to caring for her children, Nihad and his elder sister Princess Behiye. Sadly, Selahaddin and Naziknaz' eldest son had been taken from them soon after his second birthday. However, it had of course been the will of Allah; Selahaddin admired the way Naziknaz had accepted her fate so bravely. Jalefer Hanımefendi, the mother of Fuad, was much younger. She was vibrant and lively - a fashionable, modern woman in every respect. Fuad was her only child, and she did not seem particularly eager to have more. He mused that his sons were very much like their mothers in character.

Fuad's eyes wandered over to the nearby table where the backgammon board lay open. "Can I play?" he asked, already distracted. The olive-wood board was intricately inlaid with ebony, ivory and mother of pearl. The workmanship was exquisite: a geometric design decorated the centre of each half of the board, while ivory chrysanthemum heads crowned the tip of each ivory point. It had been a gift to Murad from his mother, Şevkefzâ Kadınefendi, on the occasion of the birth of his only son Selahaddin over forty years previously. Murad had taught his son, his daughters and all his grandchildren to play backgammon on this board, and it had therefore been a silent witness to many happy intimate family moments.

"We will play together tomorrow, my dear Fuad. But for the moment, I think you should go and tell your grandmother that you are now an uncle," Murad said, lovingly stroking the little boy's hair. He then turned to Nihad. "And you should inform your mother that she has become a grandmother!"

"Yes, of course," agreed Selahaddin. "They will both be overjoyed to hear the news." He smiled to himself as he thought of the pleasure it would bring his mother, Reftarıdil Kadınefendi, and especially his wife, Naziknaz, to have a baby to love – and spoil – once more. There were few secrets in the palace, so he was confident that they had heard the news, and had most likely already visited Safiru and the baby. He was also fairly certain that Naziknaz would have taken control of everything in the nursery, and would now be busy dispensing orders to the wetnurse and the maids, ensuring that the baby was properly cared for.

"Before you go, Nihad, take this," Murad said, handing his grandson a small silk pouch that had been sitting on his desk. "You know our family tradition – you must give a special gift to the *kalfa* who first brought you the happy news of your son's birth. Last week Sadık Ağa went to see an old Armenian jeweller I once knew in the Bazaar to buy these emerald earrings. When I was not much older than you are now, I bought a similar gift from him for the *kalfa* who told me of the birth of your father. I have also bought your grandmother many fine pieces of jewellery from him in the past. When I was Crown Prince, I used to visit him so often that over time we became friends." Nihad gratefully accepted the gift. "I wanted you to be able to reward your *kalfa* in the same way as I did," Murad went on. "Margos Bey still drives a very hard bargain, but his craftsmanship and stones are of the very highest quality. We would haggle over prices, arguing back and forth for hours while we drank apple tea, discussed politics and played backgammon," Murad said, fondly remembering the days of his youth when he was occasionally permitted to walk freely through the crowded streets of the Imperial capital.

"Thank you, Grandfather. It is most generous of you. You

are always so kind and thoughtful," Nihad replied, bowing his head slightly. "I will present your gift to Dilbericihan Kalfa before we meet for dinner, and will be sure to recount your story to her when I do so," he added. Then he and Fuad, who was beginning to fidget with impatience, left the study.

"Well, my son. You are now a grandfather. And I ... I am a great-grandfather. How quickly the years pass!" Murad sighed once he and Selahaddin were alone again. "There are now four generations of our family languishing in this wretched place, hidden away behind the high walls of our prison and all but forgotten by the rest of the world." Sensing the darkening in his father's mood, Selahaddin placed a hand affectionately on his arm and guided him back to his chair. Then he closed the backgammon board and placed it carefully on his father's desk. Murad seemed to be slipping into bouts of melancholy more and more often these days, and Selahaddin was becoming increasingly concerned over his beloved father's wellbeing.

Murad turned towards the window and looked out, a distracted and rather wistful expression coming over his face. "Ah well, I suppose I had better inform my brother that a new Ottoman prince has been born – as if he needed telling," he said without diverting his gaze from the distant point on the far side of the Bosphorus on which his eyes were focused. After a short pause, he turned back to face his son. "I would also like to inform the rest of the family," he began, a note of weariness entering his voice. "I know they are not allowed to receive my letters, but I wish to write to them anyway. I will try to have the letters safely delivered, of course. So can you please ask Asım Ağa to come to me with his writing box ... Oh yes, and can you ask one of the maids to bring me some apple tea?"

"Of course, Father. Please put your mind at rest. Everything will be done exactly as you wish. I will see you at dinner," replied Selahaddin, dutifully taking his leave. Reaching the door, he turned round to see his father standing before the window, absorbed in contemplating that same distant point once more.

CHAPTER TWO

Thoughts and Recollections

N O-ONE cast a second glance at the lone figure in the shabby fez struggling up the hill towards Yıldız: he was to all appearances a servant in the household of some unimportant functionary in the Empire's administration too impecunious, or too mean, to provide him with new clothes. But when this unprepossessing individual arrived at the gates of the palace, he seemed to be recognised by the guards on duty. In fact, they greeted him by his first name. Entering the guard post, he rather sheepishly produced a crumpled note, intended for Sultan Abdülhamid's Senior Equerry, from the pocket of his threadbare shalvar trousers. The sergeant snatched the note from his rough, calloused hands, and waved the cowering man away with a dismissive gesture.

❁ ❁ ❁ ❁ ❁

Alone, with only his thoughts for company, Murad sat down in his favourite leather armchair in front of the brightly burning tiled stove. He stretched out his legs, crossed his right foot over his left, placed his arms on the armrests, and rested his head back against the soft leather, doing his best to make himself comfortable while he waited for Asım Ağa, and his tea, to arrive. His eyes closed as he began to think of his family, and how it had come to pass that four generations of the most senior branch of the Ottoman Dynasty should be living in captivity in Çırağan, their 'gilded cage'.

But whatever cruel restrictions his family might be forced to live under, at least Murad had the consolation that thanks to the birth of his great-grandson, the survival of his own line was now assured. And not only had the baby been born healthy, but his mother, Safiru, appeared to be recovering as well as could be expected. This was the happy outcome he had been praying for: he knew only too well that in the past many babies had either been stillborn or had died within hours, and that sometimes their mothers had not survived the harrowing ordeal of childbirth. Murad allowed a feeling of relief and gratitude to wash over him.

The fragility of human life was a universal truth that had a special bearing on the Ottoman family as it was a constant reminder of the vulnerability of the Dynasty – and therefore, that of the Empire itself. When Murad's grandfather, Sultan Mahmud II, ascended the throne after a palace coup in 1808, he had been the only remaining prince of the Ottoman line. Indeed, there had been a very real danger that the Dynasty would become extinct for lack of a male heir.

The previous year, Mahmud's brother Mustafa had collaborated with the disgruntled Janissary Army Corps in a successful attempt to overthrow and imprison Sultan Selim III, their enlightened and accomplished cousin. Selim continued to enjoy widespread support, however, and in July 1808 Alemdar Mustafa Pasha attacked Topkapı Palace with fifteen thousand men, intending to depose the recently enthroned Mustafa IV and restore Selim. Seeing this army approach the palace, Mustafa ordered the murder of both Selim and Mahmud, thinking that as he himself would now be the only male member of the Ottoman family left alive, his life would be spared in the interests of preserving the Dynasty.

Mustafa's assassins murdered Selim, but fortunately Mahmud eluded his assailants' grasp, sustaining only a knife wound to his arm. A brave and quick-thinking *kalfa* named Cevri halted the assassins by throwing a bowlful of ash, gathered from the fire in the hammam, into their eyes, thus blinding them for long enough to allow Mahmud to escape through a window and climb onto the roof of the harem complex. In fear of his life, he clambered across the loose clay tiles and over the domes of the intervening buildings until he reached the Inner Courtyard of the palace; here, loyal attendants hurriedly tied pieces of fabric together to form a long rope – which Mahmud used to lower himself to safety. Shortly afterwards, Alemdar Mustafa Pasha's men entered Topkapı and took control, rescuing Mahmud from danger. In this way, not only was Mahmud's survival assured, but also that of the Ottoman Dynasty.

Once he had ascended the throne, Sultan Mahmud vowed that he would not be the last Sultan of the Ottoman line; therefore, in order to replenish the stock of potential heirs, he fathered thirty-six children. Unfortunately, however, the number of males in the Imperial family still remained small since of all Mahmud's sons, only two survived into adulthood: Murad's father, Sultan Abdülmecid, and his uncle, Sultan Abdülaziz.

Abdülmecid, in his turn, fathered forty children to guarantee the continuance of the Dynasty, but of these only nine were still living. Most of the others had died in infancy, or as very young children. Murad could remember many of them – some only vaguely, others rather more clearly. He had been his father's second child, and the eldest of his sons; as such, Murad was able to recall the suffering that the heartbroken mothers of many of Abdülmecid's children had endured. He could still hear the high-pitched wails of grief ringing through the corridors of the palace harems as babies died only a few days or weeks after birth, and as too many young lives were brutally cut short by the terrible diseases that plagued the city.

As a child, Murad had been grateful for the company of his many brothers and sisters. He had never thought it even remotely possible that his destiny would be to end his days as the prisoner of one of them …

☾ ☾ ☾ ☾ ☾

Murad opened his eyes. The glow from the stove was now dimmer than before, and he thought how his own burning desire to bring greater freedom to his subjects had been abruptly extinguished by the fate that had overtaken him; it made a mockery of all the dreams he had had as Crown Prince of liberalising his empire and transforming it into a modern state. Was it not ironic, he mused, that the very man who had cared so much about the ability of others to enjoy their right to freedom should himself have had to endure the curtailment of that most fundamental right? With the imprisonment of Murad, not only had the legitimate Sultan of the Ottomans been denied his birthright, but the Empire had lost a valuable opportunity to bring itself into line with recent developments in Europe.

As a young man, Murad had been overflowing with exciting new ideas and plans for reform, all aimed at reversing the Empire's decline by rendering it more democratic, more liberal and therefore more efficient and more modern. He had been inspired by the bold initiatives taken by his father and grandfather, who had led the struggle against the entrenched conservative elements in the Empire that jealously held on to their power and violently resisted any attempt to bring about change. In the face of constant opposition, his grandfather Mahmud II had begun a programme of sweeping reforms within the administration and in the fields of education, the tax system and the law, and had taken steps to modernise the army and navy. Most notably, he abolished the Janissary Corps, which had once been the most feared fighting force in the world but had become one of the bastions of resistance to change, undermining the very fabric of the Empire with its corrupt ways; it had been this rebellious body of men, in fact, who had deposed Selim III. Mahmud also introduced social reforms that horrified and enraged the conservatives: at the Ottoman Court and among the bureaucracy, for instance, the traditional oriental robes were replaced by European-style clothing, while the turban was discarded in favour of the fez.

A few months after Mahmud's death, Abdülmecid promulgated the Edict of Gülhane – thereby initiating what came to be known as the Tanzimat Period, a time of many reforms that continued throughout his reign. One of the most important of these was the guaranteeing of equal rights before the law to every Ottoman citizen, regardless of ethnicity or religion. It was hoped that this would help combat the spread of nationalism, which threatened the very existence of the Empire and was being actively encouraged by the European Powers for their own ends.

Murad had admired all that his father and grandfather had achieved, but planned to go even further than they had. In fact, he had been willing to relinquish the absolute power he would enjoy as Sultan, and establish a constitutional monarchy. He believed that unlike his predecessors, he had the advantage of being able to rely on the support of a liberal-minded elite – a generation of bureaucrats, statesmen and military officers educated in the schools and academies that had been founded during the Tanzimat Period. This influential class of people, he thought, would be eager to implement a radical change of this nature and ensure its success. In short, it had been Murad's dream to arouse the Ottomans from their slumber and create an enlightened modern empire that would be strong enough to survive for centuries to come.

☣ ☣ ☣ ☣ ☣

It was not long before thoughts of what might have been were replaced in Murad's mind by those nagging feelings of guilt that plagued him more and more frequently these days. He constantly tortured himself for causing those he loved nothing but misery. Because of him, they had been compelled to live in confinement for the last twenty-eight years, locked in this gilded cage on the orders of the usurper Sultan Abdülhamid. He chastised himself for not having been more determined and more resilient when he came to the throne in May 1876, and for allowing himself to be hounded into submission by the scheming pashas and his own ambitious, power-hungry younger brother. Everyone in Murad's family, without exception, had told him over and over again that he was not to blame, but he did not believe this for an instant. How had it all gone wrong?

Murad had ascended the throne of the Ottoman Empire on 30th May 1876 following a military coup against his uncle, Sultan Abdülaziz, that had taken place the night before. The leaders of the coup had been Avni Pasha, the Minister of War, Rüşdi Pasha, the Grand Vizier, and Midhat Pasha, a well-known liberal statesman and advocate of reform. They had become tired of the Sultan's extravagant spending, which had been a source of dangerous pressure on the Ottoman Treasury, and had grown impatient with his continued resistance to demands that he should abandon absolute power and agree to introduce constitutional government. Murad had not taken part in the conspiracy against his uncle, but rumours had reached his ears that a coup might be imminent, most likely planned for early June. He was therefore both shocked and terrified when Avni Pasha, armed with a revolver and accompanied by soldiers, burst into his room in the Crown Prince's suite at the Dolmabahçe Palace on that May night. Murad was hurriedly taken off to be enthroned as the new Sultan; meanwhile, Abdülaziz was taken prisoner.

Murad's initial reaction to Avni Pasha's arrival was to suspect that it was a trick, and that his uncle had uncovered the plot; he thought perhaps Abdülaziz wanted to test his loyalty. It also occurred to him that it might be a stratagem designed to portray him as a traitor so that he could be removed from his position as the rightful successor. For years, on the anniversary of his enthronement Abdülaziz had tried to persuade his ministers to change the laws of succession from 'agnatic seniority', the current system under which a deceased Sultan would be succeeded by whichever prince of the Imperial blood was the eldest, to 'agnatic primogeniture', whereby the eldest son of the Sultan would succeed him. Every attempt on the part of Abdülaziz to enforce this change had been thwarted by the Sheikh ul-Islam, assisted by the British Ambassador: neither of these two had wished to see the Sultan's eldest son – the petulant, pretentious Prince Yusuf İzzeddin Efendi – given preferment over the well-mannered, intelligent and enlightened Prince Murad.

Abdülaziz had envied Murad his immense popularity with the people, and had kept him in virtual seclusion in his apartments in the palace, where he lived under constant surveillance. Murad's uncle had even tried to persuade him to renounce his claim to the throne by means of bribes and threats. In these circumstances, it was entirely understandable that Murad should have been reluctant to believe that the offer of being made Sultan in place of Abdülaziz was sincere when he found himself suddenly confronted with an agitated Avni Pasha on the night of the coup.

Murad was not a devious man, and had no predilection whatever for Machiavellian conspiracies. The coup shook him to the very core of his being, and his sensitive nature was deeply distressed by the sight of the heavily-armed men who surrounded him, albeit for his own protection. Later, he was unnerved to hear of the rough treatment that had been meted out to his uncle and the ladies of his harem, who had been manhandled out of their rooms by the plotters' henchmen with not the slightest sign of respect for their status as members of the Imperial family. Rumours abounded to the effect that jewels had been ripped from their bodies, and money and personal possessions stolen from chests and cupboards; even the sick and the elderly had been treated with contempt.

The shock to his system occasioned by this night of terror resulted in episodes of strange and unpredictable behaviour on the part of Murad, but worse was to come: the trauma he had sustained developed into a full-scale nervous breakdown when he heard the news, just a few days later, of his uncle's death in mysterious circumstances. His ministers informed him that Abdülaziz had committed suicide by cutting his wrists, but Murad was convinced that this was not true. Tormented by the scene he pictured in his mind of his uncle's murder, he was seized by fits of vomiting. Over and over, he replayed to himself the horrific vision of his uncle, a well-built and powerful man, wrestling in vain with his assassins as they slashed his arms and wrists with their knives until the deposed Sultan fell to the floor, and fought no more.

The sinister countenances of Avni Pasha and the Grand Vizier led Murad to believe that they might well be capable of giving the order for such a despicable act of treachery, but the thought that Midhat Pasha might have been complicit in the murder left him completely dumbfounded. Midhat Pasha was a man Murad had trusted, fondly imagining that this able statesman might help him in the task of steering the Empire along the perilous course towards reform. His feelings of horror and betrayal were further exacerbated by the fear that his people might wrongly believe he had been in some way involved in his uncle's murder – a crime of which he was completely innocent. As these thoughts tortured his mind, sleep evaded him, and he turned to drink to drown his feelings of sorrow, bewilderment and despair. However, Murad's over-indulgence in Veuve Clicquot champagne, sometimes fortified with brandy in heady cocktails, only served to weaken his resistance to mental collapse: as he sought relief in total oblivion, he began to be plagued by frightening hallucinations in which his uncle's unquiet ghost came to haunt him.

Murad's erratic behaviour provided Midhat Pasha with the excuse he needed to depose him, and three months later the opportunity was duly pounced on. It was clear that Murad was fast recovering his faculties: his lucid moments were becoming more and more frequent as he battled successfully to overcome his demons. However, Midhat Pasha knew very well that once lost, the young Sultan's trust in him would never be regained. And so, intent on realising his personal ambitions, he turned his attention to Murad's younger brother Abdülhamid, focusing all his energies on ensuring that this new recipient of his favour came to the throne without delay. No doubt, he thought, Abdülhamid would reward him by making him Grand Vizier, and would agree to promulgate the constitution that Midhat Pasha had drawn up. For a politician not overly encumbered with scruples, it was an enticing prospect.

Allah had punished all those who had been involved in the coup against Sultan Abdülaziz. Avni Pasha was shot barely a week later by Captain Hasan, an army captain of Circassian origin who had served in the Imperial Guard and had been Yusuf İzzeddin's aide-de-camp. He was also the brother of Abdülaziz' beloved Fourth Wife Nesteren Kadınefendi, who had died only a few days after her husband; by means of this act, Captain Hasan had taken revenge for both his Sultan and his sister. Rüşdi Pasha died in exile a few years after Abdülhamid came to the throne, while Midhat Pasha totally misjudged the new Sultan's character, and was assassinated in Arabia – some say on Abdülhamid's orders – soon after being sent into exile there.

The constitution that Midhat Pasha had worked so hard to prepare, and which would have been so enthusiastically adopted by Murad, was suspended by Abdülhamid less than two years after it had been proclaimed. He showed that he had no intention either of allowing the absolute power he enjoyed as Sultan to be compromised by a constitution, or of relinquishing the position he had usurped and restoring the rightful Sultan to the throne. The fate of the Empire, now set firmly on a course diametrically opposed to that of democratisation, had thus been sealed; meanwhile, Murad and his family were condemned to a life of misery, detained indefinitely at his younger brother's pleasure.

Murad blamed himself for the fact that his only son, Selahaddin, had spent his entire adult life in a prison, and that his grandsons, Nihad and Fuad, had seen nothing of the world that lay beyond the walls of Çırağan, and had thus been denied a normal childhood. Freedom lay so tantalisingly close – just beyond the high land walls that were vigilantly patrolled on both sides by guards handpicked for their fealty to Abdülhamid; just outside the iron doors that had been installed to make the palace impregnable to any attempt to liberate its inhabitants; and just across the dangerous, fast-flowing waters of the Bosphorus, on the clearly visible opposite shore. In their worst moments, Murad and his family had the feeling of being buried alive, suffocated by the unrelieved frustration and monotony of a fishbowl existence in which normal human contact was impossible.

At first Abdülhamid permitted his sisters and two of his younger brothers, Crown Prince Mehmed Reşad and the sickly Prince Mehmed Burhaneddin, to visit Murad as he trusted them to remain loyal to him; soon, however, even these visits were stopped. From that time on, no one other than authorised members of Abdülhamid's household staff was allowed to see the deposed Sultan and his family. Visits from anyone – be they relatives, friends or state officials – were strictly prohibited; the quarantine was so rigorously enforced, in fact, that ships, caïques and small fishing boats were forbidden to pass near the Çırağan Palace in case someone caught a glimpse of the former sovereign. Abdülhamid wanted everyone, not only in the Empire's capital but also in the world outside, to forget that Murad was still alive – even that he had ever existed.

Murad's consorts and all the women of his household suffered in exactly the same way, as did his granddaughters and his one remaining unmarried daughter, Princess Fatma. It was, however, of some comfort to Murad that following the marriages of Princess Hadice and Princess Fehime, his two eldest daughters, they were now permitted to enjoy their freedom. Their uncle Sultan Abdülhamid had generously given each of them a beautiful *yalı* on the Bosphorus as a wedding gift, but the price Murad had been forced to pay for their liberty had been a cruelly high one: when his brother had finally given permission for the two princesses to marry, he had done so on condition that they should no longer be allowed to see their father or to have any contact whatsoever with him. They had been forbidden ever to return to Çırağan after their weddings, or to correspond with anyone living there, and this rule had been strictly enforced. No crueller prohibition could possibly have been imposed on such a loving and devoted father: it was a malicious and entirely unnecessary act of cruelty on Abdülhamid's part, being intended purely and simply to wound his brother – and indeed, this enforced separation was breaking Murad's fragile heart.

☹ ☹ ☹ ☹ ☹

Murad did not hear the *kalfa* enter the room, but he stirred as she placed the round silver tray on the low table next to his chair. "Thank you, Nezihe Kalfa," he said. Murad knew everyone's name in the household, from the most junior maid to the most senior administrator. They all appreciated the consideration he showed them, and they rewarded his kindness and concern for their welfare with unconditional devotion and loyalty. Nezihe's eyes remained lowered as she backed out of the room as quietly as she had come in.

Murad was thirsty. He reached down to the table and grasped the peacock-shaped handle of the silver filigree *zarf* that encased

26

the tea glass. He brought the glass to his lips, and as he drank the warm, sweet apple tea, he relaxed back into his armchair.

☻ ☻ ☻ ☻ ☻

He now began to reminisce about all he had seen when he had accompanied his uncle Sultan Abdülaziz on his state visit to Europe in 1867. What an exciting six and a half weeks it had been! Murad had been both impressed and inspired by much of what he had witnessed in Paris, London, Brussels, Vienna and Budapest. More importantly, the trip had opened his eyes to the dangerous and ever-widening gap between the Ottoman Empire and Western Europe in terms of industrialisation, military strength and progress towards fully-fledged democracy. He was not naïve enough to believe that the European Powers could ever be trusted – despite their all-too-eager overtures of friendship – but at the same time he was aware that the trip was a valuable opportunity to learn from them and about them; if the required lessons were learnt from the experience, the Empire could be strengthened as a result. Murad had been astounded by the many technological advances and new inventions that he had seen at the Paris Exhibition. He had been deeply impressed by – yet made very nervous of – the might of the British navy when he attended a naval review at Portsmouth. Murad had also greatly admired the workings of the French legal system, and had respected the system of parliamentary government that he saw running smoothly alongside the monarchy in Britain.

There had been countless balls, parties, lavish dinners and receptions, all of which he had thoroughly enjoyed. Murad smiled to himself as he remembered how Sultan Abdülaziz had reprimanded him one evening for taking too much pleasure in diversions of this kind! Initially, Abdülaziz had not wanted Murad to accompany him on his tour of Europe as he had wanted the full attention of the foreign courts and the foreign press to be focused exclusively on himself. He had also seen the trip as a chance to introduce his eldest son, Yusuf İzzeddin, to Western rulers and politicians, hoping that in this way he would be able to win their support for his son if ever a war of succession should arise. However, Abdülaziz' politically astute mother had persuaded him to bring not only Yusuf İzzeddin but also Murad and Abdülhamid to Europe as members of his entourage. She had convinced him that it would be far too dangerous to leave the popular Crown Prince and his younger brother in İstanbul as they might try to usurp the throne while he was away. Abdülaziz derived great satisfaction from humiliating and insulting the rightful heir to the Ottoman throne at every opportunity, publicly chastising him; he also kept Murad in the background at official events so that his own ten-year-old son could stand by his side instead.

None of this bothered Murad – he was enjoying himself too much to let his uncle's petty jealousies ruin the trip. He also ignored his brother, for at times Abdülhamid made it obvious that like their uncle, he too disapproved of his older brother's behaviour! One evening, Abdülhamid criticised Murad for having danced the quadrille and a waltz with Princess Louise, the vivacious and enchanting daughter of Queen Victoria. Murad could still remember the Princess's infectious laugh, her quick wit and the touch of her white kid glove in one of his hands as he rested the other lightly on her bare shoulder.

Everyone had been intrigued to meet the charming young heir to the Imperial Ottoman throne, and Murad ensured that no one who met him was disappointed by the encounter. During his time in England he developed a particularly close friendship with Edward, Prince of Wales. The young princes shared not only a similar destiny, but also a fondness for amusing diversions and beautiful women, with the result that they both took sincere pleasure in one another's company. Politicians and intellectuals were encouraged by Murad's interest in liberalism and reform, and were attracted by his eagerness to debate with them and discuss the pressing issues of the day. The ladies of the European courts were equally captivated, being fascinated by the mystery and allure that surrounded this handsome, surprisingly forward-looking prince from the Orient, and were spellbound by his dark, trusting eyes, his soft, gentle voice and his impeccably refined manners.

❂ ❂ ❂ ❂ ❂

Recently, Murad's mind was becoming more and more inclined to drift back to the past. It now turned momentarily to Ziya Pasha, a man who had once been a respected and influential writer and a political activist within the 'Young Ottomans' organisation, and who had been appointed as Murad's private secretary when he first became Sultan. However, Ziya Pasha had only held the position for twenty-four hours before being unceremoniously dismissed: it very soon transpired that tact and diplomacy were not among his virtues, thus making him utterly unsuitable for the post of Private Secretary to the Sultan! Murad had first met Ziya Pasha during his visit to London in the summer of 1867, at which time he had also met his associates Namık Kemal and Ali Suavi. In between the numerous official engagements of the state visit, Murad had eluded his uncle's spies, and had secretly arranged a meeting with them and with other Young Ottomans who were living in exile there.

He knew that these men were highly critical of his uncle's

autocratic regime, but he also knew that the Empire needed drastic reform, and thought that members of the educated elite such as these might be able to help him with the monumental task of modernisation and reform that lay ahead of him. Murad enjoyed hearing their thoughts on the subject of how Islam could be reconciled with modern ideas of government without compromising the principles of either. He also applauded their vision of creating a 'Pan-Ottoman' identity among the peoples of the Empire that would transcend all religious and ethnic divisions. If successfully established, such an identity could be an effective means of extinguishing the flames of nationalism that were now being fanned in many parts of the Empire by the European Powers with a view to seizing the Ottomans' rich and strategically important lands. The Young Ottomans, in their turn, had been surprised and delighted to find the young prince so enlightened, and had been impressed by the fact that he had risked so much to meet them: Abdülaziz would certainly have punished his nephew most severely if he had found out about these meetings.

But alas! None of these idealistic hopes and dreams had been realised. Ziya Pasha and Namık Kemal were now both dead, though their works still graced the bookshelves in Murad's study. He had always encouraged his children and grandchildren to read them. Sultan Abdülhamid had abandoned all efforts to introduce constitutional democracy, and was ruling the Empire as a despot. It hurt and angered Murad to see the damage that was being done to the Empire as a result of Abdülhamid's unyielding policies – but of course, he could do nothing.

After a while, something roused Murad from his reflections, and he caught himself staring absent-mindedly at the rows of leather-bound books arranged neatly on his bookshelves. He was irritated with himself. Why did his mind wander back to the past so often these days? Was it that he missed the people who surrounded him in his younger days? Well, yes, perhaps it was. He could not deny, after all, that he missed his brothers and sisters with a longing that seemed to get worse, rather than better, as time went on.

He had not been allowed to see any of his siblings for nearly twenty-five years, and had likewise been forbidden to correspond with them. However, with the help of Asım Ağa and other loyal servants he had maintained a secret, though very limited, communication with them all. Sadly, many of his siblings had died during this time, among them his beloved sister Princess Fatma. The thought of her beautiful, serene face and her warm, loving nature brought a tear to his eye. It rolled slowly down his cheek and was left to dry in his thinning white beard. Fatma had tried desperately to help her brother when he had first been placed in confinement, but Abdülhamid had punished her with extreme severity for what he perceived as her treachery towards him. He had ordered her to be imprisoned in her residence, the Palace of Baltalimanı, and it was only on her premature death a few years later that she was finally set free from captivity. Hers was yet another life that Murad blamed himself for ruining.

He was thankful, however, that his brother had never discovered that their sister Princess Seniha had also helped him. Soon after Murad arrived at Çırağan following his deposition, she had taken the bold step of bringing a doctor into the palace in her own carriage, sneaking him past the guards disguised as a veiled housemaid, so that the former Sultan could be treated for his nervous breakdown. The doctor had attended Murad for twelve days, kept hidden from the guards and Abdülhamid's spies by the *kalfas*. Murad knew that he owed his life to this doctor and to his sister's timely intervention: it had been this clandestine course of treatment alone that had saved him during those darkest of days.

He then cast his mind back to the time, soon after the disastrous Russo-Turkish War that ended in 1878, when his devoted brothers Prince Ahmed Kemaleddin Efendi and Prince Selim Süleyman Efendi had become involved in a reckless scheme to free him from imprisonment. With an inward sigh of relief, Murad thanked Allah that Abdülhamid had never learnt how closely Kemaleddin and Süleyman had been linked to the failed rescue attempt. Blame for this violent and bloody incident had always been placed squarely on the shoulders of Ali Suavi, the Young Ottoman Murad had once met in Europe, and on his followers – an armed band of Moslem refugees who had fled the former Ottoman territories in the Balkans in the face of the invading Russian army. The destitute refugees blamed Abdülhamid for the catastrophic Ottoman defeat and held him personally responsible for the subsequent Treaty of San Stefano – a crushing humiliation for the Ottoman Empire which not only saw the loss of huge swathes of land to Russia and the newly emerging Balkan States but also resulted in the expulsion of hundreds of thousands of Moslems and Jews from their former homelands. This ill-fated bid to liberate Murad and restore him to the throne had been put down by the local prefect of police, a man fiercely loyal to Abdülhamid who had entered the palace with his men, defeated the insurgents and bludgeoned Ali Suavi to death, thereby ending the revolt.

It was after this serious civil disturbance that Abdülhamid's fears for his security on the throne had been inflamed to the point of outright paranoia; it was then that he had given the order for those iron doors that so wounded Murad's spirit to be installed, and security at the Çırağan Palace had been so tightened that those condemned to live inside it felt suffocated by the restrictions. But in spite of all the troubles that beset him, Murad took consolation in the fact that he was blessed to have two sisters and two brothers who loved him deeply enough to be prepared to risk so much for his sake. He was also thankful to have discovered that Abdülhamid's network of spies was not infallible.

How he missed his siblings, and how desperately he longed to see those of them who were still alive! He loved them all – even Abdülhamid, though Murad's love and loyalty had been tested to the limit since the usurpation of his throne, and never more so than after the tragedy he had recently experienced. The brothers had been born on the same day, but two years apart, and this coincidence had forged a bond between them that Murad liked to think could not be broken, in spite of everything. He recalled with a glow of happiness those innocent days of their childhood when all the brothers and sisters would play and laugh together, sharing their joys and fears with one another. Even Abdülhamid had been ready to laugh as a young boy: he had not always been so serious and so afraid of the world and everything in it as he was now. How sad it was, Murad thought to himself, that his former playmate should now be a stranger to him.

Murad wondered to himself, as he took another sip of tea, how it had come about that he and his brother Abdülhamid had drifted so far apart. Was it, perhaps, during that trip to Europe with their uncle Abdülaziz that he had first sensed a change in their relationship? "Was he jealous of me, even then? Might it have been seeing me the centre of attention everywhere we went while he himself was ignored, that started it all?" Murad asked himself. Abdülhamid had not felt at all comfortable during their state visit to the capitals of Europe, especially during the social engagements they had taken part in at the various courts: he had felt self-conscious and awkward in these foreign surroundings. Not only this, but his contemptuous and haughty demeanour had discouraged ambassadors, courtiers and politicians from approaching him and engaging him in conversation, while his hard, unsmiling eyes and long, crooked hook-nose had ensured that the ladies, too, avoided him. "Poor Hamid," mused Murad. "Jealousy is such a pernicious thing. If he could only have overcome it, we might have been the closest of brothers and the best of friends. Perhaps, if we had been able to work together in spite of our different beliefs, we might have combined to create an ideal partnership that would have allowed us to protect our people from the enemies at our gates – of whom there are many!"

Nefidem returned from carrying out her previous instructions, and resumed her place on the striped silk sofa in the hall outside the study door to await any further requests from her master. A minute later, she heard Asım Ağa approaching and immediately rose to her feet. Asım Ağa was no longer a young man, and walked with the aid of a stick. The sound it made on the highly-polished parquet floors of the corridors was such a distinctive one that Nefidem could hear him coming long before he came into view.

CHAPTER THREE

Letters and Secrets

ULTAN Abdülhamid held the crumpled note in his hand. The interruption had ruined his walk in the gardens of Yıldız Palace with Princess Naime, the second eldest of his daughters. Now that she was married and had a household of her own, Abdülhamid did not see her as often as he would like, and he looked forward to his afternoons alone with her. They had been to the apiary to inspect the beehives, checking that each colony had enough sugar syrup to survive the coming winter. During one of Naime's previous visits they had helped with the honey harvest, and since then the care of the bees at Yıldız had become a shared interest for them.

Cevher Ağa, Abdülhamid's Senior Equerry, had deemed the information contained in the note of sufficient importance to justify disturbing the Sultan, and he had been thoroughly berated for doing so. Abdülhamid's mood had darkened instantly, so Naime had tactfully made her excuses and returned to her *yalı* in Ortaköy. Her father was now pacing up and down in front of the large window in his study, irritated to find that any reminder of his brother still seemed to have such an unsettling effect on him. Logic told him that

Murad was no longer a threat to his position, and that he should not be so anxious, but his conscience refused to lie down and be quiet, however much he might try to silence it: his elder brother was, after all, the rightful Sultan. This dichotomy between the confident self-satisfaction he exuded on the surface and the only half-acknowledged guilt that lurked in the depths below had haunted Abdülhamid throughout his entire reign.

He was, though he would have furiously denied it if anyone had been so unwise as to raise the subject, permanently in the grip of a fear that one day, some opposition group or other would succeed in rescuing Murad and his family from the Çırağan Palace and restore him to the throne. News of the birth of a new prince of the Muradiye line might be just the catalyst needed to bring about such an eventuality, Abdülhamid thought, furrowing his brow and beginning to replay those by now familiar fantasies in which he pictured himself being forced to give up his exalted position in a humiliating manner. Cevher Ağa should, perhaps, have guessed that the crumpled note would set off another bout of his master's paranoia: the raising of the issue of legitimacy, even in so indirect a manner, would be sure to sting him worse than a hive full of angry bees.

Abdülhamid's dark eyes, the colour of a raven's plumage, had become dilated in his agitation. His mind, meanwhile, was racing wildly as question after question occurred to him – not for the first time! Had he been right to insist on assuming the throne as full sovereign instead of accepting the position of temporary regent that Midhat Pasha had at first offered him – a position that he would have had to relinquish when his brother was eventually cured of his illness? Should he have taken the advice of his counsellors, and had Murad assassinated instead of incarcerating him in a palace prison and cutting him off from the outside world? Had he, perhaps, behaved not too harshly towards his brother, but with too much leniency?

Of one thing he was certain: the prospect facing the Empire at the time of his accession had been a dire one. It had certainly been no time to experiment with wishy-washy liberal ideas of how a government should be run. No parliament or politician could possibly care as deeply for the Ottoman Empire and her peoples as the divinely-appointed Sultan could. The Empire had simply not been ready for Murad's ideas at that time, and neither had its people: the political climate had been far too sensitive to tolerate the drastic upheaval that the introduction of constitutional rule would have brought. The history of the Dynasty had taught Abdülhamid that whenever the reins of power had been allowed to pass into the hands of the ministers of the Sublime Porte, the fortunes of the Empire had declined, whereas whenever they were held firmly in the hands of a strong, resolute Sultan, its fortunes had flourished. No, he concluded, it had been no time to hand over power to a collection of irresponsible utopian idealists.

"Murad, Murad! Forgive me, but I had no other choice," he muttered to himself. As always when thinking of his brother in a moment of solitude, Abdülhamid was racked with guilt for what he had done. He decided that he would pray for Murad; he would also pray for long life for his brother's great-grandson.

☻ ☻ ☻ ☻ ☻

"How are you, Nefidem Kalfa?" Asım Ağa asked when he eventually reached the study door.

"I am well, Sir, thank you," she replied, pleased that he had taken the trouble to acknowledge her.

"What a beautiful autumn day it is today! The leaves on the trees are just beginning to change colour. I do love this time of year," he said in his childlike, high-pitched voice. He placed his silver *qalamdan* on the small table next to the sofa, adjusted his fez and smoothed his frock coat. He then picked up the ornate box full of scribe's implements and placed it under his left arm; Nefidem knocked on the study door and opened it slowly, allowing him to disappear inside.

Asım Ağa had originally been in the service of Sultan Abdülaziz, and had first met Murad when he was Crown Prince. He had been born in the Sudan, but at the age of eight he had been captured by slave traders while collecting water for his mother at the river near his village. This had happened many years before Abdülaziz abolished the slave trade throughout the Empire. He had then been taken to Egypt – and there, with one clean swipe of a sharp blade, the future course of his life had been determined. He had survived the trauma of castration, and afterwards he had been sold to the Imperial Palace in İstanbul. By dint of hard work, he had eventually risen to the position of trusted servant to members of the Imperial family. After Abdülaziz' death, Asım Ağa had chosen to remain in this profession, and he now felt deeply honoured to be performing the function of Murad's private secretary.

Sultan Abdülhamid had dismissed most of Murad's official retinue soon after he had been sent to live at Çırağan, and had replaced all his brother's equerries and footmen with his own men, instructing them to spy on his captive's every movement. Like them, Asım Ağa had been entrusted with the task of watching Murad and his family and reporting back anything of interest to Yıldız. However, Abdülhamid never learnt anything of consequence from him since the old eunuch's loyalty to Murad was absolute. As a result, everyone in the household, from the most junior housemaid to Murad himself, felt a deep affection and respect for him.

Murad had had many private secretaries since his time as Crown Prince, but none had been as loyal or – what was equally important – as discreet as Asım Ağa. Over the years, he had earned Murad's trust, and this was something that few had achieved apart from the members of his immediate family and its longest-serving *kalfas*. Murad was profoundly grateful for the faithful old retainer's bravery. When paper and ink had been forbidden at Çırağan, it was Asım Ağa who had smuggled them in; he had even managed to find ink of Murad's preferred colour – purple. It was he, too, who for many years had been carrying secret letters between his master and those members of his close family who lived outside the palace. This action would have been seen as a heinous crime by Abdülhamid, and would have been severely punished if it had ever come to light. Asım Ağa was also Murad's main source of gossip, and would report back on everything he had heard while shopping in the bazaars or sitting in the coffee houses, thereby keeping Murad up to date with the mood in the Empire's capital.

Asım Ağa was very formal and correct in his manners, and despite Murad's objections always insisted on greeting him in the way that tradition demanded. On entering the study, he would bow low before approaching the former Sultan, and would then perform the *temenna*: this involved making a deep bow, then touching his right hand first to his lips, then to his forehead. The old eunuch had the deepest respect for Murad – not only because he had once been the Ottoman Sultan and the Caliph of Islam, but also because of his gentle, tolerant nature and his progressive beliefs. Asım Ağa now stood in front of his master, waiting patiently for Murad to address him.

"I trust you are well?" Murad enquired.

"I am, Your Imperial Highness. Thank you. And I pray that your Highness is in good health," he replied, careful not to let his eyes meet Murad's, for that would be disrespectful.

"Thank you for coming so promptly," Murad said. "I see you have brought your *qalamdan*. Good. I hope your inkwell is full – we have many important letters to write. We need to give His Imperial Majesty and the rest of my family the joyful news that a new prince has been born at Çırağan. Had you heard that the Lady Safiru gave birth to a healthy son earlier this afternoon?"

"I had indeed, Your Highness. Such wonderful news! I pray that the young prince may have a long and healthy life. *Inshallah* the noble line of Sultan Murad will continue throughout this new century and far into the next," answered Asım Ağa. His smooth, dark skin belied his advanced age: it still retained the soft, velvety texture of a ripe peach. He was tall and thin, and always dressed in the same manner – a black *stambouline* frock coat over a white collarless shirt and dark grey pin-striped trousers. He carried his walking stick everywhere he went: it was carved from a single piece of ebony and had an elaborate silver handle decorated with turquoise stones. Murad had presented him with it a few years before in recognition of his loyalty, and Asım Ağa was intensely proud of it. The old man wore his fez set quite far back on his head, and his shoes were always highly polished. Ink-stained fingers betrayed his profession and his role in the household, but they were the only flaw in an otherwise flawless appearance.

"Thank you, Asım Ağa. Please sit down at your desk. Let us begin straight away. We have much to do as I want to finish in time to dress for dinner. This evening we are celebrating the birth of my great-grandson with a family dinner, and hopefully we shall also have some music. I do not want to be late." Murad called for Nefidem and asked her to bring some more apple tea. Then he walked over to the window and stood behind his desk, turning his back to his faithful scribe as he looked out over the harem gardens. He slipped his right hand in between two buttons of his *stambouline* and let his left hang by his side. It was the stance he often adopted, especially when thinking.

"I will dictate the first letter to my brother Sultan Abdül-hamid. This will be followed by letters to my other four brothers Prince Mehmed Reşad, Prince Ahmed Kemaleddin, Prince Selim Süleyman and Prince Mehmed Vahideddin." Murad sounded assertive, as he always did when carrying out official business. "Begin each letter with all the usual salutations," Murad continued. "After that, we will write to my three sisters – Princess Cemile, Princess Seniha and Princess Mediha – and finally to my daughters." Murad paused, and his eyes glazed over as he became momentarily distracted.

After a minute or two he returned to his previous train of thought. "I am sorry, Asım Ağa. I was thinking of my beloved sister Princess Fatma, who is of course no longer in this world, and my mind began to wander. Please sit down. Let us begin."

Asım Ağa's desk was positioned at right angles to Murad's own, facing the table and chairs where Murad and Selahaddin had been playing backgammon before Nihad arrived to inform them of the birth of his son. Asım Ağa placed the *qalamdan* that Sultan Abdülaziz had given him many years ago – another treasured possession – on one side of his desk and hung his walking stick over the arm of his chair. Sitting down, he opened the drawer of the desk and removed a piece of writing paper. Then he took the black resin Waterman fountain pen he had recently purchased in the bazaar from the quill-holder of the qalamdan, unscrewed the long, tapered barrel end and, using a pipette, carefully filled it with ink. He then began to write the required salutations to His Imperial Majesty Sultan Abdülhamid Khan.

"*Birader* … Dear Brother," Murad began.

۞ ۞ ۞ ۞ ۞

Nearly two hours later the last letter was finished; it was then folded and placed in a square envelope bearing the swirling, gilt-embossed letter 'M' intertwined with a horizontal crescent that was Murad's personal monogram. The two men had been so engrossed in their task that they had barely noticed the maids enter the study from time to time to put wood in the stove and remove the trays.

"Thank you, Asım Ağa," Murad said wearily. "You have done well. Please go immediately to Yıldız Palace to deliver the letter to my brother, His Imperial Majesty. I would be grateful if you would try to deliver the other letters in the usual way this evening, before you go home. However, please do not put yourself at risk in doing so."

"Of course, Your Highness," responded the eunuch, beginning to pack away his writing tools. "It will be an honour."

"If all these letters are to be delivered tonight, you are going to need help," Murad said, standing up from his desk. "You can trust Hayriye Hanım, the midwife, to go to my daughters' *yalıs* with their letters. Their homes are next to each other in Ortaköy, so it is not far for her to go. She helped me once before, after the birth of my daughter Fatma, you know, and I am certain she will be willing to help me again." Asım Ağa was intrigued. Very little went on in the palace

42

without his knowledge, and he could not imagine how the elderly midwife could possibly have assisted Murad without him getting to know about it. Noticing his puzzled expression, Murad decided to explain.

"As you know, I named Fatma after my eldest sister. I desperately wanted my sister to learn of this directly from me, but in those days I was even more closely guarded than I am now. Hayriye Hanım offered to take a letter from me to Baltalimanı Palace, Princess Fatma's home. It was a dangerous mission, and I believe her to be a very brave woman." Murad paused, remembering the incident that had taken place twenty-three years previously. It was still fresh in his mind. He fell silent as he mentally replayed it to himself exactly as Hayriye Hanım had described it to him …

… The old beggar-woman hobbled towards the imposing ornamental gates of the palace at Baltalimanı, a few miles further up the European shore of the Bosphorus from Çırağan. She walked with a stick, and it was plain to see that walking caused her a good deal of discomfort. She was barefoot and dressed in rags. The guards at first tried to shoo her away, but not with much enthusiasm or conviction as they could see she was poor, hungry and in distress. Leaning on her stick with one hand, she held out the other towards them in a gesture of supplication. "Kind sirs," she began. "Do not turn away an old woman who has no one to care for her, and no food to eat." They exchanged glances, then shrugged, and with a toss of his head the taller of the two indicated that she could pass through the gates. He did not want to answer to Allah for the sin of denying alms to a needy old woman: he knew the kitchens would willingly give her some bread and warm soup. Once out of sight, she quickened her pace and hurried towards the door of the harem.

It was opened by a sullen-looking young eunuch who told

her sharply to knock on the kitchen door if she was looking for food. Did she not know, he asked, that this was the residence of Her Imperial Highness Princess Fatma, sister to the Sultan? Undeterred by his frosty manner, the beggar-woman demanded an audience with the Senior Eunuch, reminding the young servant of the old custom according to which every Ottoman subject had the right to an audience with a member of the Imperial House if they were willing to say a prayer for them, or swear an oath of loyalty. With obvious irritation at having his evening disturbed, he allowed her to enter and sent a *kalfa* to inform the Senior Eunuch of her arrival. This man did not take long to appear, and as soon as he was close enough for no one to overhear, the beggar-woman knelt to kiss the hem of his robe – and in doing so, whispered that she had come from Çırağan. Trying to remain calm and give no sign that anything unusual was afoot, the shocked Senior Eunuch ordered the other servants to with-draw. He then escorted his unexpected visitor into Princess Fatma's presence.

Once inside the sanctity of the harem, the old beggar-woman threw off her disguise and bowed before the noble lady. As Midwife to the Imperial House, she had delivered Princess Fatma's youngest daughter some years before, and was therefore recognised immediately. The princess wept as she held the letter from her beloved brother in her hands and eagerly read the precious words he had written to her. Without further ado, she sat at her bureau and wrote a hurried reply; then she put it in an envelope together with a photo-graph of herself, and thrust the envelope into Hayriye Hanım's hands. There was no time for conversation – the guards would become suspicious if the old woman did not pass them soon, on her way out of the palace …

… Murad came to himself with a start, as if awakening

from a dream. Turning to Asım Ağa, he apologised for his absent-mindedness, saying that it was the memory of his late sister that had caused him, yet again, to withdraw into himself. And indeed, Asım Ağa had been becoming increasingly concerned to see the former Sultan so distracted: Murad's eyes had clouded over, and for a minute or two he had appeared to have entirely forgotten where he was. Seeing the worried look on Asım Ağa's face, Murad tried to reassure him. "Asım Ağa, it is just that I loved my sister Princess Fatma dearly. I miss her terribly, and I think of her often."

He picked up the enamelled oval guilloche photograph frame that stood next to the backgammon board he had earlier been playing on. The pale apple-green enamel was decorated with laurel leaves wrought in gold, interspersed with diamonds. It was a finely-crafted Fabergé frame, and was thus an appropriate custodian of the precious image it contained. Murad stared at the faded picture of his sister: it was the only photograph he had of her. She was wearing the elaborate gold tiara, diamond-and-pearl necklace and matching diamond and pearl-drop earrings that their father had given her on the occasion of her first marriage.

When news of her nieces' births reached her, Princess Fatma had given her tiara to Hadice and her necklace to Fehime; she had also found a way of giving her earrings to Aliye, who unlike her two elder sisters had been born after Murad had been placed in confinement. Princess Fatma's own three children had all died in infancy, so she had wanted her favourite brother's daughters to have her most precious pieces of jewellery. All her other jewellery had been bequeathed to Selahaddin, to be given on her death to his children and grandchildren in whatever way he saw fit. Having lost her own children, Fatma had poured all her love into Murad's family – despite not having been able to meet them since their imprisonment. She had had to withstand a great deal of tragedy in her life, and Murad still prayed every day that she might be at peace. Fatma's sad eyes now stared back at him from behind the glass with a melancholy, despairing expression that seemed to hold a mute appeal, her lips appearing to quiver. This prompted him to describe to Asım Ağa the time when Hayriye Hanım had risked so much to get the letter to his sister, and had been given the letter and photograph in return.

"When Princess Fatma had handed her reply to Hayriye Hanım, she took off the diamond brooch she was wearing and gave it to her, telling her that it was a gift for her namesake Fatma, her newborn niece," he concluded. "My daughter often wears that brooch. You may have noticed it – it is in the shape of a crescent moon. She knows it makes me happy to see her wearing it as it reminds me of my sister." Murad's eyes returned to the photograph. "She was such a kind, gentle person, Asım Ağa – a real angel! After she died, my brother allocated her palace to our sister Princess Mediha. So you are also to carry a letter announcing the birth of a child at Çırağan to Baltalimanı Palace, although *Inshallah* you will not need to go to such lengths to obtain entry as Hayriye Hanım did that time! The princess lives there with her second husband, Damad Mehmed Ferid Pasha, and her son. You can trust the Pasha. He is no friend of my brother the Sultan."

Asım Ağa had been listening intently. He had often noticed Murad's daughter Fatma wearing the brooch, but had not been aware of how it had come into her possession. The Midwife to the Imperial House must indeed be an outstandingly brave and trustworthy woman: if reports of what she had done had ever reached the ears of Abdülhamid's spies, she would certainly have forfeited her position – and perhaps, even, her life.

"Your Highness, I will entrust the letters for the Princesses Hadice and Fehime to Hayriye Hanım, as you ask. She is most certainly a loyal servant to your esteemed family." Asım Ağa spoke quietly, his head bowed. "With your permission, I will now go to Yıldız Palace to inform His Imperial Majesty of the birth of the young prince, and will then return to perform my duties here. Tonight I will visit the homes of your noble brothers and sisters to deliver the rest of your letters."

"Asım Ağa, I am deeply grateful to you for your most valuable services. Please take care. My brother's spies are everywhere. *Yolunuz açık olsun* – May your way be open," Murad replied.

The devoted old eunuch backed slowly out of the room carrying his scribe's box under his left arm and gripping his walking stick with his right hand. In his left, he held the letter for the Sultan; the other letters, however, had been stowed away in a well-concealed inner pocket of his coat in case an over-zealous guard should decide to search him as he left the palace.

☻ ☻ ☻ ☻ ☻

Murad was alone again. He took one last, lingering look at the photograph on his desk. Then he glanced at his pocket watch. "I must wash and change," he told himself. The watch was one of his most cherished possessions as it had once belonged to his father, Sultan Abdülmecid. Manufactured by Breguet and made of gold, it was beautifully decorated. The dial was of plain design, with simple black Ottoman numerals around the edge. The watch hands were of exquisite work-manship, being inlaid with small diamonds. The enamel on one side of the casing bore a miniature portrait of Sultan

Abdülmecid, while his *tuğra* was engraved on the other. It had been a personal gift from the French Ambassador to his father in commemoration of the victorious conclusion of the Crimean War. Murad could remember his father wearing it, just as he himself did now, and he thought to himself how one day Selahaddin, then Nihad and then this new baby prince would also enjoy using such a beautiful timepiece.

It was nearly four o'clock. Everyone would be dressing, as dinner at the palace was usually served two hours before sunset. Since it was autumn and the evenings were drawing in, everyone in the kitchens would be bustling about so as to have the food ready within the hour; the housemaids would be busy laying the table, and the footmen would be attending to the stoves and lighting the gas lamps and candles. Murad knew that the ladies of the household would all be in a state of high excitement. His daughter Fatma and his granddaughters would have deliberated for hours over which dress to wear, and with which piece of jewellery; meanwhile, their maids would be patiently and expertly arranging their hair. He hoped, of course, that Fatma would choose the crescent-shaped diamond brooch.

He smiled, attempting to lift his mood. The birth of a child was indeed a special occasion, and an evening filled with laughter and amusement would be a much-needed remedy for the grief and sadness that had recently cast its shadow over the palace. Three weeks earlier, Murad's beloved youngest daughter Aliye had died at the tragically young age of twenty-three. Murad had been utterly devastated, and had hardly left his rooms since. Aliye had slipped away after catching a cold, which had then developed into pneumonia. Sultan Abdülhamid had sent his best doctors to Çırağan to treat the princess, and they had recommended that she should be moved to Yıldız Palace for a change of air. Murad had

48

been reluctant to let Aliye leave him, but had allowed himself to be persuaded owing to the seriousness of her condition. Everything possible had been done for her, but Aliye had never recovered. She had been unable to return to her family to spend her last days with them as it would have been too dangerous to move her. Murad had desperately wanted to hold his daughter and kiss her one last time, but even in these extreme circumstances Abdülhamid had refused permission for him to leave Çırağan. Murad had learnt to forgive his brother for many things, but Abdülhamid's heartlessness in this matter weighed on him heavily, and he asked himself if he would ever be able to find it in his heart to forgive him.

Nothing can prepare a parent for losing a child. It is not the natural order of things, but Murad believed that the will of Allah must always be accepted. He also believed in *kismet*, in fate, and his own *kismet* seemed to be an exceptionally unlucky one. His two eldest daughters had been lost to him when they married, and recently he had lost his youngest daughter to illness. Of all his children, only his son Selahaddin and his daughter Fatma remained with him. The loss of the daughters he so adored as a loving father had begun to affect his health: quite simply, it was breaking his heart. Tonight, however, he was determined not to allow the black depression that had engulfed his mind, and the feelings of contrition that tortured his soul, to prevent his family from celebrating the birth of his great-grandson. New life brought a reminder of the importance of family; it was an affirmation of the value of hope, and of the necessity of optimism for what the future might still hold.

CHAPTER FOUR

A Family Evening

Ali Ağa, the Head Butler, proudly surveyed the dining room, adjusting his white cotton gloves as he did so. He was calmer now, but he still felt a little hot under the stiff collar of his uniform: there had been much to prepare that afternoon, and he had become rather flustered. An order for quinces had been given to the fruiterer, but the man had been very late bringing them to the palace. This had caused mayhem in the kitchens; the Head Cook had vented his wrath on the tray-bearers and kitchen boys until the eventual arrival of a basket of the golden-yellow fruit restored the general calm. Ali Ağa thrived on grand occasions such as these, and was delighted that his master had ordered a banquet to be held to celebrate the birth of his first great-grandchild. He thought it a shame that Murad's family dined together so rarely in this beautiful room: their custom was to take their meals in the more informal atmosphere of their own apartments. But not tonight! Tonight was special, and Ali Ağa was excited to have the honour of serving the palace's distinguished residents in these majestic surroundings.

Mistress Aynifer, the Senior Lady Steward, had initially consulted Murad's First Consort, the Lady Mevhibe Eleron, over the details of the dinner. However, Mevhibe had thought-fully said that she would defer to the wishes of the former Sultan's Second Consort, the Lady Reftarıdil, in this matter. Reftarıdil was Selahaddin's mother, and was therefore great-grandmother to the newborn prince, so Mevhibe had felt it was only right that the pleasure of organising the banquet should be given to her. Everyone in the household greatly admired the Lady Mevhibe for her intelligence, and for her endurance and fortitude. She was older than Murad by five years, having married him when he was Crown Prince – still an inexperienced teenager. Unlike his other consorts, she had borne him no children, yet the two remained devoted to one another. Murad had always relied on Mevhibe for her wise counsel and balanced judgement – even more so since the death of his domineering mother, who had not been at all considerate to her.

"I hope the Lady Reftarıdil will be happy when she sees the room," Ali Ağa thought to himself with a twinge of anxiety. The housemaids and footmen had worked tirelessly to get everything ready, and he had ensured that the wishes conveyed to him by the Lady Reftarıdil and Mistress Aynifer had been carried out to the letter. He did not wish to disappoint either of them.

The formal dining room at the Çırağan Palace was a superb example of the neo-Moorish style of architecture in which Ottoman and European Baroque influences were successfully combined to create an artistic whole. Pillars of red porphyry and white Italian marble stood in rows around the room like tall, majestic trees surrounding a forest clearing; on the ceiling high above, gilded stars had been carved into a sky-like canopy of dark, heavy timber framed by deep layers of elaborately-carved coving. Crowning each pillar was an intricate ara-besque capital that could only have been inspired by the Great Mosque of Cordoba or the Al-Hambra Palace in Granada –

those priceless jewels of Moorish architecture. The walls were adorned with a series of decorative panels, interspersed with pillars, that bore various floral and abstract-patterned motifs painted in bold colours. The Çırağan Palace had been designed for Sultan Abdülaziz by the famous Garabet Balyan, and had been completed by two of his sons – Sarkis and Hagop – in 1871; it was one of the many buildings exhibiting the Balyan family's unique style that adorned the city of İstanbul and the nearby shores of the Bosphorus.

Since the times of Sultan Mahmud II, whose rule had begun nearly a century before, the Ottoman tradition of eating at low tables while seated on divans had begun to change among members of the Imperial family and the Ottoman elite. Murad's household had fully embraced the European manner of dining, and the room was furnished in a predominantly Western style. Covering the long dining table was a snow-white linen table-cloth that hung down to the floor. Sixteen high-backed Damas-can chairs, carved from walnut and inlaid with mother-of-pearl, flanked the table on each side. Upholstered in sumptuous red velvet, they were embroidered with stars in red silk. The elaborate silver centrepiece held aloft a large crystal bowl overflowing with tempting ripe fruit. Elegant silver candelabra and ornate silver jardinières filled with exotic cream-coloured orchids were spaced alternately down the middle of the table. The place cards had been written in Reftarıdil's own hand and fitted into a fan-shaped silver holder in front of each seat. Across each gilt-edged Sèvres porcelain dinner plate lay an ivory muslin napkin richly embroidered with gold and silver thread. The gleaming silver cutlery had been freshly polished, the crystal water goblets filled and the candles lit. Ali Ağa could be justly proud of what he had accomplished at such short notice.

He beat the gong at precisely 4.45pm. The doors to all the individual apartments within the main palace and the harem building opened – almost simultaneously, as everyone had been eagerly anticipating this all-too-rare festive occasion. The family was to meet in the blue salon next to the dining room, where they would wait for everyone to assemble before going in to dinner together. First to arrive were Selahaddin's four teenage daughters, the Princesses Rukiye, Adile, Safiye and Atiye. They had run across the gardens from their rooms in the harem, racing each other up the sweeping marble staircase that led up to the door of the main palace building. Then, traversing the patterned marble floor of the entrance lobby, they had skipped up the four steps that brought them into the entrance hall. Here, they had paused to catch their breath, standing under the huge crystal chandelier that hung in the centre of the hall and dominated the space between the colonnades of pillars and arches to either side. Finally, the girls had sprinted, four abreast, up the main staircase to the first floor, taking the stairs two at a time and arriving at the salon slightly flushed but giggling. Their elder sister Princess Behiye, meanwhile, had preferred to refrain from such undignified behaviour: she had followed soon after but at a much slower pace, mounting the carpeted marble steps serenely as befitted her station.

The princesses sat at the round table in the middle of the room chatting excitedly and complimenting each other on their gowns and hairpieces. They wore simple but fashionable dresses inspired by the most recent designs of the leading Paris fashion houses of Worth and Doucet. The girls often tested Sadık Ağa's patience by sending him into the city to purchase the latest issue of *L'Art et la Mode*. This popular French high-society magazine was filled with fashion ideas, and they would spend hours poring over and admiring its hand-coloured plates.

The dresses they were wearing this evening were presents from their Aunt Hadice. Hadice missed her nieces terribly now that she was forbidden to visit the Çırağan Palace, but she enjoyed treating them to extravagant gifts occasionally – they were smuggled into the palace hidden in woven baskets piled high with fresh vegetables. The guards never suspected the handsome young farmer who brought them of such subterfuges. In fact, they barely even took note of the regular suppliers who delivered their produce to the kitchen door each morning to be inspected by the Head Cook before being approved; they were certainly unaware that the young man's family had farmed the fertile fields of the Muradiye Estate in Kadıköy for decades, and were therefore prepared to risk everything for Murad and his family out of loyalty to their old lord and master. As a result, many illicit packages from Hadice and her younger sister Fehime were able to reach the palace undetected.

Hadice shared her nieces' love of Paris fashion, and had instructed her seamstresses to copy designs from *L'Art et la Mode* so that she could surprise the girls with some fashionable creations. They had, of course, been thrilled to receive the dresses and were now delighted to have an occasion to wear them. Each gown was made from silk of a different pastel colour, curving and flowing to the floor like the upturned head of a budding tulip. Intricate floral embroidery covered the bodices and skirts, while the hems were trimmed with ruched chiffon. Sashes decorated with delicate glass beads served to emphasise the slimness of the princesses' waists; the chiffon sleeves were tightly fitted at the top, billowing loosely over their arms before being caught in tight cuffs at their slender wrists. Each of the dresses suited its wearer perfectly, giving the sisters an appearance that was stylish and elegant, but at the same time feminine.

As the princesses waited for the rest of the family to arrive, they were illuminated by the late afternoon sunlight streaming through the tall windows, filling the salon with its autumnal glow. As the sisters turned to face each other, absorbed in intimate conversation, their dresses in pale hues of blue, green, lilac, pink and yellow could have been mistaken for wild flowers of different varieties swaying in the breeze in a spring meadow, while the sound of their lowered voices completed the illusion with the hum of bees.

"Behiye, have you seen Nihad yet?" Atiye asked her eldest sister. Behiye and Nihad had both been born of the same mother, so they were particularly close to each other. If anyone had seen Nihad, and would thus have news of Safiru and the new baby, it would be Behiye.

"Sadly I have not, Atiye," she replied. Atiye was the youngest and prettiest of the sisters. "But we shall see him before long, and then we shall be able to ask him about the baby," said Behiye, squeezing her sister's hand.

❁ ❁ ❁ ❁ ❁

The sound of the door opening interrupted their conversation, and the five sisters looked towards it. Ali Ağa announced Murad's four consorts, and the ladies appeared one by one, in order of seniority. First Mevhibe entered, followed by Reftarıdil, and lastly by the Ladies Şayan and Resan. As they had apartments on the same floor of the palace, all four ladies had come down together. Resan was supported on Şayan's arm as she walked slowly across the room towards the table where Selahaddin's five daughters were sitting.

Resan's grief at losing her daughter Aliye only a few weeks earlier was obvious to all: her downcast eyes were sad and empty. Since she was in mourning, she had dressed plainly and wore no jewellery. Her elder daughter, Fatma, had been a great comfort to her during these difficult weeks, and Resan's eyes now darted around the room looking for her; however, she had not yet arrived. Sensing her anxiety, Şayan whispered to her: "Princess Fatma will be here in a moment. Do not worry, dear sister." She put her arm around Resan to reassure her. Şayan and Resan were not, of course, of the same blood, but all Murad's consorts were very close, affectionately addressing one another as 'Sister'.

With her rose-pink skin, pale blue eyes and thick, wavy hair that was always dressed in the most fashionable manner, Şayan was the most beautiful of Murad's consorts. Still relatively young, she was lively and full of fun, always encouraging everyone to laugh and smile. In fact, she was very similar to her daughter Hadice both in looks and in character. This evening she was wearing a beautiful dress that Murad had given her at the time of Hadice's wedding. As they had both been forbidden to attend their daughter's wedding celebrations, Murad had wanted to treat his Third Consort to something he knew would bring a smile to her face.

The dress had been designed by the famous House of Redfern, and had been sent from London. All the ladies at Çırağan admired it for its exquisite needlework and intricate embroidery. It was made of cream silk overlaid with silk chiffon and lace; to match the colours of Şayan's eyes and cheeks, the lace had been embroidered with a ribbon design in pale blue satin that trailed down the dress, while the hem and bodice were decorated with rose-pink satin flowers. A ruched band of silk satin circled Şayan's waist, giving her a flattering silhouette. The garment had a high neckline, so Şayan did not wear a necklace; however, as the sleeves ended just below the elbow she wore a magnificent diamond bracelet to match her diamond-drop earrings.

On formal occasions, the Imperial Princesses took precedence over women who were not of Imperial Ottoman blood. However, as this was a family occasion, Selahaddin's daughters all rose from their seats to greet Murad's consorts. First they kissed Mevhibe's hand, then that of their grandmother, Reftarıdil; afterwards, they greeted the other two ladies in the same way.

"Grandmother, have you seen Nihad yet?" asked Atiye, eager to hear news of Safıru and the baby.

Reftarıdil gazed down fondly at her pretty granddaughter. "Come and sit with me by the stove, and I will tell you what Fuad told me when he came to my rooms earlier," she replied. "He was just as excited as you are!" The elderly lady took Atiye's hand and led her towards the stove: she always felt the cold, and wanted to feel the welcoming heat envelop her body before she recounted her story. The stove was covered in light blue tiles decorated with cream tulips. In fact, everything in the blue salon was blue, cream, pink or gold – as if intended as a tribute to the piercing blue eyes, cream-coloured skin and rose-pink lips of the many Circassian women in the Imperial Harem. Even the paintings – a series of beautiful Bosphorus scenes by Mıgırdiç Civanyan, one of the many talented artists who had been employed to produce paintings to adorn the palace under the supervision of Chief Court Painter Hadji Mıgırdiç Chrakyan – adhered to this same colour palette.

She adored her son Selahaddin and was a kind and thoughtful mother to him, as well as an extremely attentive grandmother to his children; she had, however, become rather plump in recent years owing to her fondness for baklava! Reftarıdil did not share Şayan's interest in fashion, and was very frugal in her habits. Today, she was wearing her favourite dusky-pink dress, cut in a style that twenty years ago had been quite the fashion. It was covered in tier after tier of ruched satin and fussy cream lace frills. She also wore a cream velvet capelet, embroidered in pink satin, to keep out the chill, together with a single piece of jewellery – a large ruby and diamond ring that Murad had given her soon after their marriage.

Despite the fact that she was approaching her seventieth year, Mevhibe looked as striking and seductive as she always had done. Murad still found her black eyebrows and heavily-kohled eyes enchanting, and was captivated by her witty, intelligent conversation. Mevhibe wore a translucent black lace and tulle dress embellished with black glass beads, overlaid on a cream silk dress with cream lace sleeves; meanwhile, a black velvet sash at her waist emphasised her slim but buxom figure. Lustrous pearls hung in tangled strands around her long neck.

Mevhibe's serene and dignified manner was fully in accord with her position as First Consort. Although she had not been blessed with children herself, and understandably felt both sad and bitter as a result, she hid her feelings well and was like a second mother to all Murad's children; she took a particular interest in Fehime, who had been left motherless after the death of Meyliservet, his Fourth Consort. Murad was always profoundly affected when a loved one died, and had been devastated by the loss of Meyliservet. His hair had turned white in the weeks following her death, and he had denied himself the pleasure of music for many months while he mourned her.

As soon as Şayan and Resan had seated themselves, the door to the blue salon opened once more to admit Naziknaz,

Jalefer and Fuad. Fuad immediately ran over to join his grandmother Reftarıdil and his sister Atiye near the stove. Meanwhile, Selahaddin's two wives approached the five princesses to greet them formally before embracing them. They then went up to each of Murad's consorts to kiss their hands as a mark of respect before rejoining the princesses at the table.

Naziknaz and Jalefer shared the responsibility of acting as mothers to all their husband's children. The Lady Tevhide, the mother of Rukiye, Adile and Atiye, had died many years ago, as had the Lady Güliter, the mother of Safiye. These sad events had brought the members of Selahaddin's family closer together, making them even more dependent upon one another.

Jalefer was the most fashionable lady in the harem at Çırağan. The young princesses had been wondering what she would be wearing, and how she would dress her hair. They were not disappointed, and gasped when they saw her. She wore a cream silk gown, expertly cut in the latest style, that curved downwards in the same way as their own new dresses did. Over this, she wore a transparent cream and black Chantilly lace dress with long flouncy lace sleeves – creating a highly dramatic effect. The dress was predominantly cream lace, with black lace forming the bottom part of the skirt. The lace was embroidered in cream silk, adding detail to the bodice and skirt, while a cream-pleated satin belt cinched in her waist. Jalefer had swept her wavy hair up into a pompadour bun, tilted slightly forward to cover her forehead. It was held in place with a diamond hair comb in the shape of a star.

Naziknaz also looked resplendent, and radiated happiness. Tulips and roses were embroidered in silver and gold thread across the bodice and skirt of her powder-blue silk gown, which was also decorated with small rosebuds made from gathered cream chiffon. Sequins on the layered cream lace sleeves twinkled in the late afternoon sunlight. She had been looking forward to the time when she would become a grandmother with keen anticipation, and was eager to tell everyone how beautiful her little grandson was.

"*Validem*, have you seen Safiru and the baby?" Behiye asked. Everyone's eyes turned towards Naziknaz.

"I have, and by the grace of Allah they are both well." Naziknaz could not contain her excitement as she continued, the words pouring out of her mouth. "I have just left her. She is resting now. She told me to tell you all not to worry. Her pains were long, but she was brave and strong throughout her labour. Oh – and she asked me to invite you all to visit her over the coming days."

Naziknaz's eyes filled with tears as she began to speak of her grandchild. "Nihad's son is such a beautiful boy. I have cradled him in my arms and kissed his lovely blue eyes. *Mashallah!* I am sure he is going to be a truly noble prince!"

"Lady Naziknaz, who does my nephew look like?" interrupted Fuad.

"I believe he looks like his grandfather," she replied, smiling fondly at Fuad. "And maybe a little like you too, my dear Fuad." That reply seemed to please him a great deal.

Everyone had a lot of questions. What colour is his hair? Is his cry loud and strong? Has he taken to his wetnurse? Naziknaz enjoyed answering each one – until the door opened again, and everyone rose from their seats.

☻ ☻ ☻ ☻ ☻

Murad entered the salon followed by his son Selahaddin, his grandson Nihad and his daughter Fatma. Mistress Aynifer followed unobtrusively behind them. The men looked very distinguished in their black tailcoats, white ties and waist-coats. As always, Fatma looked poised and regal as she glided through the doors behind Nihad. Her dress was simple but made from the finest ivory silk, with antique lace sleeves that seemed to float over her pale arms. The bodice was embellished with embroidered ribbons and bows of silver and gold thread; these also decorated the hem and train of the dress. Meanwhile, a mink-coloured velvet belt around her waist flattered her curvaceous figure. Over her heart, she wore her treasured crescent-shaped diamond brooch.

Murad smiled with satisfaction at the sight of his family gathered together. Everyone he loved most in the world was present – with the obvious exceptions of his eldest daughters Hadice and Fehime, who he hoped had by now received his letters, delivered through the good offices of Hayriye Hanım. Murad briefly thought of his dear, sweet Aliye who had so recently been taken from him. She would have enjoyed the evening very much: she loved large family gatherings, and had been looking forward to the arrival of the new baby. However, this was a festive occasion, and Murad was not going to allow himself to be seduced by melancholy. Fuad was the first to greet him, followed by his five granddaughters. They each kissed his hand and raised it to their foreheads before embracing him, and he kissed them all tenderly on their foreheads.

"My dearest granddaughters, you all look so grown up and beautiful this evening. Tell me – are these new dresses that you are wearing?" he asked.

The princesses were surprised and delighted that he had noticed their gowns. Being unused to such compliments, they could not prevent themselves from blushing. "Yes they are, Grandfather," answered Safiye. "They were a gift from Aunt Hadice."

"They are copies of the very latest designs from Paris, Grandfather," added Adile excitedly.

"Well, I think these latest Paris fashions are enchanting," Murad said. Privately, he was happy to learn that the young princesses were still very much in his eldest daughter's thoughts. "When I visited Paris as a young man, I remember thinking how stylish and sophisticated the ladies there were. I pray that one day you will have the opportunity to go to Paris yourselves; then, perhaps, you will be able to visit one of the famous fashion houses." The sisters smiled, their minds beginning to drift and dream. Murad then turned his attention to his consorts, each of whom greeted him in turn.

Once the formalities were over, he kissed the hand of his Second Consort. "Lady Reftarıdil, my honourable wife, I am happy to see you looking so well. Your new position as great-grandmother obviously suits you!"

Reftarıdil smiled up at her husband. "Thank you, my Lord. I thank Allah that the Muradiye line has been extended with this child, and I pray that he too will one day have a healthy son of his own to carry your memory forward." Murad appreciated these words: they were a reminder, once again, that in the future lay hope.

Finally, Selahaddin's two wives approached him. They bowed their heads deferentially, then kissed his hand and raised it to their foreheads.

"My dear daughters, I have been so looking forward to seeing you both this evening," Murad said. He took hold of Naziknaz's hand. "What a special day it has been for you, my dear Lady Naziknaz. It is wonderful to see you looking so happy. Have you seen the child yet?"

"I have, my Lord. He is a beautiful boy. I think I can see in him a resemblance to your son," she replied.

Murad smiled. He could still remember the day when

Selahaddin had been born, and he had looked on him for the first time. No moment in life could possibly have been more special. "I am sure this child will bring joy to your life, my dear Lady Naziknaz. You deserve to have the love of this precious boy, and to love him in return. And you will be a most valuable source of support to the Lady Safiru. Being young, she will need your help and advice, both now and in the future."

"Thank you, my Lord," she responded.

Murad then turned to Jalefer. "How Fuad has grown, Lady Jalefer! He has such great spirit and courage! I have no doubt that his penchant for adventure will lead him to achieve much in life!"

"Thank you, my Lord," she said, and withdrew to stand beside Selahaddin, her husband.

Everyone was now assembled and all the formal greetings had been performed. Murad hoped that the family would now be able to relax and enjoy the evening together.

"Come then, shall we go in to dinner?" he said.

� ☯ ☯ ☯ ☯ ☯

Aynifer Usta gave Ali Ağa the signal to open the heavy walnut doors leading into the grand dining room. Surrounded by a large, imposing horseshoe arch, they were inlaid with an elaborate mother-of-pearl design. Moorish-style arches of this kind could be seen framing windows, alcoves and niches as well as doors throughout the palace. Mistress Aynifer and Ali Ağa bowed as the family walked past them into the dining room. Murad led them in, followed by the three Imperial Princes – Selahaddin and his two sons. The six Imperial Princesses entered next: first Murad's daughter Fatma, then his five granddaughters, in order of age. Behind them came

63

his four consorts, and finally Selahaddin's two wives. This sequence reflected the order of precedence among the members of the Imperial family. However, once everyone was inside the sanctuary of the dining room the atmosphere changed: the rules of protocol were relaxed, and soon the room was filled with the warmth of a family gathering.

Fuad and Atiye helped their elders find their places, leaning over to read the name cards Reftarıdil had written out. They noticed that their grandmother had seated them next to each other and opposite Adile and Safiye, and were relieved to see that the youngest members of the family were to be grouped together at one end of the table – it would be much more fun that way! Murad took his seat at the centre; then the rest of the family sat down.

There was a palpable air of excitement in the Çırağan Palace that evening – something that had not been seen for many years. Everyone could feel it, and everyone could sense Murad's peaceful and contented mood as happy laughter mingled with the buzz of lively conversation around the table.

"The table looks beautiful, dear sister," said Mevhibe, smiling at Reftarıdil. "I congratulate you. The orchids are absolutely wonderful." The two ladies sat on either side of Murad, flanked by Şayan and Resan, his Third Consort and First Junior Consort. There was no resentment or rivalry between any of them, only friendship and respect. Mevhibe could at times be somewhat distant and aloof, it was true, but everyone accepted this aspect of her character and still admired her for her mature wisdom, for the never-failing support she gave to Murad and for her tenacious loyalty to him.

"Thank you, Lady Mevhibe," Reftarıdil replied, relieved to have been given her approval.

Selahaddin sat opposite his mother, with his wives on

either side of him. He looked to his left, where Naziknaz was sitting. Her eyes sparkled even brighter than the diamonds she was wearing, and her face was lit up by a smile. She had never looked lovelier, he thought. She felt his eyes upon her, and turned to meet his gaze.

"My dear, it warms my heart to see you looking so happy," he said with deep affection. "We have been blessed this day. *Alhamdulillah!* You must tell me all about our grandson."

As Naziknaz shared an apartment with Nihad and his wife, she had been informed as soon as Safiru's pains had begun, and it was indeed she who had sent for the midwife. So now she began to recall everything – though perhaps in a little too much detail for Selahaddin's comfort!

Nihad was still slightly stunned by the afternoon's events. He sat quietly between his mother and his aunt Fatma. His sisters Behiye and Rukiye were also at his end of the table, sitting opposite each other. They had been complimenting Fatma on her dress and her beautiful brooch. Everyone in the family knew the story of how the brooch had arrived at Çırağan, and was therefore aware of its special significance. The three ladies all waited for Nihad to tell them about his son; however, true to his accustomed manner, he was frustratingly taciturn and inhibited, and did not seem at all forthcoming.

Fatma was the first to engage him. "Nihad, we all thank Allah that your son has arrived safely! I pray that Allah may grant him the blessing of growing up with both his parents by his side, and he may enjoy good health and liberty while on this earth. I trust the Lady Safiru is recovering well?"

"Thank you for your solicitude, Aunt. It is indeed most kind," replied Nihad with his customary formality. "Safiru is so small and delicate that I did worry for her, but she amazed me by her fortitude. With rest, *Inshallah* she will soon recover her strength and return to health."

"Dear brother, I am so happy for you, and I am so looking forward to meeting my nephew," said Rukiye. "I am sure you will make an excellent father."

"Nihad, I wept with happiness when I heard the news," said Behiye. "Your son will be truly loved by us all. Look how happy this has made Grandfather, too! It is wonderful to see him smiling again." Here, a slight wobble of emotion entered her voice; however, she soon recovered herself, and could not resist poking fun at Nihad in the way only an older sister could. "Mother says he looks a little like Father, but I do hope he grows up to be rather less serious than him – and you!" she continued, trying to suppress a giggle.

Nihad smiled. He was used to Behiye's good-natured jibes, and did not resent them in any way. He loved all his sisters very much. They were all so kind and so genuinely caring, and they always knew how to make him feel more at ease. He picked up his water goblet and took a long sip, letting out a sigh as he placed it back down on the table. It was a sigh of relief – relief that by the grace of Allah, Safiru had survived the ordeal of childbirth, and that their son seemed strong and healthy. Now it was all beginning to sink in – he was a father! He had much to be thankful for …

❀ ❀ ❀ ❀ ❀

At that moment, the doors swung open – and the room was suddenly filled with the smell of almond soup spiced with nutmeg and sweetened with pomegranate seeds. Reftarıdil had planned out the menu, and the cooks had worked tirelessly all afternoon to prepare the culinary delights she had chosen for this rare feast. The tray-bearers rushed between the kitchens and the serving corridor delivering dish after dish for the *kalfas* to bring into the dining room. To the people around the table, each course seemed even more delicious than the last. The soup was followed by sea bass roasted with walnuts and spices, and served with a lemon and parsley dressing. Then came one of Murad's favourite dishes: lamb stewed with apples, apricots, raisins and cumin. This was accompanied by rice mixed with currants and pine nuts, as well as by okra cooked slowly with tomatoes, lemon juice and olive oil.

There was a choice of two puddings. Reftarıdil smiled quietly to herself as she saw Selahaddin choose the quince poached in syrup and served with clotted cream, walnuts and pistachios. This had been his favourite pudding ever since childhood. As he savoured the first mouthful, he looked appreciatively at his mother, who was sitting across the table from him. She also guessed – rightly, as it turned out – that Nihad would choose the rose-water rice pudding with pomegranate, pistachio and cardamom, this being his favourite treat.

"Reftarıdil, my dear faithful wife, you have spoiled us all with this magnificent dinner," Murad said as everyone sat back in their chairs after the meal. "That lamb was absolutely delicious. I am touched to see that after all these years you still remember how much I love that dish."

"Thank you, my Lord," she replied. "It has been an honour for me to organise this dinner for the family."

Murad smiled at her. "Look how much Selahaddin is enjoying the quince. It reminds me of how he used to eat two or three portions when he was a child!" he said, laughing.

"Yes, it reminds me too of those happy days, my Lord. How quickly the years have flown by!" Murad and Reftarıdil shared a moment of silent reflection, their minds drifting back to the days when they had lived in the Crown Prince's apartments at the Dolmabahçe Palace in those relatively carefree times before their confinement.

"I know that in many ways fate has been unkind to us, but in other ways it has been most generous, my Lady Reftarıdil! We have a beautiful son and seven wonderful grandchildren – and now a great-grandchild as well. Allah has blessed us," Murad said, with no hint of regret or equivocation. His eyes passed lovingly over the people gathered around the table.

Just then, the sound of cannon fire gave everyone a start, and all conversation stopped. Five rounds were set off in unison, each from one of the different quarters of İstanbul, and this was followed by the call to prayer.

"My brother has obviously received my letter telling him of the birth of our baby prince," Murad said to his family after the fifth round had died away. "I am pleased to see that he must have ordered the announcement to be made in the proper way. I also asked him to have five rams sacrificed in each district of the city, as required by custom, and I pray that he will honour this request as well." It gave Murad great satisfaction to know that the birth of his great-grandson had been officially announced to the people of İstanbul, and he hoped that the child would receive their prayers that evening.

He was then handed a clean napkin by Tarzınigar Usta, the Mistress of the Pantry, who was standing behind him. After wiping his hands and mouth, Murad called Ali Ağa over to him and asked him to summon the cooks. "I will join you for coffee in the drawing room after sunset prayers, but first I want to thank the cooks personally," he told Reftarıdil. "You retire with the ladies; I will be with you in a few minutes. Perhaps we could have some music this evening? Maybe Fatma and Rukiye will play for us. We are celebrating, after all."

Reftarıdil smiled at her husband, then dutifully rose from her chair and invited the princesses and the other consorts to join her in the main drawing room. They stood up and courteously took their leave. As Fatma was walking past her father, she kissed him on the cheek; then she took the arm of Resan, her mother. She could sense that her mother was struggling to contain her grief and find some way of coping with the joyful atmosphere of the evening.

"Come, Fuad," said Jalefer, holding out her hand to her son.

"I am not one of the ladies. I am a man," was his reply. "I will join you in the drawing room in a little while, *Validem*."

Jalefer was taken aback by her son's reply. Selahaddin, too, was more than a little surprised by this unexpected riposte, while Nihad was shocked at his younger brother's impertinence. Murad burst out laughing. "He is right, of course," he said. "He is not one of the ladies. However, Fuad, you are not yet a man! So what are we to do?"

Fuad shot a pleading look towards his grandfather. He did not like being treated as a child, and very much wanted to be regarded as one of the men of the household. Murad rubbed his beard thoughtfully. "If you promise me that you will always remember to treat your mother with respect, and if you apologise to her for your reply just now, which was not very polite, then you may stay here with us."

Fuad's face lit up. He turned towards his mother with a serious expression. "I am sorry, dearest Mama. It was not my intention to offend you in any way. Please forgive me."

"Of course, Fuad," replied Jalefer graciously. She was sad that her little boy was growing up, but at the same time she could not help admiring his spirit – something she knew he had inherited from her. Aware that a rite of passage was taking place, she bowed her head and seemed deep in thought as she followed the other ladies out of the dining room.

Murad invited Fuad to sit next to him. Nihad gave his little brother a disapproving look, but said nothing. Minutes later, the senior cooks of the Çırağan Palace filed into the dining room and lined up nervously, their eyes lowered in the presence of Murad, Selahaddin and the two young princes. They had hoped and prayed that the dishes they had prepared would meet with the approval of the Imperial family, but had never imagined that they would be summoned to appear before Murad.

"I want to thank you personally, on behalf of my family, for the delicious dinner we had this evening. May Allah bless your hands," Murad said, using the traditional form of words. "I know that I have adopted many Western ways, and that some of them may puzzle you, but I want you to know that I will never acquire a taste for Western food. Nothing can compare with the delicacy and refinement of Ottoman cuisine, prepared by our skilled and inventive Ottoman cooks. You are all masters of your art, and I thank you."

The cooks were at a loss to know how to react to such high praise. Tears began to well up in their eyes, which remained lowered all the while. They clasped their hands even more tightly in front of their aprons; meanwhile, their hearts thumped with pride as they experienced an upsurge of love for their master. Then the Head Cook thanked Murad, and Ali Ağa ushered them out of the room.

Murad now addressed his son and his two grandsons. "We are privileged to have the love and devotion of a household staff of forty-five special people. Appreciate all they do for you, and never take it for granted. We are fortunate indeed to have such loyal servants."

A look of concern came over Selahaddin's face. His father's state of health had been worrying him of late, and his parent's behaviour this evening had been more than a little unusual. Somehow, tonight's dinner had seemed more than just a celebration in honour of the birth of a new prince

… Was it his imagination, or was he correct in feeling that in some way this occasion was a farewell – his father's way of preparing to say goodbye?

"Good! So now let us perform our prayers, and then join the ladies!" Murad said with a sudden air of decisiveness, standing up from the table. Then he asked for the Mistress of the Ewer to bring the ablution basins and towels to him, and Selahaddin was relieved to be left to ponder without his father's gaze upon him.

CHAPTER FIVE

Music and Dancing

THE handle turned slowly, and the door opened without Hadice looking up from her book. The day before she had held an intimate 'At-Home' attended by her sister Fehime and a few ladies of the Imperial Court. Hadice had also invited the celebrated society hostess and poetess Nigar Hanım, who had greatly amused the company with tales of her infamous literary salon. Every Tuesday between the hours of two and four, ladies gathered at one of her homes in Nişantaşı and Rumeli Hisarı to enjoy the intellectual conversation that flowed there; later, between four and six, she received both men and women, and entertained them in the same way. İstanbul's most prominent politicians, as well as its most distinguished writers, artists and musicians, could all be found in her drawing room on Tuesdays.

Hadice and Fehime greatly admired Nigar Hanım, and had told her of their wish to attend one of her meetings incognito one day in order to listen to the stimulating conversations of her acquaintances, with their exciting and inspiring ideas. Nigar Hanım had promised to try to arrange this; then, before taking her leave to prepare for the following day's reception, she had given each of the sisters a copy of *Echo*, her latest book of poetry. Hadice had spent the whole day immersed in these sorrowful verses. She could relate all too easily to the unmistakable feelings of heartache that emanated from the pages. These moving words, written by a woman who had been brave enough to divorce a husband she did not love, and thus escape from him – something she had done not once but twice – inspired Hadice to fight for her own happiness.

Perizad Kalfa approached bearing a letter on a silver salver, and bowed before the princess. When Hadice looked up and saw the small envelope she felt her heart leap within her chest, her body flush with the tumultuous fires of passion and her mind begin racing wildly – was the letter from him? She snatched it eagerly from the tray and dismissed her *kalfa*. But then her eyes fell on the neat black lettering: no, this handwriting was not his. Her heartbeats slowed and the fire within her died as the anguish of disappointment consumed her. She turned the envelope over in her hands and studied the monogrammed seal: the letter was from the other man she loved – her beloved father.

☻ ☻ ☻ ☻ ☻

Meanwhile, in the neighbouring *yalı*, a young man sat in the *selamlık* composing a letter. He was Mehmed Kemaleddin Pasha, the dashingly handsome and notoriously charming husband of Princess Naime, Sultan Abdülhamid's second daughter. He felt relieved to have finally escaped the harem and the unwanted attentions of his wife, for he could think of little else but the beautiful, the captivating, the totally bewitching Hadice. He knew it was dangerous – reckless, even – to carry on a secret correspondence with her, but he did not care. He gave no thought to the possible consequences – only to the pleasures that might await him.

73

Since first seeing Hadice staring down at him from her window as he sawed planks of wood for the pergola he was building in the garden of his *yalı*, he had been totally infatuated. A week later he had engineered a meeting: he had burst into his wife's salon in the harem unannounced, interrupting her conversation with Hadice, her cousin, who was visiting her. They had both been taken by surprise; Hadice had been unveiled, yet she had made no attempt to hide her face. Instead, she had smiled her most coquettish smile. She seemed to him to be confident, exciting, modern – everything, in fact, that Naime was not. Since that first encounter, Kemaleddin had often joined the two women if he was at home when Hadice called, and whenever they were apart he had found himself longing for her next visit. He enjoyed her witty, enlightened conversation and her playful, vivacious manner. She was different from anyone he had ever met, and he found her charms utterly intoxicating.

Despite having exchanged letters for the past few weeks thanks to the good offices of his ever-devoted servant Niko, the two had not yet been alone together. However, Hadice's recent letter had given him cause to hope that she might indeed be willing to consider the idea: during her last visit, he had entertained the two princesses with one of Nasreddin Hodja's amusing folk tales (one involving a very stubborn donkey) and Hadice had laughed – really laughed – while Naime had responded only with a forced smile. He had given Hadice his silk handkerchief to wipe away her tears of laughter, and she had taken it home with her by mistake. The next day, she had returned it – with his initials embroidered in one corner, and perfumed with her own distinctive perfume.

Kemaleddin now took the handkerchief from his top pocket and held it to his nose for the umpteenth time that day; he breathed in the rich, sweet fragrance of jasmine that lingered on the silk. "It may be presumptuous of me," he thought, "but my intuition is telling me that she feels for me what I feel for her." And when it came to the ladies, he told himself, that intuition was never wrong! He decided that he would suggest a late evening tryst in the summer house at the back of Hadice's garden in two days' time: the waning moon, now only a sliver, would ensure that the evening was a dark one, so they would not be easily discovered. As he wrote his reply to her, his heart pounded in anticipation: would she come?

☙ ☙ ☙ ☙ ☙

As the princes left the prayer room, the tranquil sound of water flowing in the large internal fountain greeted their ears. Water gushed continuously from the spout, cascading into the pool in a row of glistening silver ribbons. This eternal cycle, this constant journey with no interruption and no end, was an apt reflection of the grinding monotony afflicting the lives of those souls who were condemned to live within the palace. This evening, however, that monotony had, for once, been broken.

"That must be Rukiye I can hear playing a polka," said Murad as the men approached the door to the drawing room. "She plays exquisitely, does she not, Selahaddin?"

"Yes, Father. But how can you be so sure it is Rukiye?" asked Selahaddin.

"Because she plays with such passion, such intensity. I can always tell when it is her playing. She has a really exceptional gift," he responded. Murad was an accomplished pianist himself, as well as a composer, and had encouraged a love of music in his family. He appreciated the natural talent Rukiye was blessed with, and was impressed by her dedication to achieving proficiency on the instrument; in fact, he often listened unobserved while she was practising.

The attendants then swung the doors open – to reveal a scene of such gaiety that the princes stood transfixed, afraid to interrupt the moment in case the whole picture vanished like a mirage. Even Fuad stood still. Murad had been right: Rukiye was sitting at the piano, her back perfectly straight as her fingers danced lightly over the ebony and ivory keys. She was accompanied by two senior *kalfas* who were members of the palace's musical ensemble: Lebriz Kalfa, who was playing the flute, and Dürrünab Kalfa, who was vigorously plucking at the strings of her violin as she played a pizzicato passage.

It appeared that most of the household had come to join the assembled ladies: a number of the senior housemaids and attendants were also present. Some stood around the edges of the room, while others were serving coffee and sherbet. Murad noticed that his *Gözdes*, his Favourites – the Ladies Gevherriz, Nevdür, Remişnaz and Filizten – had also been invited. He looked over towards the oval table in the corner where his consorts and Naziknaz were playing dominoes. Reftarıdil was among them, sitting nearest the stove: she was always to be found in the warmest place in any room! She had made every effort to make the evening special, thinking of everything down to the last detail and taking care of everyone's needs. In the centre of the room, the princesses and Jalefer were dancing the polka under the approving eye of Desteriz Kalfa, the Palace Dance Director. They twirled and skipped gracefully across the highly-polished inlaid wooden floor, their skirts swirling around them like Dervish robes.

Looking up from the piano, Rukiye noticed Murad, her father and her brothers watching her. She immediately stopped playing and rose from the piano stool. Everyone else, too, stopped what they were doing to stand and bow towards the princes.

"Please do not stop playing, my precious Rukiye," Murad said. "Everyone – please continue as you were before. No formalities, not tonight." So all those present bowed again and resumed their games, their conversations and their duties. "Is that Strauss you were playing, my dear grandchild?" he asked.

"Yes, Grandfather. This piece is called 'Pizzicato Polka'. Do you like it?" Rukiye replied.

"I do indeed. And you were playing it beautifully."

"Thank you, Grandfather," she said with a slight flush of embarrassment.

"Desteriz Kalfa has been teaching us how to dance the polka all summer, Grandfather," Atiye explained enthusiastically. "So we thought we would dance it tonight."

"Unfortunately, I only saw a little of the dance as I came in. Will you start again from the beginning so that I can see how well you have learnt your lessons?" Murad asked.

This delighted all the princesses, and Jalefer too. Murad, Selahaddin and Nihad sat together to enjoy the dancing while Fuad joined his grandmother, Naziknaz and the other ladies playing dominoes. The Mistress of the Coffee Service – the *Kahveci Usta* – approached and bowed low before the princes. She held a silver tray on which rested a small dish containing pieces of Turkish Delight flavoured with orange blossom and lightly dusted with powdered sugar, and beside it three fine white porcelain cups encased in enamelled silver *zarfs*. The rich aroma of the slowly-brewed coffee distracted the princes from the dancing, but only long enough for each of them to take one of the delicate cups and thank the *usta* who was serving them.

Murad also took a piece of Turkish Delight: this evening, surely, no-one could deny him this luxury!

☯ ☯ ☯ ☯ ☯

Orange blossom had always been his favourite flavour, ever since his childhood. He knew his doctors had forbidden such dangerous indulgences, but Murad's spirit had not been broken during his long confinement, and he remained as stubborn and defiant as he had always been. He quickly placed the tempting morsel in his mouth before any of his consorts noticed what he was doing, and as he chewed slowly on the sweet *lokum* it melted on his tongue, filling his mouth with the delicate, fragrant flavour. He then took the silk handkerchief from his pocket and used it to wipe away any tell-tale traces of powdered sugar that may have adhered to his neatly-trimmed moustache. For all his stubbornness, Murad had no wish to upset his consorts, knowing as he did that they would be dismayed if they caught him eating sweets.

Murad suffered from diabetes. His doctors had put him on a strict diet in the belief that this would help them manage his condition. They had studied the findings of a French doctor by the name of Bouchardat who had observed that when his diabetic patients were suffering from starvation at the time of the Siege of Paris, which took place during the Franco-Prussian War, they experienced fewer symptoms of their illness as a result of the lower level of glucose in their bodies. As a result, Bouchardat advocated a diet specially designed to control the effects of diabetes on those afflicted with the disease. The doctors of the Ottoman Court wanted Murad to follow this demanding regime; however, ever since his deposition he had been mistrustful of the medical profession, and was wisely wary of his doctors' intentions. The nervous breakdown that he had suffered after the sudden death of his uncle, Abdülaziz, had been misdiagnosed as a form of incurable madness, and Murad was convinced that the doctors had done this on the orders of Abdülhamid; he believed they had knowingly given a mistaken diagnosis of his condition at his brother's behest, exaggerating the seriousness of his symptoms and prolonging his illness in order to keep him from the throne, while at the same time lining their own pockets.

And so Murad, always eager for knowledge, had decided to read further papers on the subject of diabetes. He was particularly interested in the recent discoveries of Joseph von Mering and Oskar Minkowski, who had found that the pancreas performed a fundamentally important role in the body's functioning. They had understood that diabetes was caused by a dysfunctional pancreas, leading eventually to the patient's death. Although Murad was generally careful about what he ate, he believed these two men's research to be conclusive; he surmised that he must have an unhealthy pancreas, and did not think this condition could be treated merely by abstaining from the occasional piece of Turkish Delight! As a consequence of this self-diagnosis, Murad had instructed his *kalfas* to disobey the orders of his doctors, and also to ignore the instructions of his consorts and his daughters. He wanted to be able to enjoy sugary treats on special occasions, and this evening was certainly one such time.

After dancing the polka, the girls danced a quadrille, followed by another polka. Murad's consorts and Naziknaz continued to play dominoes, while the men sat and sipped their coffee. Despite its great size, the room was comfortably warm. All the stoves were lit, and a large Baccarat crystal chandelier shone from the gilded ceiling above. The red silk damask curtains were drawn, shutting out the world outside – that world that the people inside were not a part of – and hiding the intricately carved neo-Gothic stone pendants which dropped down outside the windows like cold, hard stalactites. The curtains, which hung from ornate gilt pelmets, were trimmed with thick gold fringes and adorned with decorative gold tassels. In each corner of the room, tall floor-standing candelabras stood on marble plinths like sentries on duty. Light flickered through their glass-etched shades onto the faces of the ladies in the room; it also partially illuminated the seascape masterpieces by Ivan Ayvazovsky that hung opposite each other, inset in the marble-clad walls.

"Are you not tired, my dear grandchildren?" Murad asked once his coffee was finished.

"Not at all, Grandfather, although I do feel a little warm and giddy," replied Adile. Then she added: "Would you like to dance the next dance with us, Grandfather?" Nihad was shocked by his sister's suggestion, and glared at her disapprovingly.

"I have been waiting for an invitation to join you," Murad said, smiling. "Yes, let us all dance." Selahaddin and Nihad exchanged nervous glances. "Come now, we cannot let the ladies have all the enjoyment! We too must share in it a little." Murad stood up. He loved to dance, but had not done so in a very long time. On his return from his state visit to Europe he had taught Desteriz Kalfa all the dances he had learnt at the European courts, and she had then taught them to his children, his grandchildren and all the ladies of the harem. "Selahaddin, I think you should dance with the Lady Jalefer, but do try not to step on her toes!" Everyone giggled.

They knew Selahaddin was not accustomed to dancing. "Nihad, I think you should ask your mother to dance with you. As a young woman, she used to know all the steps to every dance. You will be in safe hands with her!"

"As you command, Grandfather," Nihad said, unable to disguise his reluctance. His sense of duty and his unswerving belief in the principle of obedience to one's elders forced him to consent to his grandfather's wish, although he longed with every fibre of his being to remain seated on the sofa and be exempted from involvement in a pointless pastime that always made him feel achingly self-conscious.

"Nihad, my dear grandson, I love you dearly, but you do need to learn to be a little less serious and allow yourself a little more fun now and then!" Murad replied. "We are celebrating the birth of your son. If you will not dance and be merry tonight, when will you ever do so? Your mother will be so happy if you ask her to partner you, and is it not your duty to please her?"

"Yes, of course, Grandfather," said Nihad dutifully. He bowed and walked over to the table where his mother had been playing dominoes, and asked her to dance.

"Fuad, come here, dear boy," called Murad. Fuad obeyed immediately. "Now that you are a young man, it is time for you to learn how to dance. You can be your sister Atiye's partner." Fuad beamed up at his grandfather and went to take his sister's hand. "Rukiye, you have entertained us all long enough with your beautiful playing, but now it is time for you to join in the festivities. Come and dance with Behiye. Now, where are the twins? Adile and Safiye, you can dance together, too." The sisters were not really twins, but as they had been born only a few months apart and were always to be found in each other's company, the family often called them 'the twins'. By now Murad had arranged a partner for almost everyone. He knew his consorts and Favourites would not wish to dance, but would prefer instead to watch from the sides; that left only his daughter unspoken for.

Murad walked up to her. "My dear beautiful Fatma, will you do me the honour of the next dance?" he said, holding out his hand.

"The honour will be mine, Baba," she replied with her usual sweetness of demeanour.

The palace's musical ensemble had gathered around the piano with their instruments. "A waltz, I think, Dürrünab Kalfa," Murad said, addressing the director of the ensemble. "I know it may not be as fashionable as it used to be, but I do love 'The Blue Danube'!"

Standing guard at the door, Ali Ağa looked on as the music began to play and Murad's family started dancing together. Tears welled up in his eyes: it had been so long since he had seen his master and his family looking so happy – an oppressive air of melancholy usually surrounded everything that happened within the walls of Çırağan. The music was intoxicating. Even Mistress Aynifer, usually so eagle-eyed and alert, seemed distracted by the scene, and did not appear to notice that one of the lamps had burned out. Murad's consorts swayed in their seats and his *Gözdes* tapped their toes as they watched the younger members of the family float around and around the drawing room, swept along by the undulating rhythm of the waltz as if in the current of a swirling river; the dancers rose and fell in time with the music like waves lapping gently at the shores of the Bosphorus. It seemed that time had stopped.

"I see you are wearing your brooch, my dear Fatma," Murad said as he twirled his daughter around the room. She smiled.

"Why do you love 'The Blue Danube' so much, Baba?" she asked.

"It makes me feel young again, that's all," he replied with a wistful smile, spinning Fatma around yet again.

Murad had first heard 'The Blue Danube' being played at the International Exposition when he had visited Paris with his uncle Sultan Abdülaziz as guests of Napoleon III in 1867. It was there that it had been first performed as an orchestral piece, and it had been received with great acclaim. He had loved it then, and he still loved it now. As he danced with the only daughter left to him, he remembered how it felt to be happy. How he wished that the music would never end!

ꙮ ꙮ ꙮ ꙮ ꙮ

Hadice sat up in bed, her thick, dark hair tumbling over her shoulders and falling onto the satin pillows that were propped up all around her. The letter she had received from her father earlier that evening had made her feel desperately sad and lonely, reigniting her yearning for the warm, intimate family atmosphere of Çırağan. She had read about the safe arrival of Nihad's child with great joy; however, picturing to herself the happy scenes of celebration that would surely be taking place in her father's home had exacerbated her feelings of loneliness. She had cried many tears of self-pity, and had cursed herself for having been so eager to forsake such a loving, supportive environment.

Then a second letter – this time from Kemaleddin – had arrived, and her mood had undergone an instant transformation. She was now holding this letter close to her chest, which was heaving up and down as she fought to restore herself to calm after the desperate inner conflict that had just taken place. His words had excited her and aroused

83

her in ways she did not fully understand; however, her conscience had soon overpowered her desires, pouring cold water on the fires within her. Initially, on reading his suggestion that they should meet, her feelings had pressed her to agree, and fuel had been added to the flames by a sudden surge of longing to escape from the cage of convention that kept her trapped in the harem of her *yalı*; in the end, however, prudence and cool-headed rationality had prevailed. Of course she must refuse him. Yes, she would refuse him – for now at least ...

CHAPTER SIX

A Time of Accouchement

The Naming Ceremony

As the days passed Safiru regained much of her strength, while her son, who had a voracious appetite, gradually put on weight and appeared to be the healthy child she had prayed for. Nihad visited her room often: he had become besotted with the placid-natured baby boy. The young couple's happiness was infectious, and the dark veil of sorrow that had hung over Çırağan for so long was temporarily lifted as a new, brighter mood prevailed.

The baby prince was now three days old, and the time had come to bestow a name on him. After noon prayers, the family was to gather in Nihad's salon for the Naming Ceremony: this would be the first time they had visited Safiru and her son all together. Naziknaz felt fraught and apprehensive as she watched the hands of the ormolu mantle clock slowly approach the agreed hour for the ceremony. Murad was fastidious in the matter of punctuality, seeing it as an important virtue, so she knew that everyone would arrive on time. The former Sultan had taught his children and grandchildren to appreciate the value of time, telling them that since this immeasurably precious commodity is impossible to save or store and can therefore only be spent, it must always be spent wisely; in consequence, other people's time must always be respected. Naziknaz rarely hosted Murad in the apartment she shared with her son and his wife, and was anxious for everything to run smoothly so that she did not embarrass her husband, Selahaddin, or her son, Nihad.

She had been rather irritable all morning, and knew that she had perhaps behaved in an overly demanding way towards Terime, her senior *kalfa*. She now told herself that once everyone had left, she ought to apologise to her for her impatient manner and her harsh words. In addition, she needed to personally thank Zülüflü Ağa and Kasım Ağa, the two eunuchs who served Nihad's household so faithfully, for ensuring that everything ran smoothly. Naziknaz moved one of the silver vases on a nearby table slightly to the left as it was not quite centred, and played with the arrangement of heavy-headed white roses. She had picked these late blooms from the harem gardens herself earlier that morning, but it was only now, having satisfied herself that everything was ready, that she was able to take a moment to enjoy their soft, delicate scent.

Safiru sat on a day bed that had been placed in the salon for the ceremony. As she waited to receive her husband's family, her son lay sleeping on a large silk cushion next to her, while Nihad sat in a chair beside them. The bed was draped in a deep red satin fabric richly embroidered with silver and gold thread and decorated with pearls; red had been purposely chosen as it was the colour of the Dynasty. Selahaddin's daughters had worked on this cover ever since they had heard the news that she was carrying their brother's child, intending it as a present for their sister-in-law. Safiru had been deeply touched by their thoughtfulness, and was eager to thank them in person for this beautiful gift. Naziknaz, Safiru and Nihad heard voices approaching the door, and exchanged nervous glances.

Murad entered the room first, followed by Selahaddin and the rest of the family. Nihad immediately jumped up from his chair to greet everyone. Naziknaz bowed. Murad walked straight over to Safiru and kissed her on the head before she was able to rise. "My dear child, please do not try to stand. I am so happy to see you with colour in your cheeks and a sparkle in your eyes. You have made my grandson so happy, and of course me too." He looked down at the sleeping baby. "And this must be the new little prince. *Mashallah! Mashallah!* May Allah protect him from the evil eye!" he said, and kissed the boy tenderly on his forehead.

"Thank you … Thank you, my Lord," Safiru stammered. Then Selahaddin, too, kissed her and embraced her warmly. She felt uncomfortable sitting while Murad, Selahaddin and the princesses remained standing; she glanced at Nihad, hoping for a hint as to what she should do, but he was speaking with his grandfather. Safiru scanned the room anxiously for Naziknaz, but she too was busy greeting Murad's consorts. Then she felt a soft, reassuring hand on her own: she saw that it belonged to Fatma, and was instantly grateful for this kind gesture.

"My dear sister," Fatma said affectionately, "you look like a startled little bird. Calm yourself, and settle down to enjoy the afternoon. We all owe you a huge debt of gratitude for bringing this baby safely into the world. It is many years since I have seen my father this happy, and for that I thank you." Still holding her hand, Fatma smiled into Safiru's pale blue eyes. "How are you feeling? I am certain the Lady Naziknaz is making sure you have everything you need, but if there is anything I can do for you, please do tell me." Fatma knew that Naziknaz would in all probability be smothering Safiru with her well-meaning but – if the truth be told – somewhat intrusive attentions!

"Thank you, Princess Fatma. I am well, and feel so blessed. I have all I need and much more besides: the Lady Naziknaz is looking after my son and me with the utmost care," replied Safiru.

Fuad came to join the men at Safiru's bedside and looked down at the sleeping child. "He's very small, isn't he, Nihad?" he said, sounding a little disappointed. "Does he spend all his time asleep?"

"It won't be long before he's running round the gardens getting into mischief with you, Fuad, but for now – yes, he does spend most of his time sleeping!" Nihad replied with a smile of amusement.

All the ladies in the family – first the princesses, then Murad's consorts and finally Jalefer – came to congratulate Safiru on becoming a mother. They each asked after her health and gazed down on the little prince, who remained asleep on his cushion all the while. Although it was clear that they all thought him a most beautiful child, they were careful not to compliment him in any way for fear of invoking the evil eye. The innocence and purity of a newborn baby is such a precious thing that it touches everyone's heart, instantly calling forth feelings of love for the treasured child. Safiru thanked her sisters-in-law for the beautiful cover they had made for her, and noted the looks of adoration on their faces as they looked down on her son; Behiye, in particular, seemed unable to tear herself away from the bedside.

❈ ❈ ❈ ❈ ❈

The family took their places for the Naming Ceremony, seating themselves on gilded chairs at either side of the bed; meanwhile, the *kalfas* offered them water and refreshing fruit juices. It was not permitted for a woman who had just given birth to drink water until after the seventh day of her confinement, so Safiru was given yet another drink of sherbet. Over the last three days she had been regularly plied with pomegranate sherbet, which Naziknaz had said would help her regain her strength. Safiru did not like the sour taste, but she would never disobey her mother-in-law.

Selahaddin, Fuad and the princesses sat to the right of Safiru's bed, while Murad's consorts, Naziknaz and Jalefer sat to the left. The ladies pulled their fine silk scarves over their heads to cover their hair. As was his duty as head of the family, Murad lovingly picked up the baby from the cushion and passed him into Nihad's arms before sitting down next to Selahaddin. Nihad turned in the direction of Mecca and held his son so that he, too, faced the Holy City. He whispered the *Shahada* into his right ear: "I bear witness that I will worship no god but Allah, and that Muhammed is His Messenger." Then he whispered "*Bismillah* – in the name of Allah" into his left ear. Everyone waited expectantly for the name that would now be whispered three times into the baby's left ear. "Ali Vâsıb … Ali Vâsıb … Ali Vâsıb." Nihad whispered loudly so that all could hear as he revealed the name of his son.

❁ ❁ ❁ ❁ ❁

The formalities completed, the *kalfas* appeared carrying large silver trays of food and crystal decanters filled with iced sherbet drinks. A red silk ribbon was tied around the neck of each decanter, as was the custom when honouring the birth of a boy. The smell of freshly-baked puff pastry, emanating from the cheese and meat *böreks* they carried, followed the serving girls around the room, and the assembled company were also offered stuffed vine leaves and a generous selection of fruits. Naziknaz was happy to see her guests enjoying the food and relaxing in the warm atmosphere of the family gathering. She felt proud of Terime and her other *kalfas*, and decided to reward each of them later with a small gift of some lace or some silk ribbon. She brought Safiru another glass of pomegranate sherbet and a small plate of *börek* and fruit. "My daughter, I think you are looking a little pale. If you are to fully regain your strength, you really ought to eat and drink more." Safiru thanked her mother-in-law and obediently did as she was bidden.

"Tell me, Father, how did you decide on the name 'Ali Vâsıb'?" asked Behiye. It was the custom in the Ottoman ruling family for the Imperial grandfather or great-grandfather of a newborn baby to choose both its names, so everyone had assumed that Murad and Selahaddin would each choose one. As the name that had been chosen was an unconventional one for a prince of the Imperial family, everyone broke off their conversations to listen to Selahaddin's reply.

"I did not choose either of the names, Behiye, and neither did your grandfather," he replied. He then invited Nihad to answer his elder sister's question.

"I originally wanted to honour my son with the name 'Murad Selahaddin', out of respect for Grandfather and Father," Nihad said, turning to bow towards the senior princes. "But they did not approve, for reasons which I fully respect and understand."

Everyone was puzzled. This would certainly have been a highly appropriate Ottoman name, and one that would have ensured the perpetuation of Murad's memory. So now it was his turn to speak, and hopefully to resolve the mystery. He took a long, lingering look at the sleeping baby, then smiled at his ever-dutiful grandson; finally, he addressed his family. "Both Selahaddin and I thought it an honour that dear Nihad should wish to name his son after us both. However, I felt that our lives have not exactly been blessed with good fortune – as I am sure you will all agree. We did not want to be the ones to name him in case our own ill fortune should be passed on to this innocent child here. It is true that I thank Allah every day for the love I have from you all. Because of that, I count myself a most fortunate man. But this life, lived in strict confinement here at Çırağan, is not one that I would want for any of you, and certainly not one that I would wish this baby prince to be forced to endure for long. I pray that his *kismet* will be very different from my own, and that it will bring him liberty and the freedom to live his life as he chooses. It is for this reason that I asked Nihad to reconsider his choice of name."

Everyone understood exactly what Murad meant, and sympathised with him completely, but no one knew how to respond. Who could fail to agree with the sentiments he had expressed, and – more to the point – who could possibly offer consolation for what had befallen him? The highly-charged, awkward silence in the room was almost deafening – until Fuad broke it by asking the obvious question.

"Yes, Grandfather, I now understand why my nephew is not called 'Murad Selahaddin', but I still do not know why Nihad decided to give him such an un-Ottoman name," he exclaimed. "It means that if he ever becomes Padishah, he will be known as 'Sultan Ali I'. Is that not strange?" This was, of course, what everyone was thinking, but no one dared to ask. Jalefer looked anxiously from her young son to Nihad, expecting to see his face cloud over with anger, but to her great surprise he was smiling. All eyes in the room were now on Nihad.

"For me, it was an obvious choice," he began. "We all sorely miss dear sweet Aunt Aliye, who was taken from us only a few weeks ago. Before she fell ill, she was very excited about the forthcoming birth of my child – as I am sure you all remember. So I wanted to honour her memory by calling him 'Ali'. Also, I have learnt a great deal from listening to Grandfather and Father recite verses by Mevlana Celaleddin Rumi, and from hearing them discuss the ideas in his poems. One of the many quotations from that great Sufi mystic that I often heard them talk about, and cannot forget, is as follows: *'Do not grieve: anything you lose comes around in another form.'* I pray that the essence of Aliye's inherent goodness, her kindness and her gentleness will forever be carried within the soul of my son, and that it will be passed on by him to his children and grandchildren. For you see, 'Vâsıb' means 'continuous', so I felt the two names fitted together perfectly. And I pray that the sadness we all feel at losing Aunt Aliye may be replaced by the joy of welcoming Ali Vâsıb Efendi into the world."

Everyone was profoundly affected by Nihad's words. Even Murad, who had learnt from bitter experience how to conceal his emotions, had tears in his eyes. Resan, Aliye's mother, had begun to sob at the mention of her name, and she now fell at Nihad's feet. "Prince Nihad, you do me and my poor, beloved daughter a great honour. I will never forget this … this kind gesture on your part. I vow that from today, I will give all the love I had for Aliye to your son, and will love him as if he was my own child." Nihad bent down to help Resan stand up and escorted her back to her chair, where she was comforted by Fatma, her remaining daughter, and Murad's consorts.

Selahaddin and Naziknaz exchanged glances. They both felt immense pride in their son, and were inwardly touched not only by his thoughtfulness towards his Aunt Aliye and her bereaved mother, but also by this noble and ingeniously thought-out gesture towards his whole family. Murad stared in wonderment at his grandson, as if seeing him in a new light. "Thank you, my dear Nihad. You cannot imagine how much these words have warmed my heart. You have chosen a most distinguished name for your son."

It was clear that the ageing prince had been greatly moved. But now, rising from his chair, he addressed everyone: "Come, we must not impose on the Lady Safiru any longer. She must rest." He then turned to Safiru, who was privately relieved that her ordeal was about to end, and said: "My dear child, I bless you and your son, and I pray that he may have a long and happy life. May Allah grant him the blessing of growing up with both his parents by his side! I look forward to seeing you again in a few days' time for the Ceremony of the Procession of the Cradle. In the meantime, try to rest." Murad then bent down to kiss her; lowering his voice so that only she could hear, he murmured: "If I may give you a little advice, my dear child, do try not to feel intimidated by the Lady Naziknaz, who although very well-intentioned has a rather assertive character. Never forget that Vâsib Efendi is your son." Murad was worried that Safiru, with her quiet, submissive nature, might allow Naziknaz to dominate her and take control of Vâsib's upbringing, and he made a mental note to have a word with Selahaddin on the matter.

The baby prince began to stir. "I think Vâsib Efendi is dismissing us all and calling for his wetnurse to attend him," said Murad, laughing as he led the way out of the salon.

❀ ❀ ❀ ❀ ❀

Once everyone had departed, the Imperial Midwife arrived to toss cloves into a brass brazier, chanting ancient incantations all the while in order to rid the room of any evil spirits that may have slipped in along with the visitors who had come to

93

witness the ceremony. A single clove was thrown into the fire for each person who had been present, but none of the cloves exploded: this meant that thankfully, the evil eye had not been able to enter the salon that particular afternoon.

☻ ☻ ☻ ☻ ☻

The Ceremony of the Procession of the Cradle

Ottoman custom dictated that when a baby was six days old, a symbolic tie to its mother must be cut. It would no longer sleep on a cushion next to her, but in its own cradle. This was also the time when the midwife would leave the young mother and the newborn baby: it was deemed that the time of immediate danger had now passed, so they no longer needed to have her specialised knowledge and skills permanently on hand. Murad had thus ordered that the traditional 'Ceremony of the Procession of the Cradle' should be held once Vâsıb was six days old. Owing to the many restrictions that had been imposed on Murad and his family, there were some aspects of this grand ceremony which could not take place. However, Murad was determined that the baby prince should have as full a ceremony as possible, as was his right, and he had entrusted the organisation of this important occasion to his First Consort Mevhibe and his Second Consort Reftarıdil. Both had attended many such ceremonies in the past, so they knew what was expected at such a time. They, in turn, had instructed Mistress Aynifer to carry out all the necessary preparations.

The entire household was to be involved, so when the great day arrived the whole palace was filled with excitement. The ovens in the kitchen had been burning since before first light, and the palace cooks were rushing around preparing exotic delicacies to please their Lord and his family. The gardeners had been working since dawn manicuring the lawns, removing any weeds and imperfect flower heads from the flower beds, and collecting each and every fallen russet leaf. The *kalfas*, too, were working frantically to have everything ready in time; meanwhile Ali Ağa, Murad's Head Butler, and Aynifer Usta, his Lady Steward, were supervising the proceedings.

The ceremony was to be held in the salon of Nihad's apartment, and Naziknaz was doing her best to ensure that the instructions drawn up by Murad's two consorts were carried out to the letter. Zülüflü Ağa and Kasım Ağa walked the route the procession would follow to check that all was in order; meanwhile, Nihad's senior housemaids – Dilbericihan Kalfa (known affectionately by the family as 'Dilber') and Perniyal Kalfa – were watching over the junior maids as they arranged the furniture, filled the vases with fresh flowers and lit the stoves and gaslights. The ladies-in-waiting to the princesses, Murad's consorts and Selahaddin's wives were busy preparing the shoes, dresses and jewellery that the ladies they served would wear. The palace dancers and its music ensemble were practising the performances with which they were to entertain the Imperial family during the ceremony. Everyone, in fact, was busily engaged in their various duties.

Murad and Selahaddin had found refuge from all the hustle and bustle in Murad's large and impressive library in the main palace, where they were surrounded by his priceless collection of rare books and manuscripts. They were spending the afternoon playing chess while listening to Enrico Caruso sing 'La Donna è Mobile', from Verdi's opera 'Rigoletto', on the gramophone. The record had been a recent, and completely unexpected, gift from Sultan Abdülhamid. Murad was certain that his brother sent gifts of this kind only in the hope of appeasing his feelings of guilt over the way he had usurped his throne and kept him a prisoner; this particular gift, however, had been very welcome. The rich, deep tones of the celebrated Italian tenor mingled with the muffled crackling of the recording. The melodious sound rang through the room and floated out of the window – where it fell upon the unappreciative ears of the gardeners working in the gardens below. Much to their irritation, Murad kept playing and replaying the record: he found the music both uplifting and inspiring, and was grateful for his brother's thoughtfulness in this instance.

☻ ☻ ☻ ☻ ☻

As the appointed hour for the ceremony drew near, Safiru felt increasingly nervous. She was not the kind of person to crave attention, as some ladies do: in fact, she invariably shied away from it. In a vain attempt to distract her mind from what was to come, she sat on her audience bed embroidering her son's name onto an ivory satin pillowcase in silver thread. She had been working on the pillowcase since before her confinement, and had completed the foliage decoration that bordered it, but only now that her son had a name was she able to complete her task.

Nihad was sitting at the piano in one corner of the salon, quietly playing the same piece of music over and over again. Finally, he stopped playing and swivelled round on the piano stool to face his wife.

"Safiru, I have been working on a composition as a gift for our son. Will you listen to it and tell me what you think?"

"Of course, Nihad. How lovely! I had been wondering what you were doing these last few days. Your fingers have hardly left the keys!" Safiru put down her embroidery to concentrate fully on the piece she was about to hear. If the truth be told, she was relieved to have something to distract her.

"It is ... a march, my dear," Nihad said – rather hesitantly, showing that he too was feeling a little nervous, though for a different reason. "I thought it would be appropriate for the ceremony. If you think it worthy of the occasion, I will play it to my grandfather. If he, too, likes it and gives his permission, I will ask the music ensemble to play it during the procession. I have entitled it 'Green Clover'."

Nihad swivelled back round on his stool to face the piano, took a deep breath and began to play his most recent composition. At the beginning it was solemn and serious in mood, as befitted the occasion, but then it quickened in pace, becoming livelier towards the end as if reflecting the emergence of hope. Like all members of the Imperial family, Nihad had been encouraged from a young age to learn a skill or a craft. It was an important part of the family tradition that young princes and princesses should acquire a skill of their own choosing through hard work and dedication. This would be something that fully belonged to them – something neither inherited nor given to them by anyone other than Allah. Nihad had chosen to teach himself two things: the skill of musical composition (in common with his grandfather, Murad), and the craft of carpentry (like his great-uncle, Sultan Abdülhamid). He was highly accomplished at both, and worked tirelessly to improve his proficiency.

"Oh Nihad, it is beautiful, and so moving!" exclaimed Safiru once her husband had played the final note. "I think it would be the perfect piece to have played during the procession, and I am certain your grandfather will agree."

"Do you really think so, Safi?" Nihad asked. His modesty prevented him from ever trusting fully in his abilities: whatever others might say, he always doubted himself.

"Nihad, it is absolutely perfect. You should go and play it to His Imperial Highness while there is still time for the ensemble to learn the piece. Please keep the sheets of music safe: then you can present them to Vâsıb one day when he is older, as a memento of today. It will show him how much you love him, and he will treasure it as a special gift from you."

"Thank you, my dear Safı. I will do as you suggest, and go to Grandfather's rooms right away – leaving you in peace to prepare yourself for the ceremony," Nihad replied. "I want you to enjoy it – it is your big moment, you know!" So saying, he kissed his wife's hand and left the salon.

❀ ❀ ❀ ❀ ❀

Reftarıdil and Naziknaz joined Safıru in the salon a few minutes after Nihad had left. These ladies, the wives of Ottoman princes of three successive generations, first exchanged greetings; then they seated themselves and were served coffee, while Safıru was offered yet another pomegranate sherbet. It was already her third of the day, and it was not even ten o'clock in the morning!

"My dear, before we summon your maids to help you wash and dress, we thought we ought to tell you about everything that is to happen later this afternoon," Naziknaz began. "I know you have not attended a 'Procession of the Cradle' ceremony before, because at the time of Prince Fuad's birth you had not yet come to us. It is an important day for you and your son, but we want you to know that there is really nothing to be concerned about," she went on, giving Safıru a reassuring smile: she had noticed the nervous look on her face and the slight trembling in her hands. "Since it remains forbidden for guests to come to the Çırağan Palace, even to

98

pay their respects on an occasion such as this, it will be a small family affair. However, the entire household will watch the procession as it passes through the corridors of the palace and the gardens; in this way, everyone will have the opportunity to offer Vâsıb Efendi their prayers and blessings."

"Thank you, *Validem*," Safiru answered. "I am glad to hear that only family will attend, and happy too that the household will be able to share in today's celebrations. However, I have to say that I am still a little apprehensive. Knowing what to expect will certainly help me overcome my nerves."

"My dear child, it is a simple ceremony, but nevertheless an important one," Naziknaz continued. "You will sit on your audience bed and graciously accept all the prayers and blessings that are offered to you and Vâsıb Efendi. Everything that happens will happen around you, without involving you in any way: all you need do is watch and enjoy the ceremony." At this point, Naziknaz looked into her daughter-in-law's eyes once again and smiled – perhaps envying her just a little. "Only one cradle will be presented today, my dear. According to tradition, there should be three, but this is not possible since we are all but forgotten by the government of the day."

"But not by the people!" interjected Reftarıdil. "The people still love My Lord Murad, and despite all Prince Hamid's efforts they know who their rightful Padishah is." Reftarıdil often referred to the Sultan as 'Prince Hamid' as in her eyes her husband was still the Empire's rightful sovereign. She had a strong sense of right and wrong and was never afraid to speak her mind, however much she might be aware that the walls of Çırağan had ears.

"You are quite right, Lady Reftarıdil," Naziknaz said. She admired her mother-in-law's resolute loyalty towards her husband.

"One cradle is plenty. Why should I have need of three, anyway?" asked Safiru.

Amused at Safiru's naïvety, Reftarıdil gave her an indulgent smile before launching into an explanation. "The first cradle is traditionally a gift from the Valide Sultan. Since My Lord Murad's mother Şevkefzâ Kadınefendi has departed this world, it has been decided that your cradle will be a gift from Lady Mevhibe and myself. It is this cradle that will be carried in the procession from the main palace into the harem building, and then into this room. I hope you like it. We commissioned it from My Lord Murad's most able carpenter."

"That is most generous. I am very grateful to you, Lady Reftarıdil," Safiru replied.

"According to custom, the second cradle is presented by the Grand Vizier, and is carried in a long procession from his palace to your audience room. As it passes through the streets it is accompanied by imams, pashas and other high-ranking government officials, and is greeted with prayers and blessings by the people as it goes by. However, Mehmed Ferid Pasha, the Grand Vizier, will obviously not be permitted to honour Sultan Murad's great-grandson in this way. The third cradle, which is the gift of the Chamberlain of the Imperial Treasury, is supposed to follow the second in the procession. I am sorry that your child will not be accorded full honours, but please be assured that he will receive the prayers and blessings of everyone within this palace," continued Reftarıdil. Safiru felt relieved that she would not have to endure all the formalities normally required by the Imperial Court.

"Would you like to hear about my son's Cradle Ceremony?" Reftarıdil asked when she had finished her coffee and set the cup down on the table in front of her. Even before her listeners had had a chance to respond, her mind had wandered back to that day, and she began to reminisce without prompting. "It was a really grand affair. At the time of Selahaddin's birth my lord and husband Murad was Crown Prince, of course, and we were living in the Crown Prince's residence at the Dolmabahçe Palace. Anyway, on that glorious summer morning, everyone got up early … " Safiru and Naziknaz loved hearing stories of those happy times before Murad's family had been confined to Çırağan, and they hung on every word.

❀ ❀ ❀ ❀ ❀

It was late afternoon, and the procession was about to start. Safiru sat in the centre of her audience bed wearing a simple lace dress that formed a stark contrast with the bed's elaborate, deep red satin cover and its richly-embroidered pillowcases and plush velvet quilts. Safiru sat perfectly still, her small, dainty frame motionless, as if she was sitting for a portrait. She was blessed with natural elegance of posture, and looked poised; her eyes gazed straight ahead, while her folded hands rested in her lap. Meanwhile, her son lay sleeping peacefully on a silk cushion close to her. Unbeknown to Nihad or Safiru, Naziknaz had placed a small drop of poppy seed oil on Vâsıb's tongue half an hour previously to ensure that he slept throughout the long ceremony. She often resorted to her supply of this oil when Vâsıb would not settle at night; however, knowing that the young parents disapproved of such methods, she always kept the bottle well out of sight!

Just as had been the case during the Naming Ceremony, the princes and princesses of the family sat on the right of the room, while Murad's consorts and Selahaddin's wives sat on the left. When the family was ready, the sign was given

101

for the ceremony to begin. Safiru could hear the faint sound of the 'Green Clover March' being played in the distance, and the familiar tune produced a calming effect on her, dispelling all her anxieties. She felt happy for Nihad: Murad had obviously given his approval for the piece to be played. She closed her eyes, breathing in the musky scent of sandalwood that arose from the nearby incense-burner. Gradually, the music grew louder.

The procession had begun in the prayer room in the main building of the palace, and had then wound its way through the corridors and down the wide staircases into the gardens, where it was greeted by the golden rays of the autumn sun. The cortège was headed by Mistress Aynifer, the most senior lady in the household after the members of the Imperial family. After her came Hayriye, Midwife to the Imperial House, and then four specially-chosen *kalfas* carrying the cradle carefully on their shoulders. Vâsıb's wetnurse and his maid walked behind them, while the palace music ensemble, led by its director, Dürrünab Kalfa, followed. Once in the gardens, the procession slowly made its way along the recently-swept gravel pathways, wound its way between the numerous small clumps of oak, cedar and pine trees planted randomly on the lawns, and eventually arrived at the entrance to the harem building. Now the music could be heard more clearly. Safiru's heart began to beat faster, and she clasped her hands tightly in her lap. A few moments later, the door to the salon opened and the procession entered the room.

The cradle was made of rich black walnut wood, intricately carved and inset with silver gilt and mother-of-pearl. Attached to its head, as was the tradition in the case of a baby prince, was the feathery, soft white plume of a jewelled aigrette. Beneath this, on a pale blue silk ribbon, hung a blue glass bead and a pendant, inset with diamonds, bearing the word *'Mashallah'* – a prayer to protect the baby from the evil eye. A clove of garlic also hung from the cradle in a small muslin bag to ward off any evil spirits. The music ensemble disappeared into a dark corner of the salon, where they continued to play the march Nihad had composed, though now much more softly; meanwhile, the procession circled the room, first passing the princes and princesses and then the consorts and wives. As it went by, the members of the Imperial family put sumptuous fabrics and embroidered blankets, all neatly folded, into the cradle together with coins. These were gifts for Hayriye as a reward for her safe delivery of the new prince and the care and attention she had lavished on his young mother.

The wetnurse picked up Vâsıb from his silk cushion and placed him in Hayriye's arms; the midwife was kneeling in the centre of the room, beside the cradle. The baby prince, dressed in a white silk robe and wrapped in gold- and silver-embroidered swaddling bands, briefly opened his eyes and tried to focus on the elderly lady who was now holding him; however, the poppy seed oil soon took effect once more, and he closed them again. The coins and fabrics were then removed from the cradle and placed in a chest for the midwife to take with her once the ceremony was over.

Reftarıdil passed the richly-embroidered coverlet she was holding to Dilber Kalfa, who had the honour of placing it in the awaiting cradle. As she laid Vâsıb in his cradle, Hayriye recited a prayer. She then rocked the cradle three times and picked him up once more. Dilber Kalfa now approached the midwife holding a small silver bowl that contained fragrant honey from the fields and forests near Konya, in Anatolia. Hayriye put her little finger first into the bowl, then into the baby prince's mouth. The clear, sweet honey he was now tasting would ensure that in the future he spoke only clear, sweet words. Everyone prayed that the prince would grow into a good, kind adult, and that he would have a long life, lived in righteousness. He was then returned to his wetnurse; finally, the cradle was taken to his rooms, and thus the ceremony came to an end.

❁ ❁ ❁ ❁ ❁

The *kalfas* now entered the salon and offered everyone tea, coffee and sherbets. Meanwhile, tempting sweetmeats, helva and Turkish Delight were served on silver platters. These enticing delicacies were dripping with honey and sugar, so a small, damp napkin was handed to each guest. Nezihe, the junior housemaid who often brought treats to Murad's study when serving him tea, surreptitiously left a plate of Turkish Delight on the table next to his chair so that he could enjoy it without anyone noticing. Dürrünab Kalfa and her ensemble began to play a lively Chopin mazurka: she herself played the violin, while Tarzınev Kalfa played the piano and Lebriz Kalfa the flute. The lively music instantly lightened the atmosphere after the formal ceremony.

Soon after the music had begun, Desteriz Kalfa instructed her dancers to begin their performance. Everyone looked on in admiration, enchanted by their graceful movements; Teranedil Kalfa, in particular, danced the traditional Polish folk dance beautifully. The ensemble then played a series of mazurkas composed by Nihad. His sisters recognised the first piece at once: the young princesses jumped up from their chairs and eagerly joined the dancers, ignoring Naziknaz's protestations.

"Let them enjoy the afternoon," Murad said. "They are young, so they should be allowed a little merriment." He sat back in his chair, happily absorbed in watching his grand-daughters dance.

Nihad went to sit next to Safiru. "How do you feel, my love?" he asked. "Can I get you another sherbet?"

"I am perfectly all right, thank you, Nihad, but please – no more sherbets! Your mother has – very kindly – given me so many of them today that any more would be just too much," she said, smiling at her husband. "I am so pleased that His Imperial Highness your grandfather liked your composition. When I heard the first notes of 'Green Clover' being played in the distance, I immediately felt more relaxed, so after that I was able to enjoy the ceremony. It was wonderful, was it not?"

"It certainly was," Nihad replied. "The entire household lined the corridors and pathways along the route of the procession and prayed for our son, showering him with blessings. Even the guards, the warders of our prison, came to pay their respects. It was so moving! And little Vâsıb was so good – he slept throughout the ceremony and didn't cry even once! I was proud of our son today, and I am proud of you, too."

Safiru allowed herself a shy smile. "Nihad, look how well your sisters are dancing to your music," she said, attempting to divert attention away from herself. "They have learnt very well from Desteriz Kalfa, have they not?" Feeling happy and contented, the young couple watched the princesses lightly tap their feet and hop between steps as they danced the mazurka.

When Murad had at last finished his tea, he stood up and walked over to Hayriye, who was standing at the side of the room watching the dancers. As he approached the midwife, she dropped to her knees and kissed the hem of his trousers. "Please rise, Hayriye Hanım," he commanded in his soft, gentle voice. "I trust that you are well and that you have been comfortable during your stay at the Çırağan Palace."

"I have, my Lord. Thank you," she replied without raising her eyes.

"I want to thank you personally for all that you have done for the Lady Safiru and Prince Vâsıb. The birth of a new Ottoman prince brings me immense joy, and it is also of great comfort to me to know that *Inshallah* my line will now continue. I also want to thank you for your loyal service: once again you have risked much to help me, this time by taking my letters to Princess Hadice and Princess Fehime. I am very much in your debt." Murad removed a ring from his finger. "Please accept this as a token of my gratitude," he said, pressing it into the hands of the faithful midwife.

"But my Lord, I cannot accept such a gift from you. It is an honour for me to serve you," Hayriye answered. At that moment, Ali Ağa stepped forward and handed the elderly lady a brown leather pouch tied securely with a red silk ribbon. It contained a hundred liras in payment for her services. "This ... this is ... far too much, my Lord ..." Hayriye's voice trailed off as her downcast eyes filled with tears.

"Please take it. All I ask in return is that my family be always in your prayers. Pray that they will not have to suffer much longer in this prison with me. Now you may go – and may Allah be with you always, Hayriye Hanım." With this, the Midwife to the Imperial House was dismissed.

❁ ❁ ❁ ❁ ❁

The Mevlûd

After breakfast, Safiru joined her mother-in-law in the salon of the apartment they shared. The windows were open and a fresh autumn breeze wafted in through the lace curtains.

Safiru immediately noticed that the ceremonial audience bed had been removed. A week had now passed since the birth, and many of the restrictions that had been placed upon her during her accouchement would now be lifted – much to her relief. She was particularly looking forward to enjoying a glass of cold water instead of having only pomegranate sherbet to drink.

"Good morning, *Validem*," she said, bowing in front of Naziknaz. "What a beautiful day it is today!"

"Good morning, Safiru. Yes, indeed it is. How are you feeling this morning? And how is my grandson? I trust he is sleeping and feeding well."

"I am well, thank you, *Validem*. Vâsıb Efendi slept peacefully in his new cradle last night and fed from me this morning. My milk seems to satisfy him during the day, but the wetnurse now feeds him in the evenings," Safiru replied. Sitting down, she saw that the red coverlet which had been draped over her day bed now lay folded on the console table next to the door.

"That is good news, my dear. You are a very loving mother, and we are all proud of you," Naziknaz said kindly.

Safiru managed a smile, though compliments always embarrassed her. A *kalfa* entered the room and offered the ladies tea and coffee. Safiru declined, but asked for a glass of water. The maid looked at Naziknaz enquiringly, and she nodded: water was permitted on the seventh day. "May I keep the coverlet that the princesses made for me?" Safiru asked, a little nervously. "It is really beautiful, and it would mean so much to me if I could."

"Of course, dear Safiru. It is yours. The princesses made it for you: you do not have to ask. Now, I must tell you that the Mevlûd Ceremony will be taking place here in our salon after midday prayers today, so you and Vâsıb Efendi need to be ready. The princes will arrive together, and Lady Mevhibe, Lady Reftarıdil and I will also be present. This will be the final ceremony of your accouchement."

"Oh dear, another ceremony!" thought Safiru to herself. But she consoled herself by remembering that the last one had been really quite enjoyable – especially the music and dancing that followed it. And in any case, this would be the last one ...

❁ ❁ ❁ ❁ ❁

The small family group sat together in the salon. Murad sat on the pale green silk sofa in the centre of the room, with his son and grandsons on one side of him and the consorts and wives on the other. The ladies covered their heads with their veils and sat with their eyes lowered. Safiru held Vâsıb in her arms.

Murad began to recite the fifteenth-century poem by Süleyman Çelebi recounting the story of the birth of the Prophet Muhammed. The classical Ottoman words were elegant, yet simple and direct, and the verses were full of melodic beauty. Everyone listened spellbound. As Murad spoke the words of this poem, the 'Great Welcome', a ray of sunlight burst through the clouds floating in the afternoon sky and lit up the room.

Welcome, O high prince, we welcome you!
Welcome, O mine of wisdom, we welcome you!
Welcome, O secret of the Book, we welcome you!
Welcome, O medicine for pain, we welcome you!
Welcome, O sunlight and moonlight of Allah!
Welcome, O you not separated from Allah!
Welcome, O nightingale of the Garden of Beauty!
Welcome, O friend of the Lord of Power!
Welcome, O refuge of your community!

108

Welcome, O helper of the poor and destitute!
Welcome, O eternal soul, we welcome you!
Welcome, O cupbearer of the lovers, we welcome you!
Welcome, O darling of the Beloved!
Welcome, O much beloved of the Lord!
Welcome, O Mercy for the worlds!
Welcome, O intercessor for the sinner!
Only for you were Time and Space created ...

When Murad had finished reciting the poem, everyone stood up; one by one, they came to kiss his hand. They had all felt the deep love and intense emotion in his voice, and were filled with a sense of peace and serenity.

"Come now," he said. "Please sit, for we must now shave Vâsıb Efendi's head."

The Mistress of Shaving – the *Berber Usta* – brought forward a razor blade and a shaving bowl. Nihad took the sharp blade from the *usta* and slowly began to shave off his son's dark hair as he lay in Safiru's arms. Fuad stood next to his brother holding a small bronze dish into which Nihad placed each lock of hair as he cut it off. Vâsıb barely moved or wriggled – and this, of course, made the task much less difficult than Nihad had feared. Once all the hair had been removed, Lady Reftarıdil approached the baby prince and gently massaged saffron oil into the top of his head. Selahaddin then carefully weighed the hair on a crescent-shaped scale held by Perniyal Kalfa.

Ali Ağa had been watching the ceremony from the side of the room with Mistress Aynifer. Murad now called him over, and instructed him to distribute the equivalent weight of the hair in gold coins to each member of the household staff. He also asked him to secretly distribute alms to the poor in his great-grandson's honour.

"You must take great care when distributing the coins to the needy, Ali Ağa," he said with a look of concern. "If my brother finds out what we are doing, he will be angry. He does not wish the people to receive any kind of reminder that I am still alive."

"It will be done as you command, my Lord," said Ali Ağa.

"Before you go, take this dish with you," Murad added, pointing to the bronze bowl that held Vâsıb's hair. "Please arrange for this hair to be buried in the garden next to where we buried that of Nihad, Fuad and the princesses following their births." The eunuch took the dish, bowed and withdrew to carry out his instructions forthwith.

The *kalfas* brought in refreshments and fruit while everyone sat quietly, enjoying the comfort of shared silence: the effect of the ceremony, and of Murad's recitation of the poem in particular, had been profound. It was not long before the silence was broken, however: Vâsıb began to cry. Naziknaz and Safiru took their leave to attend to him. Once they had finished their tea, Mevhibe and Reftarıdil returned to their rooms in the main palace.

"Nihad, it is time to decide where to place the umbilical cord. We should take care of that now, while we are together," Murad said once the ladies had left. "It is an important decision, for it will influence your son's fate; I trust you have given the matter some thought?"

Nihad swallowed the slice of peeled apple he had been eating. "Grandfather, I must admit that I have no idea where best to place it. I have indeed considered the matter, but have reached no conclusion. Could you possibly give me some advice?" He wiped his fingers on the napkin his *kalfa* had brought him and put his fruit plate on the table.

Fuad was puzzled. Before Murad could reply to Nihad's question, he asked: "Baba, what is an umbilical cord?"

110

Selahaddin quietly explained what it was to his younger son – while Nihad scowled at him, irritated at his interruption.

"Whatever you decide will be the right choice, I am sure, my dear Nihad," Murad finally answered. "I chose to bury your father's cord in the garden of a school: as you know, I believe that education is of paramount importance in life. Your father has grown into a very learned and knowledgeable man, and he has found much solace in books and philosophy during our long confinement here. So I think I made the right decision in his case."

Selahaddin nodded in agreement. Then he addressed his son. "We asked for your cord to be buried in the courtyard of the Yahya Efendi Mosque. I prayed that you would grow up to be devout and pious. When I look at you now, my son, I can see with pride that you have indeed become such a man," he said. Nihad smiled at his father.

"So where was my umbilical cord buried, Baba?" Fuad asked.

"Yours was thrown into the Bosphorus to be taken wherever the current chose, my dear Fuad," Selahaddin replied.

Fuad looked a little dejected at this. Nihad's cord had been buried in a holy place with care and deference, while his own, it seemed, had been tossed recklessly into the sea. Murad noticed the expression of bewilderment on his face. "It was done in the hope that you would find your destiny elsewhere, far from the locked gates and high walls of the Çırağan Palace," Murad said. "You have a lively spirit, dear Fuad. I pray that you will not have to endure a life of imprisonment, as we have had to do, and that your destiny will be very different from ours." Fuad was happy with this explanation. In any case, his grandfather's observation was quite true: he dreamed constantly of adventure and exploration.

"There is only one other choice open to you," Selahaddin said to Nihad. "If you would like your son to love animals and care for them, you can decide to bury the cord in a stable. So, what course will you decide upon for Vâsıb?"

Nihad thought for a moment. "I feel torn between all the different possibilities. Please help me decide, Grandfather! And you too, Father – please help me choose," he said.

Murad answered first. "Liberty and freedom are precious things, and should never be taken for granted," he said. "Every man has the right to be free, so my advice is to choose the waters of the Bosphorus. You can ensure that your son grows into a devout and righteous man by teaching him the lessons of the Holy Quran. You can employ the best tutors and scholars to ensure that he becomes an educated man. But you cannot guarantee that Vâsıb Efendi will have liberty and freedom. That is something that, as I myself have learned, lies beyond our control, and it is for this reason that I give you the advice I do." Selahaddin placed his hand tenderly on his father's arm. He knew how much he suffered, and how much it hurt him to have to watch his family endure imprisonment at the hands of Abdülhamid.

"I agree with my father," Selahaddin said. "He speaks wisely, and from experience of life."

Nihad, moved by his grandfather's words and not wishing his voice to falter, paused for a moment to collect himself. Then he said: "You are indeed wise, dear Grandfather. The choice is clear now. Thank you for your advice, which I wholeheartedly wish to take."

Murad stood up and kissed Nihad. Then he took Fuad by the hand and led the way into the garden. As Nihad passed Dilber Kalfa on his way out of the salon, she handed him the small box containing the cord. When they had gone, she went over to the window and watched as the four princes strode purposefully over to the high wall that skirted the seafront. She saw Nihad speak to a guard standing beside the sea gate; after a certain amount of gentle persuasion, he unlocked the gate and pushed it ajar just enough to allow Nihad to slip through onto the quay beyond. Nihad then opened the box and, after saying a prayer, tossed its contents into the water lapping at his feet.

"*Bismillah*," she murmured. "May the suffering of the family of Murad have an end. May they know freedom, and may they find their destiny beyond the walls of this palace prison."

CHAPTER SEVEN

The Fortieth Day

Sunday 22ⁿᵈ November 1903

THERE was a cold chill in the air: winter was once again knocking at the door of the palace. An early morning mist shrouded the Imperial city, and an unbroken mass of grey cloud covered the sun, preventing it from greeting those who had woken early. Safiru had just finished feeding Vâsıb, and had gently placed him back under the warm feather quilt in his cradle. She pulled her shawl tightly around her shoulders and went to sit next to the brightly-burning stove, where her maid had left the breakfast tray. Safiru was feeling rather nervous, so she had not intended to eat anything; however, the smell of the warm oven-baked bread enticed her to break off a small piece. She mixed a spoonful of fragrant honey with some *kaymak* – the rich, fluffy clotted cream that she loved so much – and spread it onto the piece of bread. As the sweet, creamy morsel melted in her mouth, she thought how quickly the last forty days had gone by.

Safiru's accouchement was to end following the Purification Ceremony, which would be held in the Çırağan Palace hammam in just over an hour's time. She had never been there before: previously, she had always used the hammam in the harem building. Since today was such a special occasion, however, Murad had suggested that the ceremony should take place in the sovereign's private hammam. Safiru had heard the story of how Sultan Abdülaziz had taken Empress Eugénie of France to see the famously beautiful Çırağan Palace hammam during her visit to İstanbul in 1869, even though the construction of the rest of the building had not been completed. It is said that its splendour took the Empress's breath away. And indeed, Safiru felt overwhelmed by this unexpected gesture from Murad.

From now on she would no longer be confined to her apartment and could be left unattended, since the danger of her being taken by the 'Mother-Snatcher' had passed. Her precious son had also passed the forty-day threshold, and she humbly thanked Allah for this. She was eager to leave the apartment and take him outside before the first snows came and the large pond in the centre of the palace garden froze over; she wanted him to be able to look into the waters of the pond, gaze up into the sky and breathe in the cool, fresh air.

Her maid opened the door, and Naziknaz appeared. Safiru stood and bowed to her mother-in-law, her hands held together in front of her chest. "Good morning, my dear Safiru," Naziknaz said; then she crossed the room and bent over the cradle to kiss her grandson.

"Good morning, *Validem*. Would you like to join me for breakfast?" asked Safiru. "The bread is still warm and the *kaymak* is delicious."

"Thank you, my dear, but I have already eaten," replied Naziknaz. "I just wanted to see how you and Vâsıb Efendi were this morning. Please sit and finish your breakfast." Safiru smeared another piece of bread with honey and cream. Then Naziknaz continued: "Today is an important day for

115

you and your son. Everyone is very much looking forward to the ceremony – naturally, they want to share in the celebrations. All the ladies of the family will be coming to the hammam, and the *Gözde* have also been invited to join us. It should be a very enjoyable party: I have ordered the palace music ensemble to play some gypsy music, and the kitchens will be preparing some sweet treats for us all." The excitement showed in Naziknaz's voice as she described her plans for the occasion.

"It all sounds wonderful, *Validem*. You are so kind. I cannot thank you enough for taking such good care of Vâsıb Efendi and me."

"You know it makes me happy to look after you both, my dear girl. Now I will leave you to dress. I will return in an hour to accompany you to the hammam." With that, Naziknaz kissed Safiru on the head and left the room.

ۇ ۇ ۇ ۇ ۇ

"Mashallah! Mashallah!" Hayriye exclaimed when she saw Vâsıb in his mother's arms. "How the young prince has grown!"

The Midwife to the Imperial House had returned to the Çırağan Palace to officiate at the Purification Ceremony; she and Naziknaz had come to take Safiru and the baby to the hammam, where everyone else was waiting for them.

"Are you ready, Safiru?" Naziknaz asked gently. "Come, then, let us go." Safiru handed her son to the wetnurse and followed her mother-in-law out of the apartment, the midwife and the wetnurse walking behind them.

"My Lady Naziknaz," Hayriye said once they were in the corridor, "with your permission, I would like to return to Lady Safiru's bedchamber for a moment. Before we can

116

proceed to the hammam, I must crush the garlic that I left hanging at the foot of her bed on the day of Prince Vâsıb's birth. It must be done before we go to the baths so that pain and suffering are prevented from entering through the doors of your noble house." Naziknaz nodded her consent. The elderly midwife found the garlic still attached to the piece of red muslin, which contained an onion. Removing the muslin pouch, she quickly crushed the pieces of garlic on the threshold of the bedroom. Within a minute or two, she had rejoined the ladies.

"Make way! Make way!" Zülüflü Ağa cried as he escorted them across the harem gardens. The gardeners immediately stopped working, turned their aching backs to the ladies and lowered their heads until they had passed. Safiru closed her eyes, taking in lungfuls of the fresh autumnal air. She had sorely missed her daily walks in the gardens, and was relieved to know that she would now be able to enjoy them once again. A dry, curled-up leaf fluttered past her face, caught in the breeze on its journey to the ground. Safiru looked up and noticed how the myriad of green leaves which only a month earlier had cloaked the trees had been transformed into a tapestry of reds, burnt russets and rich golden browns. The carnations and roses, which had lingered into late summer, were no longer in bloom, so that the flower beds now looked stark and bare. Summer had turned into autumn without her even noticing.

The ladies ascended the marble steps that swept up to the entrance of the main building of the palace and made their way up the grand staircase to the first floor; then they headed towards the corner at the rear where the anteroom to the hammam was situated. They could hear music and laughter coming from behind the heavy walnut door – which was immediately opened by two attendants, allowing them to enter the elegantly-furnished chamber. Zülüflü Ağa remained outside, leaving Mistress Aynifer to greet the ladies. Safiru nervously surveyed the room. The dancers were performing traditional folk dances to the accompaniment of lively music while the princesses, Murad's consorts, Jalefer and the *Gözdes* all looked on, savouring the sugary delights that were being served to them. Since the day was gloomy and the sun had still not broken through the clouds, the gaslights had all been lit, and the glass-etched red shades threw a soft, warm glow around the room. A large Samsun carpet lay across the parquet floor; the deep red and gold hues in it echoed the colours of the leaves that were falling from the trees in the garden, while its muted blues held the colour of the Bosphorus that flowed outside the windows.

The midwife disappeared into the hammam beyond the anteroom to prepare for the ceremony. First, Naziknaz and Safiru greeted Princess Fatma. She was sitting on a crimson silk sofa with her mother, the Lady Resan. Murad's other consorts and Jalefer sat next to them on delicate gilt-framed chairs; all were drinking lemon mint sherbets while they watched the entertainment. Naziknaz and Safiru greeted them respectfully and thanked them for coming to attend the ceremony.

"May I hold Prince Ali Vâsıb?" asked Resan eagerly. She had visited Safiru many times during her accouchement, and had come to feel a deep love for the little prince. With each visit, her despair at losing her beautiful daughter Aliye had seemed to lift a little. The baby was just the tonic she needed to help repair her shattered heart.

"Of course, Lady Resan. My son is blessed to receive such love and affection from you," Safiru answered. She nodded to the wetnurse, who gently placed the baby in the consort's arms. Safiru and Naziknaz bowed towards the young princesses, then went to greet them. The princesses, who had been accompanying the music ensemble on small tambourines, now stopped playing and warmly embraced their sister-in-law and Naziknaz. Finally Murad's Favourites, the *Gözdes*, were greeted. The Ladies Gevherriz, Nevdür, Remişnaz and Filizten were sitting together at a marquetry table, inlaid with red tortoiseshell and brass, that stood on the other side of the room. They rose and bowed before the Imperial wives; then they kissed Naziknaz's and Safiru's hands before raising them to their foreheads. They were delighted to have been included in the family celebrations. Naziknaz gave Safiru a reassuring smile as they joined the *Gözdes* at the ornate boulle table and sat waiting for the ceremony to begin.

Soon the Mistress of the Baths appeared, bowing low to everyone and inviting them to enter the hammam. The ladies now proceeded to the dressing area, where they removed their shoes and garments. The musicians and dancers, meanwhile, went into the cool room. The princesses put on loose-fitting silk bathing robes and towering high-heeled *nalıns*. These wooden bathing clogs were decorated with silver and gold filigree, and inlaid with mother-of-pearl. The leather straps that held their dainty feet in place were decorated both with silver and gold embroidery and with pearls and tiny silver bells that tinkled as they walked. The other ladies put on flowing robes made from fine cottons and linens. Their bathing clogs were less ornate, and lower: the heels of the various ladies' *nalıns* varied in height according to their rank within the harem. Once Safiru had undressed, Mevhibe presented her with a set of elaborately-embroidered cream linen towels, which she wrapped about her naked body. The largest towel went around her hips, and the second largest across her shoulders; the smallest was tied in a turban on her head.

"This is a small gift from me," Mevhibe said. "After today, you will no longer be a *loğusa*, a new mother. May Allah bless you and your son!"

Safiru kissed her hand and raised it to her forehead. "Thank you, Lady Mevhibe. They are absolutely beautiful."

Everyone admired Mevhibe's gilded embroidery. Of all the ladies in the harem, she was the most accomplished at needlework; in recognition of this fact, Murad only wore shirts made by his First Consort. Reftarıdil then approached Safiru and presented her with a new pair of *nalıns*. Her name had been embroidered in gilded thread across the leather band, and the heels were decorated with small turquoise stones.

"My dear Safiru, I have had these made especially for you. May Allah protect you and Vâsıb Efendi." Reftarıdil kissed her grandson's wife on the forehead. "Please remember me when you wear them," she said, cupping Safiru's face in her hands.

"Lady Reftarıdil, they are exquisite. You have greatly honoured me. Thank you," replied Safiru, putting on her new bathing clogs. Now ready for the ceremony, she was led into the hammam supported by two bathing attendants. Everyone followed – except for the wetnurse and Vâsıb, who remained in the cool room. Here, the musicians began to play soft, soothing music that was much more relaxed in mood than the lively tunes they had been playing earlier.

The hammam at Çırağan was one of the jewels of the entire palace. Smoky grey veining of different shades ran through the glistening white marble that covered the floors, walls and ceilings. The rooms were flooded with natural light that

120

streamed in through the large windows overlooking the Bosphorus and the lower terraces of the gardens of Yıldız, as well as from roof lanterns cut into the domes above each chamber. Yet more light filtered in through windows in the ceilings, each one shaped like an eight-pointed star. The raised relaxation areas running along each side of both chambers were separated from the lower level by a marble balustrade in an arabesque design, and were divided into sections by pairs of tall marble pillars. Set into the thick marble walls were ornate arched alcoves and recesses holding oil lamps and candles which flickered as they burned, creating dancing shadows behind them. Elaborate friezes with interlaced geometric patterns were carved into the architraves around each door and window, and every marble panel and niche was decorated with intricate floral motifs and symmetrical latticework. Tiered marble *muqarnas* projected out from beneath the ceilings, giving the impression that honeycomb was dripping down onto those below. The constant sound of water flowing from the bronze taps into the marble basins soothed the ear, ensuring a harmonious and relaxing atmosphere.

Safiru willingly submitted to the firm but skilful hands of the Mistress of the Baths. She sat on a wooden stool while warm water was poured over her head and body from silver bathing bowls engraved with prayers and floral designs. The olive oil soap, scented with rosemary and laurel, was repeatedly lathered into her ivory-smooth skin with a silk bath glove until it ran off her onto the floor like foam on the surface of the sea. After being rinsed, Safiru felt a coarse palm-root mitt being rubbed vigorously over her skin, and her body began to tingle. It was as if she could feel her soul being purged while her body was purified. Once this was done, Safiru shut her eyes and surrendered herself to the pleasure of being washed and massaged again. Oblivious to the whispering voices of the princesses and the Imperial consorts, wives and *Gözdes* in the hammam, she drifted into an unexplored realm that lay somewhere between consciousness and sleep.

When Safiru eventually came to herself, she did not know how long she had been in the hammam. She was dried, then dressed in a beautiful robe trimmed with gold embroidery. Her hair was dried with a small towel by a bathing attendant; after that, it was combed with a fine-toothed comb made of ivory inlaid with pretty silver flowers. The *kalfa* wound a thin white muslin scarf around her head to hold up her damp hair. Finally, Safiru stepped into her bathing clogs and returned to the cool room. She was *loğusa*, a new mother, no more.

She kissed her guests' hands and sat on a sofa next to Naziknaz. Relaxing into the deep, soft velvet cushions, she tried hard not to let her eyes close. A *kalfa* bowed to her and poured chilled rose-water sherbet into a golden goblet. Safiru's throat felt parched, so she gratefully took the refreshing drink from the tray. Another *kalfa* approached with a plate of thinly-sliced melon, which she also graciously accepted. As she listened to the gentle chords played by the musicians and sipped her sherbet from the cold, hard rim of the heavy goblet, time seemed to evaporate like the steam that billowed upwards and lost itself high up in the domes of the hammam.

❁ ❁ ❁ ❁ ❁

It was soon the baby prince's turn to be bathed. Hayriye took him from the wetnurse and carried him into the hammam. The ladies followed to watch the ceremony and sat quietly on benches that had been placed on the raised platform behind the marble balustrades. First the Midwife to the Imperial House, holding Vâsıb in her arms, recited the names of the forty Saints of Islam. Then a bathing attendant lathered up some soap on a silk bathing glove and passed it to Hayriye – who washed the little prince thoroughly, covering him in a veil of soapy suds so that he felt to her like a slippery eel wriggling and squirming in her frail arms. Next, she poured warm water over him and rinsed away the suds. Safiru watched anxiously, afraid that her precious child would slip out of the midwife's arms and fall onto the hard floor.

Following this, a bowl containing a beaten duck egg was brought forward by one of the bathing attendants. Since ducks have a close affinity with water, this action symbolised the baby's close bond with water. Being the origin of all life, water was sacred, and was revered for the important role it played in sustaining life and purifying the body. Hayriye gently rubbed the beaten egg into Vâsıb's soft white skin. As she did so, his bright blue eyes gazed up into the old midwife's wrinkled face. He did not cry: instead, he seemed mesmerised by her large hazel eyes, the colour of roasted Arabian coffee beans.

"*Allahu Akbar!* Allah is Great! *Allahu Akbar!*" Hayriye proclaimed. She then recited the first chapter of the Quran three times, calling upon Allah to guide the baby prince on his journey through life. When the prayers were over, a small golden key was dipped forty times into a basin of warm water, and the duck egg smeared over the baby's body was washed off into the basin. Then the baby prince was dried and wrapped in a thick, warm towel before being returned to his wetnurse. His very first hammam bath was complete.

☻ ☻ ☻ ☻ ☻

The ladies retired to the cool room for further refreshment, music and dancing. Now that the Purification Ceremony was over, the celebrations could begin in earnest. Mevhibe thanked the midwife, who had performed the final part of her duties at the Çırağan Palace, and gave her permission to take her leave. Then the *kalfas* appeared carrying large, round silver trays bearing a variety of sweetmeats and fruits. Steaming pots of apple tea and dark coffee and crystal carafes of iced sherbet were poured into delicate cups and ornate goblets; these were then served to the princesses and the Imperial consorts, wives and *Gözdes*. Napkins were distributed and the various delicacies offered round.

"*Validem*, you must try a piece of this *revani*," Fatma said to her mother. "The cook has made it with orange-blossom syrup today, and it is delicious." Resan chose a piece of the semolina cake and took a small bite.

"Oh my! It truly is delicious, my dear," Resan replied after swallowing her first mouthful. "The kitchens really are spoiling us today."

The musicians now began to play some folk music, and the fast melodies were infectious. The ladies sat swaying on their chairs as they watched the flamboyant movements of the dancers, who were circling the room. As they danced, they played the *zills*, their brass finger cymbals, which they clicked together with their long, elegant fingers. The young princesses took up their tambourines once again and tapped, shook and jingled them in time with the music while Naziknaz, Jalefer and the *Gözdes* clapped their hands. Safiru, sitting quietly but happily on her own, looked on.

"Look how expertly Dürrünab Kalfa plays the violin," Mevhibe said to Reftarıdil and Şayan. "Her bow seems to glide across the strings like a swallow gliding through the air, diving and darting gracefully in ever-changing directions." The ladies both nodded, their eyes remaining fixed on the violin all the while. Dürrünab Kalfa was being accompanied by Lebriz Kalfa on the clarinet and Tarzınev Kalfa on the *bağlama*, an instrument similar to a lute; it was the violin, however, that was creating all the emotional power in the music.

"I wish I could dance like Teranedil Kalfa," said Adile to her sister Safiye. "Look how she is floating across the room – as if she were being carried by the breeze!" The sisters watched as the dancers slid and shimmied on the parquet floor, admiring how they rolled their hips and stomachs while making exaggerated circles and figures of eight with their bodies. Their hips twisted and thrust to the beat of the music, while their arms extended and waved through the air like slithering snakes.

"But dear sister, you can dance so beautifully!" Safiye exclaimed. "I think you dance as gracefully as a butterfly in a field of flowers. You certainly dance far better than I could ever hope to do." The 'twins' smiled at each other as they went on playing their tambourines along with Behiye, Rukiye and Atiye.

Putting down her tambourine, Behiye left her sisters to sit beside Safiru. "How do you feel after the hammam, Safiru?" she asked.

"It was wonderful, thank you, Princess Behiye," Safiru replied. "And the room itself is magnificent. I feel as if I have bathed in paradise, and that I have been completely cleansed and reborn as a mother – but I must admit that I am feeling a little sleepy now."

"Then you must eat something to restore your energy," Behiye replied. She beckoned to a maid who was holding a tray of 'Lady's navels'. "I have eaten so many of these that I have lost count. They are heavenly," she said. Safiru took one of the small, round pastries. In the centre it had a tiny hollow, intended to resemble a navel, and there were chopped pistachios sprinkled on top. The pastry had been soaked in a sweet honey syrup, and it melted on Safiru's tongue.

"You are quite right, Princess Behiye. They taste wonderful. I must remember to take some back with me – I know Nihad would enjoy them very much."

"In that case, we must wrap a few in a napkin before they are all devoured," Behiye suggested. She asked for a clean napkin and laid it over her knees; then she placed six of the delectable sweetmeats in the centre and tied the four corners together, making a neat little bundle. She handed it to Safiru. "My brother is a lucky man to have a wife who so clearly adores him!" she said.

The music and dancing continued into the late afternoon. Safiru did not return to her rooms until darkness had descended, but she found Nihad waiting for her in her bedroom when she did.

❂ ❂ ❂ ❂ ❂

Nihad was not the only man waiting for his love on that cold November evening. After over a month of gentle but determined persuasion, Hadice had finally agreed to meet Kemaleddin alone in the summer house at the back of her garden. Far too excited to sit down, he was pacing back and forth across the rugs that lined the floor of the dimly-lit kiosk.

Getting into Hadice's garden without being apprehended had been quite an adventure for him. He had waited until Naime had retired to bed, and had then met his manservant Niko in the garden of his own house, by the side of the pergola that he had now finished building. Niko had arranged everything – two tall ladders, which were to be used to scale the wall between the two gardens, the unusual present Kemaleddin had ordered for Hadice, and a basket of sherbet and sweet pastries.

Niko was a very resourceful person; he had served for many years in the Ottoman army, ending his career as an orderly in the service of Kemaleddin's distinguished father, Field Marshal Osman Pasha. He had been born to a Bulgarian peasant family of Orthodox Christians, but on the death of both his parents he had been taken in and raised by a childless Turkish couple in a nearby village. Niko never forgot the heartless way he had been treated by the people of his own village: no one had wanted an extra mouth to feed, and at the age of only eight he had been left to fend for himself. He had lived off his wits for a week or two before eventually being found by the *imam* of a neighbouring Moslem village asleep under a tree, having eaten nothing at all for three days. He would not have survived if it had not been for the compassion of the people of this village who, poor as they were, all helped to feed, clothe and educate him. As a result, at the time of the Bulgarian uprisings Niko had remained fiercely loyal to that which he held most dear – the Ottoman state.

Hadice had felt nervous all day. Fehime had called on her that afternoon, and had instantly sensed that her sister was restless and uneasy; however, when asked what was troubling her Hadice had said nothing. The afternoon had seemed interminably long. Fehime had talked animatedly about the idea of engaging a photographer to come to her *yalı* and take a series of photographs of them both which they could then send to their father as a gift. She had expected Hadice to be as excited as she was at the prospect of engaging in such a risqué exploit, but as she told her about the 'Sébah and Joaillier' photographic studio on the Grande Rue de Péra, she had had the impression that her sister's mind was

127

elsewhere, and that she was only listening out of politeness. A highly-respected lady of the Imperial Court had recently visited this studio – unbeknown to her husband – and had sat unveiled while being photographed by one of the owners, a young Syriac-Armenian by the name of Jean Pascal Sébah. This lady had shown the resulting photographic portrait to Fehime, who had been captivated by it and had felt inspired to do the same. The portrait was a work of art, and the composition both clever and tasteful: there the high-born lady sat, captured for all eternity in a moment in time – and more importantly, perhaps, flouting tradition by acting in defiance of her husband. Fehime had been assured of the photographer's tact and his absolute discretion and professionalism, and she was determined to arrange a sitting whether her sister joined her for the occasion or not.

The idea had of course enthralled Hadice momentarily, but owing to the battle with her conscience that was raging inside her over the impending meeting with Kemaleddin, she had soon become distracted, and thereafter was unable to muster any enthusiasm for her sister's scheme. She had feigned a migraine, and Fehime had taken her leave without attempting to disguise her irritation. Hadice felt guilty for not having taken her into her confidence, but the truth was that she had not wanted to make her sister an unwitting accomplice in what she was about to do. Only Zeynel Ağa and Perizad Kalfa had been let into her secret, and she was determined that it would stay that way – for now at least.

Accompanied by her eunuch and her *kalfa*, Hadice walked gingerly along the stone path towards the summer house. She could hardly see where she was going: they had not dared to light the lantern for fear of being seen by one of the guards. The newly waxing crescent moon was barely visible in the night sky, and there was little or no moonlight to help them

128

navigate their way through the shadows. Her heart was racing as she tiptoed behind Zeynel Ağa, clutching tightly at her sable-lined *ferace* as if it offered some kind of magic protection. Then panic set in: her hands became hot and clammy, her breathing quickened and she began to feel faint and dizzy. Part of her questioned what she was doing – how could she be so foolhardy? She must turn around immediately, this inner voice insisted, and go back to the harem before it was too late.

But it was too late! There he stood in the open doorway, his handsome face thrown into relief by the flickering light inside. He bowed and made way for her to pass into the kiosk, with its welcoming warmth. With a nod, he dismissed Niko, Zeynel Ağa and Perizad Kalfa, who took up positions around the summer house to keep watch. Sitting next to the burning brazier, Hadice removed her *ferace* and slowly unpinned her *yashmak*, thus surrendering her final defences; meanwhile, the butterflies fluttered wildly in her stomach, and she tightened her grip on the embroidered reticule she was holding in her lap as she watched Kemaleddin close the door on the outside world – and on the protection afforded by the rules of protocol. She hoped that he would be understanding and undemanding, as she was painfully aware of being completely unprepared for what might happen next. Kemaleddin showed no sign of nervousness – quite the contrary, in fact. As Hadice watched him pour two glasses of mandarin sherbet and pull out a bowl of *saray lokması* from the picnic basket, she wondered how experienced he was with women. Her instincts told her that he had had many lovers; in fact, she was quite sure of it. What she was less certain of, however, was the nature of his intentions towards her.

He placed the bowl of dainty, syrup-coated doughnuts on

the table and sat down in the chair beside her own. He was so close that she could smell his eau de cologne – a once-familiar fragrance that sparked memories of her father. She wanted to touch his beautiful face with her fingertips, lose herself in his kind green eyes and feel the touch of those moist, fleshy lips that were hiding beneath his moustache against her own. She had dreamed of this moment for weeks, but now that it was here she was paralysed, torn in two by her desires on the one hand and her merciless, unrelenting conscience on the other. Neither of them spoke: they did not need to. There seemed to be a mutual understanding between them that all they wanted was to have the opportunity to absorb one another's presence without disturbance or inter-ruption. And so they sat in silence at the little iron table, staring mutely into each other's faces – until a sharp, high-pitched yapping sound broke the spell.

Hadice jumped, but Kemaleddin just laughed. "Do not worry, my dearest Hadice. That is only Aslan!"

"And who is Aslan?" she asked with a coy smile.

Kemaleddin stood up and walked towards the basket in the corner of the room. She watched his every stride, blushing inwardly as she imagined how his broad shoulders must look beneath his frock coat. He opened the lid of the basket and lifted out a wriggling bundle of silky beige fur. "This is Aslan. Do not be deceived by his diminutive size, for he is rather feisty, just like you, and like you he desires only love and affection. He is yours." He held her eyes for just a little too long, and Hadice looked away in embarrassment.

"Kemaleddin Pasha, I think you forget your place to speak to me so plainly," she replied, feeling her face and neck redden as she spoke. "Thank you, but I cannot possibly accept such a generous gift. Forgive me – I must return before I am missed." She stood up and made for the door with as much dignity as she could muster, but he blocked her path, smiling that very same boyish smile that had first attracted her to him. Before she could protest, he thrust the puppy into her arms; as he did so, his hands brushed lightly against hers, sending her heart racing all over again.

"Aslan will keep you company whenever we are apart, so that you will never feel lonely again." With that Kemaleddin bowed, opened the door and disappeared into the darkness before Hadice had had a chance to reply. "Yes," he thought to himself with satisfaction, "I am pleased with how our first meeting has gone." His intuition had been right: without any doubt, she loved him just as much as he loved her.

And so Hadice was left standing in the doorway of the summer house holding the wriggling puppy. She had expected that at this point she would be feeling pangs of guilt stabbing deeply into her body; this had not happened, however, for Kemaleddin had behaved like a gentleman, and had not pressed her to do anything she need be ashamed of. Yet she knew that something within her had changed, and she feared that she would now be unable to turn back from the course she had set for herself. After a few moments, she looked down at the puppy in her arms. "And what am I going to do with you, then?" she asked, stroking his soft, furry ears. He responded by licking her affectionately on the cheek. This made Hadice giggle – and in this way much of the tension she had been holding inside her during the illicit encounter was released.

Just then, Perizad Kalfa appeared. She had waited until Kemaleddin had climbed back over the wall into his own garden before emerging from her lookout post, while Zeynel Ağa had been waiting patiently on the pathway, ready to escort Hadice back to the harem. If Perizad Kalfa was shocked to see her mistress unveiled and holding a puppy, she certainly did not show it. Without saying a word, she picked up Hadice's *ferace* from the chair and wrapped it around the princess's shoulders, then pinned her *yashmak* in place. Hadice well knew, however, that her other servants were not nearly as discreet as her trusted *kalfa* and her loyal eunuch: questions would surely be asked both by them and by her friends as to how she had come by such an unusual dog. He was quite obviously a rare pedigree breed, not a common mongrel that had strayed into the garden of her *yalı* by accident; consequently, she needed to come up with a credible story to explain his presence – and quickly!

As she walked back along the path behind Zeynel Ağa, an idea suddenly occurred to her. If she wanted to keep the puppy, which she very much did, there was no alternative but to take Fehime into her confidence. She was, quite naturally, reluctant to take such a radical step and had hoped against hope that she would be able to avoid involving her sister in her duplicity, but she needed Fehime to pretend that the puppy had been a gift from her: there was no other way its arrival could possibly be accounted for. She decided that she would call on her sister the following morning, tell her everything and ask for her help. She was certain that Fehime would not judge her, though she did fear reading disappointment in her sister's eyes. Hadice's pace quickened as she neared the harem door while Aslan, hidden under her *ferace*, snuggled closer to the warmth of her tingling body.

PART II

CHAPTER EIGHT

The Calm Before the Storm

May 1904

LIFE at Çırağan began to return to normal after Safiru's
accouchement came to an end. The birth of the new
Ottoman prince and all the ensuing ceremonies had
provided a very welcome respite from the boredom and
monotony of everyday life in the palace. The long, cold
winter had passed without incident and had now given way
to a hopeful, vibrant spring. The pastel pink and ivory-
coloured blossom, which heralded the arrival of spring each
year with its explosion of colour, had long since disappeared
from the trees. Two months earlier the ever-faithful white
storks had flown home to İstanbul, obscuring the skies over
the city with their black-tipped white wings. As they went in
search of suitable nesting places, the flocks of birds had
seemed to the city's inhabitants like fast-moving clouds.
Their chicks had since hatched, and were now keeping their
parents busy with continual demands for food, sending them
on never-ending forays to the fully-stocked larders of the
Bosphorus and its wooded shores.

It was early lunchtime, and Safiru and her sisters-in-law
were enjoying a picnic in the harem gardens. Ali Ağa had
arranged for a canopy to be erected on one of the lawns to

135

shield the ladies from the rays of the midday sun. Spread under it was a hand-woven carpet from Uşak, a town in the Aegean Region that had been supplying carpets to the Ottoman palaces for hundreds of years. With its soft pastel colours and floral design, it made an entirely suitable accompaniment to a springtime picnic. In the middle of this carpet, a silver tray covered with small dishes of stuffed vine leaves, cooked meats, fresh fruit and pastries lay across a low wooden stand inlaid with mother-of-pearl. The ladies, seated on large floor cushions of emerald-green velvet, were nibbling at the food and sipping sweet, violet-flavoured sherbet from silver goblets. A warm, gentle breeze brought with it the light fragrance of freshly-mown lawns, and from the leafy branches of the trees up above came the cheerful sound of bird song. In the flower beds, honey bees were busy flitting between the wide-open heads of flame-red tulips, which although nearing the end of their season still freely offered up their golden pollen as they swayed in the breeze. Nothing, it seemed, could possibly disturb the peace and tranquillity of this idyllic scene.

Adile, Safiye and Atiye were kneeling around Vâsıb, smothering him with attention. They were playing peek-a-boo with him as he chewed determinedly on his silver rattle and sucked at a silk stocking filled with marzipan to dull his pain. The little prince was teething: nevertheless, he giggled uncontrollably each time he was tickled, making everyone laugh. Rukiye, meanwhile, was engrossed in *The Hound of the Baskervilles* – the most recently-published adventure of Sherlock Holmes. Abdülhamid had become an admirer of the novels of Sir Arthur Conan Doyle, and would have each new book translated as soon as it appeared so that it could be read to him in the evenings. He would send copies of these translations to Çırağan, and Rukiye would eagerly devour

136

each one as soon as it arrived: she enjoyed the stories every bit as much as the Sultan did.

"Rukiye, I really do not know how you can read those gruesome English mystery novels!" sighed Behiye. "Surely you can find something more appealing in Grandfather's library?"

"But Behiye, you really must read this one," Rukiye replied. "I think it is my favourite one to date. It is absolutely thrilling, and the plot is so clever!" Rukiye did not wait for a reply; her eyes immediately returned to the pages of her book.

"I think I will leave Mr Sherlock Holmes to you, dear sister," Behiye said with a dismissive gesture. Then she turned her attention to Safiru, who was gazing down upon her son's round face. "It will not be long before little Vâsıb begins to crawl," Behiye said. "Then we will all be kept on our toes!"

"You are quite right, Princess Behiye," Safiru replied with a faint smile. "The winter months have passed by so quickly! I find it hard to believe that Vâsıb is already able to sit on his own, without support." These words were scarcely out of her mouth when the baby prince suddenly fell backwards onto one of the soft, plump cushions that had been placed behind him, and everyone in his circle of admirers burst out laughing once again. Safiye scooped Vâsıb up in her arms and tickled him, making him giggle even louder than before.

"I hope the breeze carries the sound of Vâsıb's laughter over the walls and up the hill into the grounds of Yıldız Palace, until it reaches the ears of Sultan Abdülhamid. I want the Padishah to know that the spirit of the people he is keeping in confinement here has not been broken," said Behiye, suddenly bristling with defiance. A woman of resolute and determined character, she was the strongest-

137

willed and most intelligent of the five sisters. She rarely complained about their situation, but like everyone else she had days that she found harder than others. Today was obviously one such day, and she was unusually irritable.

"Princess Behiye, would you like another *köfte*?" asked Safiru, attempting to distract her sister-in-law from her train of thought by holding out a plate of succulent lamb meatballs – which she rightly guessed Behiye would be unable to resist.

❀ ❀ ❀ ❀ ❀

Selahaddin and his son Nihad were also enjoying being out in the garden on this perfect spring day: they were sitting reading the morning newspapers on the other side of the main palace building, in the shade of a large oak tree that grew outside the marble summer kiosk in the far corner of the *selamlık* gardens.

"Father, there is a very good article in this newspaper on the accord that was signed last month between Britain and France. It is indeed surprising, and not a little worrying, that now that they have signed the Entente Cordiale these two countries, who were enemies for centuries, seem to have become firm friends." Nihad was concerned that this treaty would have far-reaching implications for the Ottoman Empire, and that it would affect the precarious balance of power in Europe, North Africa and the Middle East; he had therefore been following developments closely. In fact, he had been taking an interest in European political affairs for some years – ever since reading about the 'Fashoda Incident', when France had made an unsuccessful attempt to wrest control of South Sudan and the headwaters of the Nile from the British. This territorial dispute, part of the so-called 'Scramble for Africa', had revealed the eagerness of both these imperialist nations to increase their power and influence in the region, and had almost led to war between them. On that occasion Nihad had been alarmed, and the fact that the two countries now appeared to have moved much closer to one another had aroused his suspicions.

"It is of deep concern to us, my son – not only for our empire, but also for all those who love peace throughout the world," Selahaddin said sadly. "The European Powers are beginning to polarise themselves into two opposing groups, and this will only lead to further antagonism: perhaps, even, to war. I had long feared that such an agreement was in the making. Do you remember that King Edward VII, my father's old friend, paid an official visit to Paris in May last year, and that this visit was reciprocated by Émile Loubet, the French President, in the summer? When we read about it in the newspapers, your grandfather warned us that something was afoot. They were obviously trying to rally popular support for an alliance, as relations between Britain and France had become extremely tense after the Fashoda Crisis. That wily British Foreign Secretary Lord Lansdowne, and the equally crafty French Foreign Minister Théophile Delcassé, must have been planning this for some time."

"Perhaps if our paranoid Sultan had ordered his secret police and his network of spies to infiltrate and influence foreign governments instead of spending their time spying on his own subjects, we might have been in a position to prevent such an agreement from being signed," Nihad responded with more than a touch of bitterness in his voice.

"Perhaps, but I doubt it," Selahaddin replied calmly. "Unfortunately, our government no longer has the power and influence it once had. We have allowed that power and influence to be eroded, and in any event we have never been as good at the subtleties of diplomatic intrigue and espionage as the British and French." Selahaddin put down the newspaper he had been reading. "As the new century begins to unfold, it is time our government planned the future of the Empire and ensured that we are in a position to protect our people and our borders on our own terms. If we neglect to do this, one day we will be presented with a fait accompli by those foreigners who want to destroy us. My fear is that the fanatical expansionism of Britain and France will know no limit. We must not forget that France is also allied with Russia, so it is even possible that a Triple Entente may be signed one day. I have always greatly feared the Russians: they have never abandoned their dream of ruling our Imperial city, turning the Slavic peoples in our European provinces against us and acquiring our eastern territories. These are dangerous times indeed."

Selahaddin adjusted the cushion that had slid down behind him and sat back on the white wrought iron bench. Sunlight flickered through the bright green leaves of the ancient oak tree under which the two men were sitting, falling on them in irregular patterns. Selahaddin was wearing a light tweed suit, a red silk tie and a dark crimson fez that hid his greying hair; a pair of reading spectacles was perched precariously on the end of his nose. The latest Ottoman, British, French and American newspapers lay scattered over the table that stood between him and Nihad, who was sitting on the bench opposite him. Every morning, Sadık Ağa went out to bring the daily newspapers to Çırağan. The three adult princes would often read them together: they would peruse all the articles with great enjoyment and then discuss them – so great was their thirst for information about what was happening in the world outside the palace. Today, however, Murad had decided to remain in his study after breakfast, thus giving Selahaddin and Nihad some time to spend alone together in the gardens.

After a short pause Nihad returned to the subject of the

newspaper article he had been reading. "As you will no doubt have guessed, Father, there are certain to be some secret articles to the agreement, but it is sure to have resolved many of the territorial disputes that have existed between Britain and France since the Fashoda Incident, and will therefore allow them to establish a new understanding. I think it unlikely that any military obligations will exist between the two countries at this stage, but the fact that France no longer objects to the British occupation of Egypt must be of great importance. Britain will view the agreement as a great success because she will now have a free hand to govern our protectorate as she sees fit." Selahaddin nodded. Then Nihad went on: "France will also feel that she has won a victory as Britain has finally acquiesced in her hegemony over Morocco and has granted her territories in Gambia, Nigeria and Senegal. She will feel that she now has the buffer she desires against possible future German aggression in Africa."

"I agree. Both nations will be feeling pleased with this agreement," Selahaddin said. Then he added: "You have a commendable grasp of the intricacies of international politics, Nihad, especially for one so young, and in particular for someone who has had no experience of the outside world. *Inshallah* your obvious ability will one day serve our empire well."

Inwardly, Nihad appreciated these words of praise from his father; outwardly, however, he pretended to ignore them, continuing as if he had not heard them. "I have to admit, Father, that it still makes me very angry to think how Sultan Abdülhamid allowed the British to establish a de facto protectorate in Egypt without putting up a stiffer resistance. Although the Khedive is still a loyal Ottoman vassal and Egypt is still a province of the Empire, in allowing this to happen we have shown a weakness that will no doubt be taken advantage of in the future. I am sure that in the long run the British will not tolerate a Khedive who is so strongly pro-Ottoman; nor will they be satisfied to allow Egypt to remain a 'veiled protectorate'."

"Yes, indeed. It is shameful that we have ceded our rights in Egypt in so meek and subservient a manner," Selahaddin replied. "And this new agreement will only serve to weaken our position there even further," he went on. "It will encourage the British to believe that one day they will be able to make Egypt a formal protectorate."

Selahaddin beckoned to Tirazan, his maid, who was standing a discreet distance away. She had entered Murad's service as a young child and was similar in age to Selahaddin. As children, the two had played together in the gardens of the Crown Prince's quarters within the Dolmabahçe Palace complex when Murad was living there; on Selahaddin's coming of age she had joined his household. "Tirazan Kalfa, may I please have some more tea?" he asked. "Nihad, would you like some more, too?" Nihad nodded. Tirazan removed their empty tea glasses and returned moments later with fresh mint tea and a crystal bowl filled with slices of peeled apple on top of crushed ice; she knew this was Nihad's preferred way of eating his favourite fruit.

When he had eaten a few pieces, he resumed the conversation. "I think Germany may well be feeling as concerned as we are. Do you not agree, Father? Their colonialist ambitions in Africa will no doubt be significantly affected by the signature of the Entente, and they will naturally feel inimical towards Britain and France. It seems that Britain now sees Germany and the Kaiser, rather than France, as her main rival in Europe. But is this not strange, Father? Britain and Germany have always been allies, and even the English King and his family are German."

"I agree, Nihad. However, I think the British have their suspicions with regard to the reasons behind the rapid expansion of the German fleet. Britain has long enjoyed absolute naval supremacy, but her dominance over the seas might now be under threat," Selahaddin said. Then he continued: "It is indeed perplexing that a traditionally-minded kingdom such as Great Britain should have a foreign family as its rulers. You could even argue that an English king has not sat on the English throne for nearly a thousand years. After all, William of Normandy was French, and of Viking descent. Later on, there were kings from the three French houses of Blois, Anjou and Plantagenet. These were followed by the Welsh Tudor monarchs, and they in turn were succeeded by the Scottish Stuarts. After that, the Hanoverian Dynasty, who were German, arrived. The current king is from the German house of Saxe-Coburg-Gotha, I believe. Can you imagine our great empire being ruled by someone who did not have any Turkish blood in their veins? I find it very odd that the English are able to accept an arrangement of this kind; I do not believe the Turkish people ever would."

"Yes, Father, it is very odd indeed," Nihad replied. "It is certainly something to be proud of that our family has ruled uninterruptedly, as one single dynasty, for over six hundred years. The blood that runs through our veins is of course the same as that of our illustrious Turkic ancestors who established our empire in order to ensure that the Turkic people would forever have a safe homeland."

"We are honoured to belong to such a dynasty, my son," Selahaddin said. "However, the world is changing rapidly all around us, so we must never be complacent. It is possible that one day our people may forget all that the family of Osman has done for them, and acquire new heroes to revere."

143

He paused for thought. Then he went on: "All monarchies rely on the love, trust and devotion of the people they serve. Never forget that!"

"I won't, Father." Nihad shifted in his chair. A growing feeling of anger and resentment had been festering inside him for a while now, and he badly wanted to unburden himself to his father; however, he was nervous about doing so. After a short pause to summon up his courage, he began: "I know that we must all accept our fate, and that we must never question the will of Allah, but I have never felt so frustrated by my imprisonment as I do now." Knots tightened in his stomach as he saw an expression of pain spread across his father's face, and he immediately wished he had not spoken. However, having once steeled himself to broach this painful subject, he was determined to continue until he had told his father everything that was on his mind.

"I know it is selfish and inconsiderate of me to say this to you, Father, and I am only too aware that you have suffered far longer than I, but there is so much more that I could be doing," he went on. "Our empire and its people need our family to act decisively. They need it to lead the way in bringing about radical reform, rapid modernisation and a drastic remodelling and reorganisation of the Empire before it is too late. If we do nothing, the vultures circling over our heads will start to pick away at our territories. I have some ideas that I would like to share with our Padishah, but I know Sultan Abdülhamid will never agree to meet a grandson of Sultan Murad. In any case, he is too conservative and authoritarian to appreciate that change is essential to our survival, and he is blind to the fact that it must come eventually – whether he commands it to or not," Nihad said, the anger gradually mounting inside him.

"I understand your pain and frustration, Nihad. Believe

me, I do. But be careful, my son," said Selahaddin. "This palace has eyes and ears. Sultan Hamid's spies are behind every door and every tree, and will report any dangerous talk of this kind back to him. I do not want anything to happen to you, my precious boy."

Selahaddin had noticed the change that becoming a father had wrought in Nihad. His elder son was no longer content to spend his days reading, composing and working in his carpentry workshop: he wanted his life to have a purpose, and that purpose – the one he believed he had been born to – was to serve the Empire.

"I am sorry to worry you with all this, Father. But I am not afraid of Sultan Abdülhamid. What really frightens me is what the future might hold for the people living under the protection of our empire and our family," Nihad replied.

Selahaddin smiled. "Once again, it makes me proud that you should have such sentiments, Nihad. However, for all our sakes, you must bide your time and be patient. There is little you can do from inside this prison."

Nihad knew there was wisdom in his father's words. He picked up one of the newspapers lying on the table and returned to the article on the implications of the Entente Cordiale that he had been reading. Glancing across at Selahaddin, he saw that he had removed his spectacles and closed his eyes. Nihad knew that soon his father would be drifting off into a doze.

☪ ☪ ☪ ☪ ☪

Murad had spent the morning in his study, where he had been busy sorting through the last of the boxes containing his private papers; he had burnt a good many letters and documents, and filed others away. Having felt the need to set his affairs in order, he had spent a lot of time during the winter cataloguing the large and valuable collection of rare books in his much-prized library and organising his musical compositions into bound volumes. He had also written his last will and testament; in doing so, he had made sure that no one in the household was forgotten, and that his most treasured possessions were all assigned to those dearest to him. However, he had left the mammoth task of dealing with his private papers to the very end. There had been so much to sift through; every sheet of paper had brought back its own special memory, and every time a new box was opened Murad had stopped to reminisce about the past. As a result, the exercise had taken far longer than he had anticipated, so it was with a sigh of relief that he now lifted the lid of the final box, which was labelled 'The Brotherhood'.

He opened the small velvet pouch lying on top of the pile of papers, which were tied together with a black silk cord, and took out the octagonal gold seal that the pouch contained. It was a Freemason's seal bearing his personal membership number – 272 – etched in Ottoman numerals below the engraved symbols of the square and compass, those essential tools of every stonemason. The seal had been given to him by Cleanti Scalieri, Grand Master of the Proodos Lodge into which he had been initiated when he was Crown Prince. He had been introduced to Scalieri by Namık Kemal, the Young Ottoman intellectual who had entered the Brotherhood himself, and had become a close friend. Murad stroked his white beard with his thumb and forefinger as he fondly remembered these two figures from his distant past, and that strange day of clandestine ritual at the house in Kadıköy of 'Brother' Louis Amiable, another member of the French Obedience. The initiation ceremony had begun precisely at noon on 20th October 1872 and had ended at exactly midnight. Intense secrecy had surrounded the proceedings as it was feared that if Murad's uncle Sultan Abdülaziz discovered that he had become a Freemason, he might rouse the conservative elements in the city against his nephew; if the truth of Murad's initiation were generally known, it might be used by Abdülaziz as an excuse to alter the line of succession in favour of his son Yusuf İzzeddin – something that the Sultan had always been intent on doing.

Murad had first been introduced to the teachings of Freemasonry during his state visit to Europe; Edward, Prince of Wales, who was also a member of the Brotherhood, had done much to persuade him of its merits. Murad had always been open to new ideas and new ways of thinking, irrespective of their origins; this was in part due to the influence on him of the writings of the thirteenth-century Sufi scholar Mevlana Celaleddin Rumi. It was one of this revered Persian theologian's sayings, in particular, that had encouraged him to investigate the values of Freemasonry and explore the possibilities it might offer: *'I am neither of the East nor of the West; no boundaries exist within my breast.'* It was this motto, in fact, that Murad had chosen to live by. Initially, he had been struck by the similarity of the philosophy of Freemasonry to that of Sufism; he had been attracted by its progressive humanism and its aim of achieving the material and moral perfection of mankind through the study of ethics and the practice of charity and goodwill to all, guided by the light of scientific truth.

The values of freedom, inclusiveness and mutual respect and toleration for others irrespective of race or religion were extremely important to Murad, and he thus found it easy to acquiesce in the core principles of the Brotherhood, which exactly mirrored those of the French Revolution – liberty, equality and fraternity. He saw no conflict with Islamic belief or with his future position as Caliph, so his conscience was clear when he joined the order: after all, Freemasonry accepted the existence of one God as Supreme Being, and this meant that Mohammedan, Christian and Jew should stand together as brothers. Murad thought this notion could serve to unite the subject peoples of the Empire, reviving their sense of being 'Ottoman' – citizens of a state that embraced all the creeds of its many and varied peoples without distinction, thereby inspiring the loyalty of all. In fact, he cherished the hope that he might be able to use Freemasonry as a weapon in the fight against nationalism, the insidious and ever-growing threat that 'Ottomanism' was designed to counter.

Murad untied the black cord and flicked through his old correspondence – until his eyes eventually fell upon a letter from the Grand Secretary of the Grand Orient de France, the oldest of the French Freemasonry Lodges to which the Proodos Lodge was affiliated. It was dated May 1st 1873, just over six months after his initiation into the Brotherhood. Murad had not even once looked at this letter of welcome since he had received it all those years ago, and had never reread its optimistic predictions of a more stable and progressive future for the Empire. He remembered how in his reply he had pledged to work tirelessly to unite all the peoples of his diverse Empire – peoples who were currently so divided by cultural, ethnic and religious differences – so that they would be able to enjoy a peaceful and enlightened co-existence. He had even proposed the establishment of a Turkish Lodge, to be named 'Eastern Light', so that the influence of the foreign Obediences within the Empire could be curtailed while at the same time maintaining and upholding the Freemasons' ideology. But like so many of his plans, this one too had come to nothing.

Murad decided to keep most of the correspondence in the box in the hope that future generations would understand the purity of his intentions and be apprised of the motivations that had first brought him onto the path that eventually led to his attainment of the rank of Master Mason of the eighteenth degree. He knew that many dark rumours were circulating with regard to the mysterious order, and that he would be criticised not only for joining such a notorious organisation himself, but also for encouraging two of his younger brothers, Ahmed Kemaleddin and Ahmed Nureddin, to do the same. However, perhaps the contents of the box would one day speak for him when he was no longer there to speak for himself. Reverently, he replaced the seal in the small velvet pouch, retied the black silk cord around the bundle of papers and replaced the lid on the wooden box. His final task had now been completed.

☻ ☻ ☻ ☻ ☻

In all the time he had been in Sultan Abdülhamid's service, Cevher Ağa had never seen him so angry. He was like an erupting volcano, the fury flowing out of him like wave after wave of molten lava. Standing frozen in terror in the Sultan's study at Yıldız Palace, the equerry flinched as his master launched into a fresh tirade.

"Every day I have to deal with the European Powers and their devilish plots, and with threats from anarchists and socialists, not to mention constant criticism from the opposition, those vexatious fools – and all this at a time when I am battling night and day to hold the Empire together. Is it really too much to ask that my own family refrain from adding to my burdens? Is it really too much?" he yelled. His voice was already hoarse from shouting; his whitened knuckles gleamed as he pounded the desk with his fist and his dark eyes blazed in wild fury.

"So how did you come by these letters?" he demanded, picking up the offending sheets of paper from his desk and waving them in the face of Fehim Pasha, one of his most trusted – although corrupt – intelligence agents. Fehim Pasha remained perfectly calm, however: he was secretly thrilled at the prospect of arresting two members of the Imperial family and being able to interrogate them in whatever way he pleased.

"Your Majesty, they were sent to me by Princess Naime's *kalfa,* Lârundi Kalfa. She found them hidden in a casket in Kemaleddin Pasha's dressing room," he replied in his usual ingratiating manner – but the Sultan held up his hand to prevent him from continuing any further. Fehim Pasha had wanted to add that the *kalfa* also suspected Kemaleddin of slowly poisoning his wife: in recent weeks Naime's health had been in decline for no apparent reason, and as Kemaleddin had insisted on administering all her medicine personally, Lârundi Kalfa had grown suspicious. She had served Naime faithfully for many years, and it had broken her heart to see her mistress become increasingly distressed over the fact that Kemaleddin was no longer visiting the harem at night. It was abundantly clear to her, as indeed it was to the other servants, that Kemaleddin had fallen in love with Hadice, but Naime seemed entirely unaware of the chemistry that existed between her husband and her cousin whenever they were with her in her salon.

Blood rushed to the Sultan's head and his face became redder than ever; the veins in his neck looked as if they would explode. Not only was he incensed to learn that for months an affair had been going on between his favourite niece and his son-in-law, but he was roused to utter fury by the knowledge that his network of spies had failed to uncover this scandalous deceit much earlier.

"How is it possible that you did not learn of this sooner? Do you not claim to know everything that happens at Court, and indeed in the whole of İstanbul, Fehim Pasha? It seems you are losing your grip!" Knowing that no answer was required, Fehim Pasha hung his head and stood there in what he hoped the Sultan would interpret as abashed silence. Meanwhile, Abdülhamid went over in his mind all the times when he had seen Kemaledddin and Hadice together at Yıldız. Had there perhaps been a stolen glance during a performance at the palace theatre, or had there been a chance for them to be alone together in the gardens? He did not think so – they had at least been discreet.

"The audacity of this Kemaleddin Pasha truly astounds me! How dare he say here that he worships Hadice? How can he, in all conscience, possibly worship anyone other than Allah? And how dare he refer to me as 'the usurper of the throne'! He will die for this! Being the son of Field Marshal Gazi Osman Pasha is not going to save him!"

Kemaleddin's father had become a national hero following his brave defence of the city of Plevna, in the Principality of Bulgaria, during the Russo-Turkish Wars. Abdülhamid had admired and respected him greatly, and had bestowed the title of 'Marshal of the Imperial Household' on him in recognition of his unswerving loyalty to the Empire. He had also invited Gazi Osman Pasha to join him on a number of occasions in his weekly carriage ride to the mosque to perform the *Selamlık* ceremony – a rare honour that was accorded to none outside the Imperial family. Furthermore, it was because of the high regard in which the Sultan held his old Field Marshal that he had given his own two eldest daughters in marriage to the distinguished soldier's two eldest sons – a decision he now deeply regretted. Recently, he had been considering marrying his third daughter, Naile, to the Pasha's third son, but of course that was now out of the question. "It appears that 'the fruit of a tree does not always fall near its roots'," he thought to himself. "How is it possible for a son to be so different from his father?"

Now that the initial shock was over, the Sultan was slowly beginning to recover his composure, and he began to issue commands. "Fehim Pasha, you are to go immediately to Ortaköy and arrest Kemaleddin Pasha. Cevher Ağa, you are to summon Princess Hadice to court, where she will explain herself to my sister Princess Cemile." Continuing in a much gentler tone, he said: "And Cevher Ağa, I want my poor, dear Naime brought here immediately. She must not be left alone in her *yalı*." Then he turned to face the window, thus indicating that the audience was over. Lost in thought as he stared unseeingly through the glass, he muttered to himself: "She will need all the love her mother and her sisters can give her if she is ever to recover from this abominable betrayal." For the moment, the loving, caring father had replaced the Sultan.

CHAPTER NINE

A Spring Scandal

Thursday 19ᵗʰ May 1904

SELAHADDİN was still asleep when Ali Ağa approached the table under the oak tree. His manner was hesitant, and he looked nervous. Addressing Nihad in hushed tones, he said: "Your Highness! Please accept my apologies for disturbing you, but I have been ordered to find your father and escort him to the receiving room immediately."

"Can it not wait, Ali Ağa?" Nihad asked with a hint of irritation in his voice. "You can see my father is resting."

Chagrined by this answer, which left him in an awkward position, Ali Ağa began wringing his hands with embarrassment. "Your Highness," he said, "Cevher Ağa has arrived from Yıldız Palace, and has demanded an audience with your father. He appears to be in a terrible rage, and is insisting that Prince Selahaddin come at once." As Senior Equerry to Sultan Abdülhamid, Cevher Ağa was the man who acted as intermediary between the Sultan on the one hand and Murad and his family on the other. The tyrannical palace administrators who had been appointed to oversee the security and daily running of Çırağan reported to him, and it was through him that any requests from members of the imprisoned family were made.

"This is an outrage! Who is Cevher Ağa to demand anything from my father?" Nihad retorted. Although he was accustomed to the rudeness, vindictiveness and blatant disregard for protocol with which his grandfather and father were customarily treated by the Sultan's henchmen and his spies in the palace, he deeply resented it; he knew, however, it would be unjust to lay the blame on his faithful servant. "I am sorry, Ali Ağa. I know this is not your doing. I will wake my father and accompany him to the receiving room."

"Thank you, Prince Nihad," Ali Ağa replied with a bow. "I am sorry, but Prince Selahaddin is to come alone. Cevher Ağa was quite specific on that point."

Nihad looked a little surprised, but stood up and walked over to the other side of the table. Knowing that sleep often evaded his father at night, he was reluctant to wake him. Nihad gently placed his hand on his father's shoulder and whispered in his ear: "Father! Father! Cevher Ağa is here to see you."

Selahaddin woke with a start. "What does the man want?" he mumbled, looking up at Nihad through bleary, half-closed eyes.

"I do not know, Father, but it seems to be a matter of some urgency," Nihad replied. "I am not permitted to accompany you, so I will wait for you here. Once your meeting is over, perhaps we can have a short walk around the gardens with Fuad? His lessons will be finished soon, and I know he would like to see you."

"Very good, Nihad. Perhaps we can persuade your sisters and your dear wife to share their picnic with us: it is such a beautiful day, and it would be lovely to eat outside. Come, Ali Ağa, let us see what this infuriating man wants of me." With that, Selahaddin rose from his seat, popped a piece of rose-petal *lokum* in his mouth and disappeared across the lawns towards the main palace with the faithful Head Butler following close behind.

☸ ☸ ☸ ☸ ☸

When Selahaddin reached the entrance hall, an attendant opened the door to the receiving room. As he passed through the doorway, he noticed that she looked both worried and frightened. He found Cevher Ağa pacing up and down the room, his hands clasped behind his back; the man's cold, hard eyes seemed focused on the detailed pattern of the Hereke carpet beneath his polished boots. Seeing Selahaddin approach, Cevher Ağa stopped pacing and glared angrily at the prince, showing no sign of respect or deference – only the arrogance and disdain of a jailer towards his prisoner. But before either man could speak, the Lady Mevhibe, Murad's First Consort, appeared. She, too, had been summoned.

Cevher Ağa seemed to be struggling to control his anger: indeed, as he forced himself to greet the prince and the Imperial consort he appeared to be trembling beneath his uniform. Mevhibe went to sit in a chair on the opposite side of the room. Selahaddin followed, but remained standing beside her.

"I am so appalled by what I have to tell you that I hardly know where to begin," said Cevher Ağa. He paused for a few moments to allow his words to take effect. Then he continued: "The honour of the Imperial family has been brought into disrepute. Yesterday evening we learnt of an unimaginable scandal that has shocked and outraged His Imperial Majesty. His fury was of such intensity that we could barely restrain him."

"And what is this scandal that is a source of such shame

155

for the Imperial family, Cevher Ağa?" asked Selahaddin calmly.

"Sir, I will speak plainly. Your sister, Her Imperial Highness Princess Hadice, and His Excellency Damad Mehmed Kemaleddin Pasha have been having an affair for the last few months," he replied in a suave and matter-of-fact manner. All the aggression had now departed from his voice, and he actually seemed to be taking pleasure in giving this piece of news and relishing the hurt it would cause.

Mevhibe did not allow her expression to alter: she refused to give Cevher Ağa the satisfaction of showing her sudden fear. She kept her eyes fixed on the virginal white petals of the tulips that stood in the vase on the table in front of her, their drooping heads bowed low. The only clear thought that occurred to her among a swirling chaos of emotions was that if this were really true, it would grieve her husband so sorely that he might well lose his will to live – a will that for years she had battled tirelessly to keep alive. Selahaddin froze, at first unable to respond to the terrible accusation that had been levelled against his sister. Then he slowly sat down in the nearest chair.

Cevher Ağa had obviously not finished. "Together they plotted to murder Princess Naime so that one day they would be able to marry," he said. "The innocent princess has recently been suffering from a slight malady. Their treacherous plan was to persuade the physician treating her to inject her with poison instead of medicine."

Selahaddin jumped up from his chair and shouted at the equerry. "That is a lie! A slanderous lie! What insolence! How dare you speak of my sister in this manner? She is not capable of such a thing." Mevhibe was startled by the vehemence of Selahaddin's reaction: he was usually so controlled and calm. His face had turned bright scarlet, and his eyes had narrowed in anger. "Your venomous spies are determined to dishonour the name of His Imperial Highness Prince Murad and that of his entire family. It seems they will stop at nothing to do so, and are even willing to stoop so low as to attempt to besmirch his daughter's reputation in their efforts to discredit him. Does the Sultan still fear my father so much that despite having imprisoned him for nearly twenty-eight years he still feels the need to spread malicious lies, and add fuel to vile rumours of this kind?"

"I suggest you sit down, Prince Selahaddin," Cevher Ağa replied – sweetly, and with a patronising smirk on his face. "I can assure you that these are not lies or rumours, but facts. Facts which were investigated and substantiated during the course of the night."

Selahaddin sat back down in his chair. He could feel his heart beating as though it would burst; his mouth was dry and his palms were sweating. Mevhibe asked Tirendaz, who had entered the room to wait in attendance soon after Selahaddin's arrival, to bring two glasses of cold water. The elderly *kalfa* had heard everything, and her face betrayed the cold fear that she, too, was feeling. She picked up the silver pitcher from the console table and slowly poured the iced water into the crystal glasses, then placed them on the table between Selahaddin and Mevhibe. Selahaddin gratefully drank a full glass, and this seemed to restore his composure a little.

Cevher Ağa now launched into a full account of the investigation, adopting the manner of a policeman reporting a crime, while Selahaddin and Mevhibe listened in stunned silence. He explained how the lovers had used ladders to scale the wall separating their two *yalıs*, and how they had had illicit meetings in the gardens on many evenings. Both mansions had been searched and numerous intimate letters

157

had been retrieved – as had certain potions suspected of being used to poison Naime. "The evidence of the letters is irrevocably compelling, and I am sure that after the chemicals have been analysed the plot to poison His Imperial Majesty's esteemed daughter will also be confirmed," the equerry said with an air of thinly-disguised satisfaction.

"You have indeed been very busy during the course of the night, Cevher Ağa," answered Selahaddin, speaking with as much control as he could muster. But before he could say anything further, he was interrupted. "I have not yet come to the real purpose of my visit, Prince Selahaddin," Cevher Ağa said with an air of smugness. "And that is to impart a message to your father from His Imperial Majesty." Selahaddin and Mevhibe exchanged nervous glances.

"His Imperial Majesty commanded me to remind your father that at Prince Murad's request, he organised the marriage of the Princess Hadice, provided her with a beautiful mansion furnished in the most luxurious style, and ever since that time has ensured that she wants for nothing. His Imperial Majesty wishes to ask his brother whether he thinks he deserves to be repaid for his kindness by having the Princess Hadice embark on an affair with the husband of his own daughter the Princess Naime, while at the same time participating in an attempt on this esteemed Princess's life." For the first time since she had entered the room, Mevhibe allowed her gaze to drift away from the tulips and fasten on the contemptible, self-righteous man who stood before her. Selahaddin said nothing.

Clearing his throat, Cevher Ağa gave a sly smile: he had now come to the part that would afford him the greatest pleasure. Speaking with a harsh edge to his voice, he said: "His Imperial Majesty has already decided on the punishment that Kemaleddin Pasha is to receive, but he insists that as her father, Prince Murad must determine an appropriate punishment for Princess Hadice. He awaits Prince Murad's prompt decision on the matter."

"All we have heard so far is malicious slander," Mevhibe said with a dismissive wave of her hand. "You have failed to present us with any evidence to support your accusations."

Selahaddin leaned forward to look Cevher Ağa squarely in the eye. "I will not permit His Imperial Highness Prince Murad to be troubled by this matter until I myself am convinced of the truth – or otherwise – of what you have told us," he said firmly. "Further investigation is required, and it is imperative that we learn the results of the analysis of these … these so-called 'potions' before taking any action. Furthermore, I insist that Princess Hadice be allowed to recount her version of events to me. See to it that she is permitted to write to me, without interference or censorship. I will await her letter. Now, Cevher Ağa, you may leave us."

"But Prince Selahaddin, His Majesty ordered me to return with an instant decision from your father on the fate of Princess Hadice," Cevher Ağa replied, an unwonted degree of nervousness entering his voice. He had not anticipated that Selahaddin would react with such assertiveness, and had been caught completely unprepared. This imprisoned member of the Imperial family had until then always been conciliatory and compliant; however, this slur on his sister's reputation had called forth all his resources of inner fortitude, spurring him to defend his family with the utmost resolution when they were under threat.

Cevher Ağa was all confusion. Lost for words, he stood there shifting his weight from one foot to the other, totally dumbfounded. In spite of the extreme gravity of the situation, Selahaddin and Mevhibe could not help but feel a twinge of amusement at seeing their jailer so flustered. They knew that

159

their robust response would surely send Abdülhamid into paroxysms of rage, and that his anger would equally surely be vented on his equerry.

"Did you not hear what I said, Cevher Ağa? Now you may scurry back to Yıldız Palace and tell my uncle, Sultan Abdülhamid, that if my sister is proven guilty of having had an affair with Kemaleddin Pasha, and if she has indeed plotted to murder our cousin Princess Naime, then I will kill her with my own hands for bringing shame on our family. If, however, she is proven innocent of the crimes of which she is accused, I will expect a full apology to be made. Now get out of my sight!"

Cevher Ağa bowed and hastily backed out of the receiving room. Once the doors had closed behind his retreating figure, Selahaddin let out a deep sigh. His hands were shaking, and his breathing had quickened.

"I am proud of you for standing up to that vile man, Prince Selahaddin," Mevhibe said tenderly. "But I am afraid he will soon be back for an answer. What are we to do? We cannot tell Prince Murad about this appalling business with Princess Hadice. I fear for his health. He is not strong, and I do not believe his heart could withstand being broken again so soon after losing Princess Aliye."

"You are absolutely right, Lady Mevhibe: we cannot tell Father. We must try to protect him from the repercussions of this dreadful scandal," Selahaddin said. He was slowly recovering his poise after the painful interview with Cevher Ağa. "Hamid would of course greatly enjoy discrediting our branch of the family, and I suspect that he may already have ordered certain details to be made public. The affair may be reported in the press tomorrow, so we must be prepared – we must ensure that Father does not see any newspapers until we have checked them for disparaging articles."

Mevhibe, too, was slowly recovering from the distressing

160

confrontation, and the practical side of her nature now came to the fore once again. "I will instruct Sadık Ağa to take the newspapers straight to your apartment as soon as they arrive tomorrow so that you can scrutinise them carefully before sending them to your respected father. I will also speak to all the *kalfas* and try to stop any palace gossip from reaching Prince Murad's ears," she said.

"Thank you, Lady Mevhibe. I know I can trust you to take care of everything. We rely on you for so much – I do not know what we would do without you," Selahaddin said, giving the elderly consort a smile of appreciation. "Now, are you all right in yourself? All this must have been a tremendous shock to you: I know how fond you are of Princess Hadice. You have been like a mother to her, as indeed you have been to me."

"I am perfectly all right, thank you, my dear Selahaddin," she replied. "Experience has taught me that life is little more than a series of difficult and painful trials; however, I also know that with faith, and with the love and support of family, we can endure almost anything." Her usual coolness of demeanour had melted away like a spring frost, to be replaced by a warmer, gentler and more thoughtful manner. "I know what your dear sister Princess Hadice is like," she went on. "She is a romantic, it is true, but she is definitely not a calculating murderess. She has filled her dreamy head with so many French novels that it has affected her vision of the world, and she has come to believe that life is one long, exhilarating adventure. She is in love with the idea of love. That is all she is guilty of, I am sure of it. And I have no doubt that her letter, when it arrives, will prove that I am right."

"I pray that you may be right, Lady Mevhibe." Selahaddin gave a sigh and shook his head. "It is a bad business, for sure."

"I think I ought to go and speak to Lady Şayan," Mevhibe

continued. "I feel she has a right to know about the accusations that are being levelled against her daughter, and I do not want her to hear about them from anyone else. If you agree, and if you will excuse me, Prince Selahaddin, I would like to speak to her now."

"Of course, Lady Mevhibe. Of course you must speak to her, and I am grateful to you for thinking of it," Selahaddin replied. "I must go back to the *selamlık* gardens – Nihad is waiting for me there. We were going to join my daughters and Lady Safiru for a picnic, seeing that the weather is so beautiful today. It is ironic, is it not, that all this should happen on a day that is so utterly paradisal? Now our enjoyment of it has been irrevocably spoiled."

☪ ☪ ☪ ☪ ☪

Selahaddin made excuses and left the picnic early; then he hid himself away in his apartment for the rest of the afternoon with orders that he was not to be disturbed. As he sat alone in his salon trying to make sense of it all, Cevher Ağa's words went round and round in his head. How could the outlandish accusations that had been made against his sister possibly be true? Surely Hadice would never behave in a way that would bring dishonour to her family? There must be some reasonable explanation for it, he told himself in his desperate struggle to believe in his sister's innocence. The hours slipped by, but just as dusk was creeping into the room there was a timid knock at the door.

Tirendaz Kalfa entered carrying a small silver tray with a letter on it. She bowed before Selahaddin and apologised for disturbing him. "Sir, this has just arrived from Yıldız Palace, addressed to you. The messenger's orders were that it be brought to you immediately."

Selahaddin invited her to approach and took the letter from the tray. He immediately recognised his sister's elegant handwriting on the ivory-coloured envelope. "Thank you, Tirendaz Kalfa. I have been expecting this," he said. "You may draw the curtains and light the lamps before you go."

Tirendaz bowed her head, set down the tray and did as she was bidden. It pained her to see Selahaddin, the noble prince she served, in such torment. She had dedicated her life to his welfare and cared deeply for him. Her greatest wish was to be able to protect him and shield him from all danger, just as she had done when he was a young man. As she carried out her duties, she remembered how she had helped him escape from the Çırağan Palace at the time of the Ali Suavi Incident, which had taken place when he was sixteen years old. How different the lives of Murad and his family would have been if the soldiers of the Beşiktaş Guard had not reached Murad before his rescuers did, and if they had not been able to hide him from them in the tunnels beneath the palace until the fighting was over and the rebellion had been quashed! Tirendaz was proud, however, that she had succeeded in evading the guards that day, and had taken Selahaddin to a rowing boat that was moored to the quay outside the palace, waiting to take him to safety on board the formidable battleship *Mesudiye*, the flagship of the Ottoman Black Sea Squadron. Here, he had at least been able to enjoy a few hours of freedom. As she lit the last gas lamp in the room, the elderly maid wondered how she had ever found the courage to do such a thing; it must have been the recklessness of youth, she concluded. How she wished she could now help her master find relief from the pain he was suffering!

Once Tirendaz had left the room and closed the door behind her, Selahaddin broke open the red seal on the envelope and took out the folded letter inside. As he held it

163

in trembling hands, he could not at first bring himself to read the words on the paper: he was too fearful of what they would say. His eyes wandered over the flowing Ottoman script, written in dark purple ink as was his sister's custom. After a few moments, he began to focus on the gold-embossed crown at the top left-hand corner of the letter. Seeing Hadice's personal crest and inhaling the familiar scent of jasmine that lingered on the delicate paper restored his morale and gave him the courage to renew his trust in his sister. Finally, he reached for his spectacles and began to read.

My dearest and most esteemed brother,

I write this letter to you in haste, and with shame and regret at having undoubtedly caused you a great deal of concern and anguish. Since I have been given little time in which to write, I will dispense with formalities and communicate to you only the facts as I know them to be. I thank you for your benevolence and consideration in asking to hear my account of events.

I have hidden my profound unhappiness from you all for so long that to speak of it now is almost a relief. From the moment I set eyes upon my husband, Vasıf Pasha, I knew that our marriage was doomed. I felt I had to hide this truth from Father and Mother since they had sacrificed their own happiness by granting my wish to marry and allowing me to leave our loving home. As you know, our uncle Sultan Abdülhamid arranged a lavish wedding for me, bought me a beautiful villa on the Bosphorus as a wedding gift, and bestowed on me a most generous dowry; for all of this I remain eternally grateful. However, his attempts to find suitable husbands for Fehime and myself proved far more problematic, and far less successful.

It seems that many of the eligible bachelors in İstanbul were so concerned for their own personal advancement that they went to extreme lengths to avoid marrying a daughter of Sultan Murad. I know that Father is no threat to our uncle, but it seems there are many who still believe that he may be. I was insulted to learn that Tahir Bey, the son of Tunuslu Hayreddin Pasha, the former Grand Vizier, even grew a beard to dissuade Sultan Abdülhamid from choosing him as a potential husband for me. As you know, Imperial bridegrooms are not permitted to have beards, so this ruse was a clever one. As a result, our uncle, in his wisdom, chose Vasıf Efendi to be my husband – a man who was a lowly palace scribe, and the son of a palace servant who waited at table. He is absolutely detestable: apart from being tall and lanky, and very ugly, he is sullen, never smiles, and has a permanent frown on his face. Not only this, but he is bigoted, parochial, narrow-minded and vulgar, and is in addition neither kind nor respectful.

It is not easy to tell you this, dear brother, but you must know everything if you are to understand the situation fully. For weeks after the wedding I resisted my husband's unwanted advances, but there came a time when I could refuse him no longer. The memory of that accursed night will never leave me, and ever since then I have continued to refuse him. I cannot bear to be in his presence; I have banished him to the selamlık and given orders that he must never be permitted to visit me in the harem again. I have petitioned our uncle many times asking for the marriage to be annulled, but each time he refuses my

165

request. On one occasion, I even chastised him for choosing such unsuitable husbands for Fehime and me. I asked him why his own daughters Princess Zekiye and Princess Naime had been wedded to the dashing sons of Field Marshal Osman Nuri Pasha, while we had been married off to undistinguished men far beneath our station. He reprimanded me for my impudence, but thankfully he swiftly forgave me. I know that Father will be angry with me for having confronted the Padishah in this manner, but you know how hard I find it to control my emotions on occasions.

In case you begin to worry needlessly about Fehime, I want to assure you that she is not as unhappy as I am. Even though she does not love her husband, unlike me she is able to tolerate him, for he is kind and understanding; she also finds solace in her music.

As you may know, my yalı in Ortaköy sits between that of our dear sister Fehime and that of Princess Naime. Since we became neighbours, Princess Naime and I have developed a close friendship, and have spent many enjoyable afternoons visiting one another. This fact makes my actions even more reprehensible and fills me with a deep sense of guilt which I honestly believe will remain with me forever. Princess Naime is kind and gentle by nature, and it is to my eternal shame that I have wronged her in the way I have. Some say she is Sultan Abdülhamid's most favoured daughter as she was born in the month of his accession to the throne, so he sees her as his auspicious talisman.

One afternoon in early October, I caught a glimpse of Princess Naime's husband for the first time. Mehmed Kemaleddin Pasha was building a wooden kiosk among some trees in his garden, just the other side of the wall between our two properties. Something made him look up from his work just as I was staring down at him from my window, and our eyes locked together. Neither of us could look away. I could hardly breathe: I felt as if I had been struck by a thunderbolt, and my lungs had been emptied of every ounce of breath. Soon after that first encounter, we met by chance in the salon of Princess Naime's harem during one of my visits to her. It was all I could do to conceal my feelings in his presence, but soon I realised that he felt the same way as I did. From that day onward Kemaleddin Pasha would often join us when I called on his wife, and before long we began to exchange letters. We met alone for the first time in my summer house early in the winter; once spring came, we would meet in my garden. We would sit and talk for hours among the spring flowers, hidden by the blossoming trees and guarded from prying eyes by Zeynel Ağa, my faithful eunuch, and Perizad, my most trusted kalfa. When we were together, it was as though I had broken free of the chains of my desperately unhappy marriage, and for those brief moments I could forget all the sadness of my empty, lonely existence.

Dear brother, we fell in love. Kemaleddin Pasha is a brilliant young army officer – chivalrous, handsome and passionate, and his letters are ardent and roman-tic. He wrote beautiful poetry for me, and painted exquisite miniatures as gifts. I admit that he stirred such deep feelings in me that I have been quite unable to extinguish the raging fire in my heart. I admit that I replied to his letters, that I reciprocated his love and that I sent small tokens to him in return. But – and this I swear to you by all that I hold sacred – we were never

167

physically intimate with one another. I promise you this, dear Selahaddin, and I implore you to believe me, for I speak the truth. I know that I have acted shamefully, that I have brought disgrace upon our family, and that I have also betrayed my dear cousin's trust; but I pray that you will be able to forgive me, and that one day Princess Naime will be able to do the same.

I know, too, that I am accused by Sultan Abdülhamid's secret police of attempting to murder Princess Naime in order to make it possible for Kemaleddin Pasha and I to marry. This is nothing more than a malicious lie, and I refute this slanderous accusation with every fibre of my being. It is true that a few weeks ago our cousin appeared to become ill: she began to wither and fade away like an autumn rose at the approach of winter. The doctors could find no explanation for her condition, but she took me into her confidence and told me the real reason for it. Before she discovered that her husband and I had begun corresponding and meeting in secret, she told me she suspected that Kemaleddin Pasha had fallen in love with another as he had become distant towards her and no longer visited her rooms. Brother, Princess Naime was never ill, and the doctors and investigators will never find a trace of poison in any of the potions they are testing, however meticulously they conduct their search: the source of her affliction is a breaking heart, and nothing more.

The Sultan will no doubt grant his daughter a divorce, and I am sure I will now have to face his wrath. I pray that in the end he will consent to grant me the divorce I crave, and perhaps even allow me to return home to all of you at Çırağan. Whatever the outcome may be, I accept my fate – but I vow that I will never marry Kemaleddin Pasha, even if one day we should both be free to do so. It would be wrong, and our union could never obtain Allah's blessing after all the pain I have caused to so many in my family. Through my selfishness I have tarnished Father's honour, damaged our family's noble reputation and destroyed our cousin's happiness. I do not deserve to live my life with the man I love, and am fully resigned to enduring this punishment until I die.

Now you know the facts of the case; they are exactly as I have described above, and as I recounted to Princess Cemile when I was summoned to Yıldız Palace earlier today. Do with them what you will, but I beseech you to do your utmost to keep Father from hearing about what I have done. I ask this not in order to save myself from his anger and his feelings of disappointment, but in order to save him from having to endure any more pain and heartbreak than he has already suffered. I do not expect you to forgive me, because I will never forgive myself; all I ask is that you should try to understand me.

With love and affection,

Your repentant and ever-devoted sister

Hadice

Tears streamed down Selahaddin's cheeks.

CHAPTER TEN

Newspaper Reports

Friday 20th May 1904

SELAHADDİN had risen early, long before dawn prayers, having passed the night without sleep. A bright moon still hung in the heavens, illuminating the clear sky; its reflection shimmered on the rippling surface of the Bosphorus that flowed endlessly in front of the palace. He read and re-read his sister's letter until at last the call to prayer from the nearby mosques broke the torturous cycle of grief, despair, hope … and grief once again. Removing his spectacles, he walked over to where a silver ablution basin and ewer stood on a large mahogany chest on the other side of the room. He picked up the ewer, its spout shaped to resemble the arched neck of a swan, and slowly poured the water into the basin. Then he unrolled his prayer rug and laid it reverently on the floor facing the direction of the holy city of Mecca; after performing his ablutions, he began the first of his daily prayer rituals. That morning he prayed for the guidance of the Almighty in the matter of how his father might be shielded from the scandalous news, which Selahaddin knew would grieve him in the very depths of his being; he prayed, too, that his sister would be spared the full wrath of Abdülhamid.

☻ ☻ ☻ ☻ ☻

A few hours later, Sadık Ağa came to Selahaddin's apartment. Tirendaz Kalfa showed him into the study, where he waited patiently for an audience with the prince. He placed the heavy pile of newspapers he was carrying on the large desk in the centre of the room. Each one had been carefully ironed as soon as it had been delivered to the palace in order to ensure that the ink on the freshly-printed sheets was dry. In the course of performing this duty, Sadık Ağa had noticed that every single one of the newspapers carried an official statement from Yıldız Palace informing the city, and indeed the whole of the Empire, of the scandal involving Princess Hadice and Kemaleddin Pasha. It was not long before the entire household staff had also heard the news: gossip of any kind invariably spread like wildfire through the service corridors of the Imperial palaces. All the servants at Çırağan were feeling anxious over the threat that this whole affair would pose to Prince Murad, their lord and master, and to the beautiful, vivacious Princess Hadice.

The eunuchs and *kalfas* were incensed; many voiced speculations and expressed strong opinions regarding what had happened. Hadice was widely acknowledged to be one of the most beautiful of the Imperial Princesses of the day: she was certainly one of the most fiery and passionate. Some of the housemaids thought Abdülhamid had, albeit unintentionally, created the problem himself by marrying Hadice off to such a loathsome man. They felt it was wrong that the Sultan's plain – and, if the truth were told – rather dull daughters had been wedded to handsome, dashing young army officers of talent and ability while Hadice and Fehime had had to settle for low-ranking servants of the state who were moreover devoid of any outstanding personal quality.

171

Others hazarded the opinion that in view of the fact that Hadice was so unhappy in a marriage that was plainly unsuitable, she might have decided that her only means of escape was to force her uncle to grant her a divorce by arranging for the bundle of love letters to be discovered by his spies. A few even speculated that the princess might have planned the whole thing with the sole purpose of wounding the Sultan in revenge for all that her father and the rest of her family had suffered at his hands during their confinement. Hadice knew how much Naime, Abdülhamid's much-favoured daughter, adored her husband. Perhaps she had thought that by seducing Kemaleddin Pasha and causing Naime to descend into the depths of despair, she would be able to fire an arrow into the cold heart of her treacherous uncle.

After a few minutes, Selahaddin entered the room. Sadık Ağa bowed. "Thank you for bringing the newspapers to me this morning, Sadık Ağa," Selahaddin said. "Is it as I feared? Have the press reported anything of the incident involving Princess Hadice and Kemaleddin Pasha?"

Sadık Ağa was at a loss to know how to reply. He fidgeted nervously, clasping and unclasping his hands behind his back while keeping his eyes lowered to hide the pained expression on his face. "Yes, my Prince," he said at last. "I am afraid so. All the newspapers have printed the same short statement from the Palace." He waited in trepidation for Selahaddin's reaction.

The prince remained calm and walked towards his desk, where he opened the first newspaper in the pile. The article he was searching for leapt out at him immediately:

Owing to various audacious and irregular circumstances, the Council of Ministers has taken the decision

*to strip His Highness Damad Kemaleddin Pasha of his
military rank, grant an immediate separation from his
wife Princess Naime, and banish him from the Imperial
capital.*

The notice was brief, but the inferences were clear.
Selahaddin leafed through each newspaper in turn: each one
reported the incident in exactly the same way. He knew that
as information filtered out of Yıldız Palace over the course
of the next few days, further details would inevitably reach
the eyes and ears of the outside world. İstanbul and the whole
of the Empire, not to mention the wide world beyond it,
would soon be learning of the scandal that had rocked his
family.

"My father must not see today's newspapers, Sadık
Ağa," Selahaddin said. "If he does, he will ask too many
questions, and I fear what effect it would have on his health
to hear the answers. You did well to intercept the newspapers before they were taken to his rooms." The eunuch
bowed in response, placing his hand on his heart. "Please
ask Aynifer Usta to meet me in Lady Mevhibe's apartment
immediately," Selahaddin continued. He then picked up a
selection of the newspapers and disappeared through the
door. Sadık Ağa followed him out of the study and set out
on his search for the High Hazinedar.

❀ ❀ ❀ ❀ ❀

Mevhibe had been informed that the newspapers had been
delivered to the palace, so she had been expecting Selahaddin
to visit her at any moment. She was not alone in her salon
when he was announced: Şayan was sitting on the sofa beside
her. The two ladies greeted him warmly, but it was evident

that he was not the only one who had been unable to sleep the previous night. Mevhibe looked tired and drawn, her face revealing the worry and fear she was harbouring inside. Şayan's eyes were red and swollen from shedding a flood of tears that had scarcely been interrupted since she had first heard of her daughter's troubles. The ladies were anxious for news, so Selahaddin showed them the newspapers he had brought with him. After they had read the articles, he gave Şayan Hadice's letter. Mevhibe edged closer to Şayan and placed a comforting arm around her shoulder as they read the letter together.

"My poor, dear Hadice! How unhappy she must have been to do a thing like this!" Şayan said once she had finished reading it, only just able to suppress her sobs. "How could Sultan Abdülhamid marry my beautiful angel to a hideous monster like that, when all she wanted in life was to fall in love with an honourable man, marry him and have children of her own? Is there no end to that man's cruelty?" Şayan's eyes began to fill with tears once again, but she resisted bravely and blinked them back. One single tear escaped her long, dark lashes, however, and ran down her cheek. Mevhibe, showing sisterly compassion, took out her lace handkerchief and wiped it away.

"I do not know, Lady Şayan," said Selahaddin with a sad shake of the head. "How has Hadice's innocent yearning for love and romance led to this? I recall that when we were young, she would often rebel when it was time to study, but never when it was time for French classes with Father and Lady Gevherriz. She would work really hard in those lessons – she was intent on becoming fluent so that she could read all the romantic French novels in Father's library! Do you remember how she used to sit reading them for hour after hour, lost to the world in escapist fantasies?" The three of them smiled as they recalled the dreamy young girl Hadice had once been.

"I remember that her favourites were *Madame Bovary* and *Dangerous Liaisons*," Selahaddin continued. "Both those novels are about love, seduction and the ruinous struggle between idealised romanticism and the harsh reality of social constraints. And now my poor, dear sister is facing similar struggles to those of her tragic heroines. Things have come full circle." Selahaddin understood his sister Hadice better than anyone else did, and he was determined not to let this affair ruin her reputation. "Ladies, you must not worry," he said, a note of resolution entering his voice. "My duty now is to protect my sister so that she does not suffer for love, as Madame Emma Bovary and Madame Marie de Tourvel did."

Mevhibe and Şayan, who were not at all convinced that things would be as easy for Selahaddin as he seemed to think, exchanged nervous glances – but before either could respond to what he had just said there was a firm knock at the door and Mistress Aynifer, the Senior Lady Steward, entered the room. She was dressed in the traditional Ottoman manner, as indeed were all the *kalfas*; as she bowed and approached Selahaddin and the ladies, her sapphire-blue robe billowed out behind her. This richly-brocaded silk kaftan was held in place by a silver belt set with jewels, and from it hung a small embroidered purse that contained the keys to the harem's storage vaults and safes. She also wore a short jacket richly decorated with silver and gold embroidery, and a sapphire-blue silk *hotoz* headdress to match her kaftan. As a mark of her rank as Lady Steward, she had a long strand of golden hair attached to the back of her headdress and falling below her waist. Everyone in the palace appreciated the skill with which she oversaw life in the harem, ruling over it with calm authority and absolute efficiency.

"Aynifer Usta, as I am sure you are aware, certain rumours about Princess Hadice have been circulating in the palace since yesterday afternoon," Selahaddin said. "The coming days are going to be very difficult for us all. I would like you to take the household in hand and make sure that no one speaks of this matter in Prince Murad's presence. Everyone is to go about their duties as normal. Is that understood, Aynifer Usta?"

"Of course, Sir. As you command, my prince," she replied.

"Good," said Selahaddin. "Now I will leave you with these ladies. No doubt Lady Mevhibe will have further instructions for you. I know we can trust you to ensure that our wishes are carried out." With that, Selahaddin asked Şayan to return his sister's letter, which he folded and put back into the envelope.

Murad was unsettled: the late arrival of the newspapers had caused a disruption to his morning routine. Having watched the fishermen pull in their catch from the deep waters of the Bosphorus and scanned the bustling district of Üsküdar on the opposite shore for reminders of the normal, everyday life of the city, he put down his binoculars. He had had a number of pairs of binoculars confiscated on Abdülhamid's orders, but with the help of his faithful eunuchs he had always been able to replace them with better and more powerful ones, and was now much more adept at hiding them from the guards than he had been. These binoculars and the daily newspapers were his only links to the outside world, so both were highly valued. He carefully replaced the binoculars in their leather case and returned them to their hiding place – a secret compartment that Nihad had very cleverly cut into the back of one of the armchairs. Still the newspapers had not arrived, and Murad was becoming increasingly fidgety.

He decided to sit at his piano to take his mind off this annoying situation, and after a few moments he tentatively lifted the lid. Murad had not played his treasured Erard piano since the death of his youngest daughter, Aliye, but since – most unusually – the newspapers had not yet been brought to his rooms, something pulled him towards the keyboard. The piano was an invaluable solace, a never-failing source of peace and comfort that relieved his otherwise banal and claustrophobic existence: when he played, he felt as free and untroubled as a bird set free from its cage. Music allowed him to grow wings that carried him soaring out of the windows, away from the cruel guards, over the oppressive walls of his prison and up into the boundless skies above his beloved İstanbul.

Murad was soon lost in happy memories of his youth, his fingers instinctively flitting lightly and expertly over the smooth keys. He played one of his own compositions, a waltz in E flat that he had written a few years after coming to live at the Çırağan Palace. Tarzınev Kalfa had assisted him with its composition by patiently playing and replaying each bar back to him while he tinkered with the notes until he felt that it was now perfect. Written to commemorate the birth of his daughter Fatma, it was one of his favourite compositions – a lively, spirited piece that would certainly have received enthusiastic applause if performed in any of the grand European ballrooms. As a young prince, Murad had been especially influenced by the work of two Italian musicians, both of whom had been Directors of Music at the Imperial Ottoman Court: first Giuseppe Donizetti Pasha, and later Callisto Guatelli Pasha, who had been Murad's own music tutor. Consequently, Murad's compositions were a combination of the European style and the Oriental – a harmonious fusion that was in keeping with the way he saw the Empire's future as a meld between the two cultures, and was moreover a reflection of his own nature.

Murad's father, Sultan Abdülmecid, had always actively encouraged his son's interest in music; he naturally knew of Murad's particular admiration for Erard pianos, and the reason for it. During the summer before his seventh birthday Murad had accompanied his father to a concert held in the old Palace of Çırağan – the one that had preceded the current building. His father had invited the famous Hungarian composer and virtuoso pianist Franz Liszt to perform in İstanbul, and had ordered that an Erard piano be purchased from Paris specifically for the concerts that were to take place. Listening to Liszt play that night had been the catalyst that brought about Murad's musical awakening: it had sowed a seed in the young prince's heart that eventually took root and became a magnificent tree in whose welcoming shade he could always find shelter from his troubles.

That evening, Liszt had played a programme of pieces by Italian composers. First, he had flattered Giuseppe Donizetti Pasha by playing 'Andante de Lucia de Lammermoor', a work by the Pasha's brother Gaetano Donizetti. The next item had been 'Casta Diva' from Bellini's opera 'Norma', and this had given Sultan Abdülmecid a good deal of pleasure. Murad remembered how his father had called for his *narguile*, and had smoked the water pipe throughout the entire performance, filling the room with scented smoke. The piece had been played with such sensitivity and tenderness that Murad still remembered how he had sat spellbound throughout. The concert had concluded with Rossini's rousing 'William Tell' Overture. Murad had never forgotten that night – the night he had fallen in love with music, with

178

all its beauty and enchantment – so much more intoxicating than women or champagne. He also felt privileged to have been present at a concert at which Liszt had performed: the Hungarian maestro was not only a uniquely gifted pianist and composer, but also a charitable and philanthropic man whom Murad respected and admired. Since it had been an Erard piano that Liszt had played in İstanbul, from that day on it had been Murad's dream to do the same himself one day.

With all this in mind, Sultan Abdülmecid had asked Guatelli Pasha to arrange for the purchase of an Erard piano for his son, and the Pasha had been able to do this thanks to the good offices of Signor Demetrio Paspalli, his brother-in-law. The piano had arrived in İstanbul in the spring of 1861; owing to his failing health, however, instead of waiting to present it to Murad on his twenty-first birthday, as he had originally planned, the Sultan had decided to give it to his son immediately. Murad had been totally overwhelmed: his father could not have given him a more thoughtful or a more precious gift. It was, however, to be the last present he received from his father, for soon afterwards Sultan Abdülmecid's health had deteriorated rapidly, and he had died without seeing his son celebrate his birthday.

As Murad played the last note of his waltz, his mind drifted back to that day in June 1847 when as a child he had sat in the old palace watching Franz Liszt perform. Unwittingly, his fingers began to play Bellini's 'Casta Diva', and his eyes started to glaze over: he was yet again absorbed in replaying scenes from the past. A particular evening now flashed into his mind – an evening when he had been staying at Buckingham Palace during the State Visit. Edward, Prince of Wales had invited him to play the Erard piano that had once belonged to his late father Prince Albert. It stood in one of the state drawing rooms, and its ornate gilded frame and elaborately painted panels depicting cherubs and monkeys had instantly caught Murad's eye. It was the most beautiful piano he had ever seen, and as he played it he had been impressed by the tight tension of the strings, the strong, solid frame and the clear, incisive sound of the instrument. However, in Murad's eyes nothing could ever compare with his own, considerably more modest piano – whose only decoration was a simple brass bordering inlaid in each panel, and the words 'A Son Altesse Impériale Mehemmed Mourad Effendi' inscribed in brass on the lid of the keyboard. After a while, he took out his father's old pocket watch to check the time. "This is odd! I wonder what has happened? The newspapers have never been this late before," he thought to himself.

He summoned Nefidem Kalfa. "Please can you find out where the newspapers are?" he asked.

She looked agitated, and more than a little flustered. "My Prince, they have not come yet," she replied. Her cheeks turned pink with the shame she felt at telling her master an untruth, and her dark eyes began to dart about nervously. Murad's suspicions were immediately aroused.

"Nefidem Kalfa, whatever is the matter?" he asked calmly. "You have not been yourself since yesterday afternoon."

"Nothing is wrong, my Prince," she replied, the blush in her cheeks deepening to berry red.

"That is good. Now please bring me today's newspapers," Murad repeated, a little more firmly this time.

Nefidem bowed and backed out of the room. She did not know what to do. As she was standing in the corridor wondering how she could obey her master while at the same time obeying the First Consort's orders, she noticed Lady Reftarıdil walking towards her.

"You look worried, Nefidem Kalfa. Has Prince Murad been asking for the newspapers?" she said with a knowing look. She had thought all along that Selahaddin's plan to simply keep the newspapers from his father would never succeed. Murad was stubborn, and he was also a man of ingrained habit. She knew that he would insist on having the newspapers brought to him, and that if they did not appear he would become suspicious and demand to know where they were. Like everyone else in the palace, Reftarıdil was concerned for Murad's health and wanted to protect him from anything that might cause him distress. However, she felt that attempting to conceal the recent painful incident from him would be not only impractical, but also improper. She knew Murad would be sure to notice the whispers and strange behaviour of the household staff, and would detect the general air of nervousness and unease among the members of the family. She also felt that as Princess Hadice's father he deserved to know the truth about what had happened, and moreover that he had the right to correspond with his brother the Sultan on the matter.

After Selahaddin had left Mevhibe's apartment, he had gone to visit his mother; it was then that Reftarıdil had persuaded him to permit her to show Murad the newspapers and Hadice's letter. She now had them safely hidden in her beaded bag, ready to show her husband if the opportunity presented itself.

Nefidem nodded. "Yes, my Lady. I told him they had not yet been delivered to the palace, but I am certain he did not believe me."

"Thank you, Nefidem Kalfa. Do not worry. I will speak to Prince Murad myself."

Entering Murad's apartment, Reftarıdil kissed her husband's hand and raised it to her forehead. She noticed that the lid of his piano was open and was delighted to see that he had begun playing once again.

"Lady Reftarıdil, my venerable wife, I trust you are well," Murad said, embracing her warmly.

"Thank you, my Lord: I am. And I hope you are also in good health?"

"Praise be to Allah – I am well," he replied.

"I see you have been playing the piano," she said with a smile.

"Yes, I was playing some pieces that reminded me of the past, and it has done my soul a great deal of good." Looking over towards the piano, Murad gave a wistful sigh of satisfaction. Then he sat down on one of the sofas and indicated to Reftarıdil that she should sit next to him. "I must admit that over the last few months I have greatly missed playing my piano."

Looking into her gentle face, he then continued: "As you know, I usually finish reading the newspapers before you visit me, but today I am still waiting for them to be brought to my rooms, which is highly irregular. Nefidem Kalfa has been acting very strangely all morning, and yesterday, when Ferengiz Kalfa was attending me, she too behaved strangely. Selahaddin did not pay his usual visit on me yesterday evening, or this morning either, and I fear that even you, my dear wife, do not appear to be your usual self. Something is troubling you all. I fear that something has happened which everyone is trying to keep from me. If that is the case, I ask you to tell me what it is here and now."

Even though Reftarıdil knew that her husband would be devastated by the news she was about to impart, she had always been obedient to his wishes. She was also very much aware that there was no alternative but to show him the newspapers. Without speaking, she opened her bag, took one of them out and handed it to Murad. Taking it from her, he opened it out. The official notice from Yıldız Palace immediately caught his eye, and his furrowed brow betrayed agitation.

"My Lady, read this to me!" he commanded, pointing at the announcement that was staring boldly up at him from the page. Reftarıdil read the words aloud slowly and deliberately, trying to keep her voice steady all the while.

"And what do they mean by 'various irregular circumstances'?" he asked when she had finished. Reftarıdil did not reply. "Princess Hadice and Princess Fehime live in neighbouring mansions to that of Princess Naime and Damad Mehmed Kemaleddin Pasha, do they not? What could have happened there?" Still Reftarıdil remained silent, so Murad went on: "These 'irregular circumstances' of which they speak must be related to me or to my daughters in some way – since the newspapers have been kept from me until now, and everyone has been acting so strangely. Lady Reftarıdil, I demand that you tell me all you know."

This was the moment Reftarıdil had been waiting for all along. She uttered a silent prayer, took a deep breath as unobtrusively as she could and calmly recounted to him all she knew. She then showed him the letter that Hadice had written to Selahaddin the day before. When he had finished reading his daughter's words, Murad seemed to become a little calmer. He stood up and walked over to the window, prompted by a sudden need to feel the warm breeze caress his face as it blew in through the lace curtains. He had not seen Hadice for about six years, ever since she had left Çırağan some time before her marriage, and he missed her desperately. He longed to hold her in his arms, kiss her eyes and tell her that all would be well. "She must feel so lonely and unhappy!" he thought to himself. He turned to Reftarıdil and looked her in the eye. "Is everyone in the palace aware of the situation?" he asked. She nodded, and he turned back to face the window. "I want to see my son and Lady Mevhibe in the library immediately," he said, his voice dropping almost to a whisper.

Reftarıdil slowly backed out of the room. Her heart was pounding. She had not expected Murad to remain so imperturbable on receiving this piece of news, which could only be a devastating blow to him, and his lack of any visible sign of emotion worried her deeply.

�ை �ை �ை �ை �ை

"Why did you try to hide all this from me?" Murad asked Selahaddin and Mevhibe as they stood before him in his library, its walls covered from floor to ceiling with fully-stacked bookcases.

Without hesitation, Mevhibe replied: "My Lord, we wanted to protect you from the pain and anxiety we knew it would cause you, and prayed that the matter could be resolved without our needing to disturb you. Please do not blame Prince Selahaddin, for the blame rests entirely with me. I beg your forgiveness." Selahaddin was taken aback, not having expected that Mevhibe would answer before he was able to speak, and certainly not having anticipated that she would take all the blame on herself.

"Father, I …" Selahaddin began – but before he could finish his sentence, he was interrupted by the First Consort.

"My Lord, everything I did, I did out of love for you," Mevhibe said. She caught Selahaddin's eye and gave a barely perceptible shake of the head to tell him not to contradict her.

She knew Murad was likely to be less harsh on her than he would be on his son, and despite the fact that she was not Selahaddin's biological mother, her protective maternal instincts had come to the fore.

"Tell me exactly what Cevher Ağa said when he came here yesterday. Word for word," Murad said evenly.

Mevhibe recounted the conversation she and Selahaddin had had with the Palace Administrator the previous afternoon, taking care not to leave anything out. Murad's face turned white with rage as he listened, his face betraying utter astonishment at the accusations levelled against Hadice.

Once Mevhibe had finished, there was a long pause during which Murad was obviously struggling to overcome the violence of his emotions, his breast heaving up and down. Meanwhile, Selahaddin – for whom the wait was agonising – stood before his father dreading what would come next. But when, at long last, Murad took out his handkerchief, mopped his brow and broke the silence, he seemed to have collected his thoughts and come to a decision. Although his face bore a grim expression, he spoke with perfect equanimity. "Yet again, my brother has made a vicious personal attack on me and my family," he began. "These lies have, as you may well imagine, wounded me to my very core. But that, of course, was the intention. It is clear to me that by directing this vile slander against my daughter, my brother and my enemies are making yet another attempt to humiliate me in the eyes of the world."

After a short pause, he began pacing up and down in front of his bookshelves. "These accusations are preposterous. Hadice would never have entered into an intimate affair with Kemaleddin Pasha, and most certainly would never have plotted to take the life of her cousin. I have read her letter, and I believe every word of what she says. I am absolutely

185

convinced that she is guilty only of entering into a totally inappropriate – and to tell the truth, more than a little naïve – correspondence, for which of course she should be punished."

He began to stroke his thinning white beard, and a pensive expression came over his face. "However, my brother must bear some responsibility for what has occurred since he wronged my daughters by marrying them both to such patently unsuitable men. I fully understand that Hamid did not want either Hadice or Fehime to become pawns in the hands of politically ambitious husbands, but I did believe – foolishly, as it turns out – that he would at least choose kind, educated men for them. I will not forgive this betrayal on his part, coming as it does after I had entrusted their happiness to him." Murad now stopped pacing and went over to the shelf on which his substantial collection of French novels was displayed. He scanned the faded brown leather spines until his eyes eventually rested on the gold lettering that spelt out the title of Flaubert's *Madame Bovary* – thus showing that like Selahaddin, he too understood Hadice through and through.

"My Lady Mevhibe," Murad said, "you told me that yesterday, Cevher Ağa insisted that I determine the punishment to be given to Princess Hadice, and that Sultan Abdülhamid had demanded an immediate response from me on the subject."

"Yes, my Lord," she replied.

"Please summon Asım Ağa. I wish to dictate a letter to my brother before Cevher Ağa returns. After that, you may retire to your apartment." Murad's face softened as he looked into the dark eyes of his First Consort. To him, time had only served to enhance her beauty, increasing the grace and poise she already possessed. He took her soft hands in his. "Please

186

know that I am thankful for the love you have always shown me, and that I understand that your intentions in this matter were good. However, my loyal, faithful wife, I am your husband, and it is I who should protect you – not you who should protect me, although that is exactly what, to my shame, you have tried to do in this case, as I am very much aware." With that, Mevhibe kissed Murad's hand and withdrew, leaving Selahaddin with his father.

☢ ☢ ☢ ☢ ☢

Once they were alone, Murad turned to Selahaddin with a faint smile on his face. Selahaddin was relieved to find that his father was not at all angry with him, but perplexed by his seeming composure after what had just been revealed to him. "Selahaddin," Murad began, "you did well to stand up to Cevher Ağa yesterday, and I am particularly impressed by the fact that you were able to contrive a way of ensuring that your sister was able to write to us with her own account of events. That was very clever. My dear, beautiful Hadice has suffered so much because of me, and yet my brother has now ordered me to decide on what he calls 'an appropriate punishment' for her. How can I possibly do this, when all my heart's desire is to look upon her once again and hold her in my arms?" Murad looked earnestly into his son's dark hazel eyes. "Hadice's dreams of happiness have been thwarted because of Hamid's insecurities, and because of the jealousy he feels towards me. As you well know, Hamid's fear of me stems entirely from the fact that he knows his rule is not legitimate. This is why in the coming days, he will no doubt do everything in his power to publicly shame Hadice, hoping thereby to bring shame and dishonour on me. Ever since he usurped my throne by spinning a web of lies, concealing from everyone the true nature of my state of health, he has lived in constant fear that one day he will be called to face divine retribution. He is afraid of losing the throne that he coveted so desperately. And he will indeed be punished, for Allah sees all, and He is just."

"His fate is written, Father. No one can hide from Allah – not even the Caliph of Islam," Selahaddin said with a sad shake of the head.

"You are right, of course, Selahaddin. However, you must be wary of your uncle. Never underestimate him. He is dangerous, and he is very cunning. Once I am gone, I believe he will feel a deep sense of guilt for the way he has treated my family and me, and I pray that these feelings of remorse on his part will bring no harsh repercussions for you. I hope that instead, you will be granted your freedom, and that you will all be let out of this accursed prison to live your lives in peace and freedom. But whatever happens, you must promise me that when the time comes, you will take care of your sisters, your children and all the ladies and servants of our household. Promise me this, Selahaddin."

There was alarm in Murad's voice, and it worried Selahaddin to hear his father speak in this way: it reminded him of the time when they had first arrived at the Çırağan Palace – that time when Murad's fear and despair had left him a pitiful shadow of his former self. Those dark days still haunted Selahaddin, and ever since then he had always been fearful that one day his father might relapse into the same deep depression that had then held him in its grip.

"Father, please do not speak like this. You must not worry about such things."

"Come, my dear Selahaddin," Murad said, holding his arms open to embrace his son. They remained locked together for a few moments. Murad kissed his son lovingly on both cheeks, but Selahaddin sensed that a change had taken place

– a change that he could not describe, but that gave him a terrible sense of foreboding.

"The Lady Şayan will be worried. She will be waiting anxiously for news. Please go and tell her that I believe Hadice to be innocent of all the things she is accused of. Inform her that I am going to write to my brother telling him of this fact and requesting that he put an end to any further investigations. I will state that the punishment I deem appropriate for Hadice is that he should grant her an immediate divorce, and allow her to return to Çırağan to live in confinement with her family. I will then add that since Hadice has already endured the punishment of being married for two and a half years to Vasıf Pasha, leniency is required."

Murad turned to his bookshelves, reached up to one of the higher shelves and took down a book that he knew his daughter had read many times. As he opened it, a pressed flower – a pale blue forget-me-not – fell to the floor. He remembered how in Hadice's youth she had enjoyed picking flowers, putting them between the pages of books, and then sticking them carefully into her journals. Here was one such flower that had been inadvertently left for him to find. "I will forget you not, my dear Hadice," Murad said to himself as he bent to pick it up.

He scarcely noticed when Selahaddin took his leave, doing no more than murmur a faint goodbye as he stared down at the flower – now faded and fragile after so many years. A minute later, when Nefidem Kalfa announced Asım Ağa, he showed no reaction at all. The eunuch stood in the doorway holding his scribe's box under one arm and leaning on his ebony walking stick with the other while he waited for Murad to give him permission to approach.

CHAPTER ELEVEN

Consequences and Repercussions

Late May 1904

THE days following Murad's discovery of the scandal saw the Çırağan Palace once again cloaked in deep melancholy. The precious respite of joy and laughter that the palace's inhabitants had enjoyed after the birth of baby Vâsıb had proved but ephemeral, and had all too soon been replaced by renewed anxiety and depression. Murad retreated to his rooms, and in his seclusion slipped further and further into the dark abyss of despondency. He was reluctant to eat or drink: even his favourite delicacies were no longer able to tempt him. Sleep evaded him, and the dark rings around his eyes grew even darker. As the torment in his heart weakened his body, his stoop became more pronounced and his speech slowed. It was obvious to all that in the space of no more than a few days he had aged by several years. Murad's family, and indeed the entire household, was becoming increasingly concerned that his old illness would return.

Abdülhamid had completely ignored Murad's letter. He had refused to grant Hadice a divorce, believing it to be more appropriate that she should suffer the long, lingering punishment of remaining married to the husband she found so

190

abhorrent. He had ordered her to remain in her mansion in Ortaköy, and forbidden her to leave it; she had in addition been barred from appearing at Court. It goes without saying that all this had greatly upset and angered Murad. Kemaleddin Pasha, meanwhile, was to be divorced from Princess Naime. Stripped of all his titles and his military rank, he had been banished from the capital and sent to live in Bursa under guard. There was, however, a minor consolation in that the ludicrous claim that Hadice and Kemaleddin Pasha had plotted to poison Naime had not been taken any further, though of course no apology had been made for the hurt this malicious accusation had caused.

Hadice was, as she had been ever since the discovery of her clandestine relationship, distraught. She was standing at the window from which she had once seen Kemaleddin sawing planks for the pergola he was building in his garden; now, however, she was staring blankly towards the empty summer palace of Beylerbeyi on the opposite side of the Bosphorus, an insistent feeling of loss, emptiness, guilt and despair gnawing at her insides. Aslan sat at her feet: he could sense her pain and was doing his best to console her, though she scarcely noticed him. Despite the fact that it was late afternoon, she was still in her night clothes; her hair was undone, and fell tangled and unbrushed down her back. For the second day running, she had eaten neither breakfast nor lunch. All she could think of was the shame she had brought on her father, the pain she had caused her cousin Naime, and the uncertainty that hung over the fate of her beloved Kemaleddin, who by now would have arrived in Bursa to begin his life in his place of banishment – and all this because of her foolish vanity and her selfish longing to feel loved and adored.

"Surely there has to be more to life than the dreary, grinding, meaningless existence I wake up to every morning," she thought to herself. The warm rays of the afternoon sun streamed through the ivory lace curtains that fluttered gently at the open windows; nothing, however – not even the welcoming warmth of a balmy spring day – was able to bring solace to Hadice's wounded heart. On a nearby table the bronze mantle clock, mounted on a base of white marble and adorned with gilt bows and swathes of gilded flowers and fruit, slowly ticked away the hours as Hadice sat grieving for the happiness she knew would never return. She freely admitted that she had everything most people could only dream of – a beautiful waterside mansion furnished with elegant and tasteful furniture and surrounded by lovely, tranquil gardens; wardrobes, cupboards and drawers filled with the finest and most fashionable clothes, exquisite pieces of jewellery and many rare and precious gems; and, of course, loyal and faithful servants to minister to her every need. Hadice wanted for nothing, yet she would willingly have exchanged everything she had without a moment's hesitation for a far more modest life with the man she loved, and who loved her. Over the last few months, her only too vulnerable soul had come to resemble a bloody battlefield: her conscience had fought long and hard to vanquish her sensual desires and had ultimately triumphed, thus staving off the threat of total ruin – but the victory had come at a terribly high price.

It seemed to her that her life's story, far from being the fairytale that ever since her youth she had excitedly imagined it would be, had proved in the end to have been scripted as a tragedy – much like the one in her favourite novel, *Madame*

Bovary. And yet, in spite of all that had happened in recent days, there was one thing that Hadice was still thankful for: she had at least been privileged to experience the intensity of those feelings that accompany true love, and so profound had that intensity been that she believed it would remain with her to the end of her days. The memory of how his softly-spoken declarations of love had made her feel, how the light touch of his hands had made her quiver, and how her heart had pounded beneath her tightly-laced corset every time he looked into her eyes, could never be erased from her mind no matter what humiliations and disappointments she was made to endure, and nothing and no one could take the memory of those precious moments from her.

Yet another tear ran down a channel in her already salt-encrusted cheek as yet again she acknowledged the bitter truth that never again would she feel as alive as she had done when alone with him. "Love is daring, and at least I can say that once I dared," she said to herself. But something inside her had died, and a little of that bubbling, ever-hopeful spirit that she had once possessed, and that she had naïvely assumed would always be with her, had been lost forever.

☻ ☻ ☻ ☻ ☻

The house was small yet comfortable. Situated on the outskirts of the city, it enjoyed breathtaking views of the mountains, of the alpine meadows and dense forests of firs that adorned their slopes, and of nearby wild orchards of cherry and plum trees interspersed with patches of deciduous woodland. Kemaleddin had been in Bursa for nearly a week now; he was sitting next to the window in an armchair upholstered in dark blue Bursa silk, looking up at the mountain range that towered over the former Ottoman capital. It was dominated by Keşiş Dağı, the 'Mountain of Monks' – so named as during early medieval times it had provided sanctuary for a good many Byzantine monks. One of these had been Saint Joannicius, the 'Hermit of Mount Olympus', who had found the solitude he craved in this untamed wilderness. Monks no longer lived in hermitages in the high valleys or wandered through the mountain passes, but even so this upland region was far from deserted. From his window, Kemaleddin often saw golden eagles soaring up above, and at night he heard the haunting sound of howling wolves. He had been told that bears, coyotes, foxes and wild boar were to be found there in abundance, and thought that when he felt up to it, he might one day go on a hunting trip and explore the glacial lakes, mountain streams and water-falls.

To Kemaleddin, the Sultan had been relatively merciful: the terms of his banishment were far from strict, and although guards were stationed at his door he was allowed to leave the house whenever he chose. He was not, however, permitted to leave the city of Bursa. In addition, he was forbidden to communicate with anyone without the prior consent of the Governor of Bursa, who in turn was obliged to defer to the wishes of Yıldız Palace. It was this last restriction that Kemaleddin found the most heart-wrenchingly difficult. It was perhaps understandable that he should be prohibited from writing to Hadice, but Abdülhamid had also gone so far as to refuse to allow any correspondence between him and his two young children.

In Kemaleddin's memory, the events of the foregoing week were surrounded by a haze. He had been seized while dining alone in the *selamlık* section of the *yalı* he shared with his wife, Naime. Soldiers had burst into his private apart-ments with pistols drawn, dragged him from the table and

194

thrown him to the floor in front of their commander, Fehim Pasha, who had read out the warrant for his arrest. Kemaleddin had then been taken outside, hurled into a carriage with his hands tightly bound together and taken to Yıldız for questioning. Interrogating the privileged husband of an Imperial Princess had given Fehim Pasha a good deal of perverse pleasure, and he had used extreme – and completely unauthorised – methods of coercion in his determination to make his uncooperative prisoner talk. Kemaleddin's handsome face still bore the cuts and bruises he had sustained under the beating administered by his torturer, and his body ached and throbbed in the places where ribs had been cracked. However, he had not given Fehim Pasha the satisfaction of extracting any information from him, and the despicable man's frustration had been further exacerbated when Abdülhamid, just a few hours later, ordered that the interrogation be stopped. It seemed that the Sultan's fury had soon abated: being the son of Field Marshal Gazi Osman Pasha had saved Kemaleddin after all. At the same time, an order had been issued to the effect that he was to be sent to his place of banishment the following morning, and that no harm was to come to him.

All Kemaleddin had been able to think of since his arrest was his beloved Hadice: at first, he had been assailed by pang after pang of worry and guilt over what might happen to her if Fehim Pasha should be permitted to interrogate her. Much to his relief, however, his faithful servant Niko had been able to discover that the Sultan had forbidden Fehim Pasha to arrest Hadice. Instead, she had been summoned to Yıldız and subjected to comprehensive questioning by Princess Cemile, Abdülhamid's favourite and most trusted sister, who as the most senior princess of the Imperial House had authority over all affairs to do with the Imperial Harem. After this protracted and painful audience, Hadice had returned shaken but unharmed to her *yalı*, where she was now living under house arrest.

The sound of a woodpecker hammering the trunk of a tree in the garden made Kemaleddin look up. He noticed the buttercups and daisies dotted over the lawn, their pretty faces smiling up at the warm sun; meanwhile, the breeze filled the room with the musky scent of the grape hyacinths, with their bell-shaped blue and white flowers, that grew between the rocks. Everything seemed to be conspiring to remind him of the times he had spent in Hadice's garden reading poetry to her to make her smile, sketching her beautiful face to capture the way she looked at him, and lying in the grass by her side as they watched the clouds drift across the sky.

"My poor Hadice! What a dreadful, unnatural thing it is for such a free spirit to be shut up in a cage yet again! Oh my beloved, what have I done to you? Please forgive me, my dearest! Please, oh please forgive me!" he said to himself, hanging his head in shame.

Niko had been permitted to accompany him to his place of banishment, and now appeared in the room carrying a round silver tray. On it was a plate of melon and white cheese, a bowl of ice – no doubt collected from Keşiş Dağı, which for centuries had supplied ice to all the palaces and grand mansions of İstanbul – a bottle of *rakı* and a short, narrow glass. He set the tray down on the table next to Kemaleddin, poured the clear *rakı* into the glass and dropped into it a single piece of ice. The liquid slowly turned milky-white, and the 'lion's milk' was ready to drink. The taste of the sweet melon, the salty cheese and the aniseed-infused *rakı* was a welcome and much-needed distraction for Kemaleddin. How could he ever manage without his ever-loyal Niko?

"Niko, why don't you get another glass and sit with me a while? *Rakı* should never be drunk alone. Come! Please join me," Kemaleddin said.

This unexpected invitation made Niko feel slightly awkward, but in this, as in all things, he dutifully obeyed his master. It hurt him sorely to see such a courageous army officer, the son of the great field marshal he had once served in the Balkans, stripped of his military rank and reduced to living far away from the capital and in such reduced circumstances. Since that dreadful night when he had been powerless to prevent Kemaleddin from being seized and taken away for interrogation by Fehim Pasha, he had felt guilty for not having attempted to protect him. But then, he told himself, it would have been futile: he would have been shot on the spot if he had tried to do any such thing, and then his master would have been condemned to suffer his banishment alone. Just before their departure from İstanbul, he had sent word of their fate to Zeynel Ağa so that Hadice would not worry, and had received in return a hastily-scribbled note informing him that Hadice was – for the time being, at least – safe. He had managed to pack a few things of value that would be useful during the months, or maybe years, that they might have to endure in Bursa, and had nursed Kemaleddin's wounds ever since their arrival.

For all that it represented a place of punishment for his master, Niko liked Bursa: it was, without any doubt, both a beautiful and a fascinating city, and far quieter and less crowded than İstanbul. He felt that they had been lucky not to have been exiled to Taif, in the Ottoman Province of the Hejaz, where so many of Abdülhamid's enemies were sent and then left to rot, their very existence forgotten. The city they were now in appeared to be a prosperous and thriving place. Its wealth was perhaps not as great as in its heyday, when it had been a trading centre for raw silk from China that had been transported through Persia before arriving here to be bought up by Italian merchants, but now silk production in the immediate locality had vastly increased, and field upon field around Bursa was devoted to the growing of twisted mulberry trees covered in precious silk cocoons.

Bursa had been the first Byzantine city to fall to the Ottomans: it had been captured in 1326 following a protracted siege, and had then become the Ottoman Empire's first capital. Every Sultan who had died before the conquest of İstanbul now lay resting in eternal sleep in this ancient city, and Niko had vowed to pray at the tomb of each one. There was now little evidence of the devastating earthquake that nearly fifty years previously had killed so many people, destroyed hundreds of homes, and damaged many mosques, buildings and monuments – including the tombs of Sultan Osman I, the founder of the Ottoman Dynasty, and his son Sultan Orhan I. Like much of the rest of the city, these tombs had been destroyed in the earthquake, but they had subsequently been completely rebuilt on the orders of Sultan Abdülaziz and now stood ready to receive the prayers of all loyal Ottoman subjects.

The two men drank together until the sun had set and the bottle was empty …

❀ ❀ ❀ ❀ ❀

Thursday 26th May 1904

Murad was reading the newspapers in his library with Selahaddin, as he did most mornings. The foreign newspapers, in particular, were full of reports of the Russo-Japanese War that had been raging in Manchuria and Korea since early February.

198

Both the Russian and the Japanese Empires saw these territories as of great strategic and economic importance. Russia badly needed to keep possession of Port Arthur, on the north-east coast of Manchuria close to the Korean border, as access to a warm water port on the Pacific coast was essential for the fulfilment of her trading and naval ambitions. Japan rightly feared Russian expansion and aggressive encroachment into her sphere of influence, and had suggested a compromise in order to avert the possibility of armed conflict. The Emperor had in fact offered to acknowledge Russian control over Manchuria in exchange for recognition of Japanese suzerainty in Korea; Murad could not understand why the Tsar had rejected this proposed solution, choosing instead to countenance the prospect of war. The compromise seemed a perfectly reasonable one to him, but it obviously did not satisfy the Russians' overweening ambitions.

Murad remembered how his father had often talked about Imperial Russia's expansionist designs, and how these designs had to be resisted at all costs since İstanbul would always be in their aggressive neighbour's sights. During his father's reign, the Ottoman army had fought bravely in Moldavia and Wallachia to protect the Empire's European provinces from Russian encroachment; the Ottomans, together with their British and French allies, had then defeated the Russians in a war on the Crimean peninsula that lasted from 1853 to 1856. Years later, however, after the Russian Bear had licked his wounds clean, he had come back – and was now even more ferocious and determined than before. In 1877, the Ottoman army had again been drawn into conflict in the Balkans and in the Caucasus, and this time the Russians had been victorious. In December of that year the surrender at Plevna of Osman Nuri Pasha, Kemaleddin Pasha's father, after a long siege had put an end to nearly five hundred years of Ottoman rule in huge swathes of territory in the Balkans. Now Russia had her eyes on south-east Asia, and Japan was understandably suspicious of her intentions.

"Reading about this war in Manchuria has reminded me of an occasion when the Japanese people showed genuine friendship towards our Empire, and great respect for us," Murad said to his son, looking up from his newspaper. "Let me tell you about an incident that took place a few years ago." Selahaddin smiled to himself: he knew that his father was about to recount once again the sad tale of the *Ertuğrul* and her crew. However, he was delighted to see something of Murad's enthusiasm for life return, so he sat back in his chair to listen to the story.

"When I was Crown Prince, I accompanied my uncle Sultan Abdülaziz at the launch of a magnificent frigate that had been built in our shipyard on the Golden Horn. The vessel was named the *'Ertuğrul'* after our distinguished ancestor, and I remember that it was a beautiful ship with three tall wooden masts. For a time it anchored in the Bosphorus, right in front of my apartments at Dolmabahçe Palace; once I was even invited on board to tour the ship and meet her crew. At that time our Imperial Navy was the third largest in the world after those of Britain and France, and I felt incredibly proud of our fleet." As he spoke, Murad's manner became more and more animated.

"After my brother came to the throne, a senior member of the Japanese Imperial family by the name of Prince Komatsu Akihito visited İstanbul. He presented Hamid with the Order of the Chrysanthemum, which is Japan's highest decoration. Grateful for this noble gesture, my brother ordered that the *Ertuğrul* should set sail for Japan in order to present Emperor Meiji with the Order of Distinction, and that she should fly

200

the Ottoman flag for all to see as she crossed the Indian Ocean and the South China Sea. When the vessel arrived in Japan, Rear Admiral Ali Osman Pasha and his officers were received most graciously by the Emperor and his Empress. I understand that they attended a large number of ceremonies, dinners and receptions. Since our two nations, though their cultures are widely different in many respects, are both steeped in tradition, a good deal of mutual respect seems to have developed during the visit. Just after the *Ertuğrul* had begun the long journey home, however, she ran into strong winds; these soon blew up into a devastating typhoon, and great damage was caused to the ship. She then drifted helplessly onto a reef just off the coast at Kusimoto, which I believe is the southernmost point of Japan's main island, and broke into many pieces. She sank quickly, and over five hundred souls were lost – including the Rear Admiral himself. Only sixty-nine of the crew were rescued, and these men were brought back to İstanbul aboard two small Japanese warships. The Japanese buried those bodies that they had been able to recover from the sea in accordance with the practices of our religion, treating them with great respect. This act of reverence should always be remembered, Selahaddin, and that is the reason why I admire the Japanese as a people and hold their Emperor in such high regard."

"What a tragic fate for our beautiful ship and her brave crew!" Selahaddin commented – as if he had just heard the story for the first time. "It seems we owe much to the Japanese for showing such concern for those poor Ottoman sailors who died so far from home."

"Yes, indeed," Murad said, nodding in agreement, and returned to the article he had been reading.

Murad hoped that the Japanese, who had enjoyed initial successes against the Russian Pacific Fleet at Port Arthur, had sufficient reserves of strength and endurance to over-come the Ottomans' old enemy in the long haul. He had been particularly interested to read of the death of Admiral Makarov a month previously, when the Russian flagship, the *Petropavlovsk*, had struck a mine laid by the Japanese at the entrance to Port Arthur, and had sunk within minutes. It seemed to him to be the will of Allah that Makarov should die in this way – it was *kismet*. Murad knew that during the Russo-Turkish War of 1877-78 Makarov had been the captain of the Russian torpedo boat that had carried out the world's first successful wartime attack with a self-propelled torpedo: in consequence, an Ottoman ship had been sunk off the coast of Batumi in Georgia, and hundreds of Ottoman officers and seamen had lost their lives.

Soon Murad looked up from his newspaper again, this time with an expression of surprise on his face. "Selahaddin! It seems the Japanese army has crossed the Yalu River and marched into Manchuria from Korea," he said. "They have defeated the Russian Eastern Detachment, and are landing more troops every day along the Manchurian coast. The Russians have been outflanked, and have retreated north to Port Arthur. According to this article, the Japanese army now has well-trained, highly disciplined soldiers who are as brave and as fearsome as their Samurai warrior forebears. Their army and navy are now equipped with advanced artillery, rifles and ships of the highest quality. It appears that they have completely modernised their armed forces – as indeed we must continue to do – and that as a result they are now threatening to upset the global balance of power by capital-ising on Russia's weaknesses."

"The European Powers will not like this unbalancing of the status quo, and the fact that an Asian empire has become so strong will no doubt be a source of anxiety for them," said

202

Selahaddin pensively. "This could have important repercussions for Western control over colonies such as China, India, Indonesia, the Philippines and Vietnam. It could also, perhaps, be an inspiration for people living under European rule in south-east Asia, showing them that the Great Powers are not omnipotent and encouraging them to rise up against their colonial overlords."

"You are absolutely right, Selahaddin. But it may also encourage people living under Ottoman rule to believe that their nationalist dreams of independence are capable of being realised, and thus rebel against us," Murad said. "I have an idea that the world order we have known for so long is about to undergo monumental changes."

Murad picked up the *New York Times*. As he was fluent in French, it was the French newspapers that he preferred to read when he wished to glean a foreign viewpoint on world affairs; however, he liked to leaf through the British and American newspapers as well in order to expand his limited knowledge of English. One article in particular caught his eye, and his expression changed instantly. The blood drained from his face, and his eyes widened in an unblinking stare. The newspaper slipped from his fingers and dropped to the carpet.

"Father, what is it? What is wrong?" Selahaddin asked with urgent concern. He jumped up and collected the pages of the newspaper that now lay scattered across the floor at his father's feet.

Murad did not seem to hear his son's anxious voice: to him it was but a distant echo reverberating off the bookshelves. "Father, are you all right?" Selahaddin asked once again.

Murad's gentle brown eyes closed for a second or two, and when they re-opened he answered his son in a tone that

Selahaddin recognised from the days of his father's illness, and that he had fervently hoped never to hear again in his voice – one that was full of hopeless sadness and resignation. "Now the whole world knows of Hadice's shame. Today it has been reported in the pages of the *New York Times*, so people are even reading about it in the Americas. Her name and mine are both mentioned in the article, so yet again we find ourselves the butt of malicious gossip."

As Selahaddin did not speak English, once the newspaper was back in his hands and his breathing had calmed down Murad slowly read the short article to him:

"CONSTANTINOPLE, May 23rd – Kemal Pasha, the Sultan's son-in-law, and other high officials have been arrested and sent into exile in consequence of the discovery of a secret correspondence between Kemal Pasha and Princess Khadidje – Hadice" (Murad corrected) – "daughter of the imprisoned ex-Sultan, Murad."

When he turned to look at his son, Murad had tears in his eyes. "I simply cannot bear this life any longer," he said. "I have no luck, my son – my fate is utterly relentless. Until now I have upheld my dignity, but now I am tired – tired of all the lies, tired of it all."

CHAPTER TWELVE

Death of a Sultan

July 1904

THE roses were now in full bloom in the formal gardens of the Çırağan Palace. The heavy, perfumed heads, like outsized jewels, covered every bush. The kitchen garden, meanwhile, was bursting with aubergines, beans, cucumbers and tomatoes, and in the fruit garden apricots, peaches and cherries were waiting to be picked. Summer had arrived, and as always İstanbul was stiflingly hot and humid. Unlike the other members of the Imperial family, those who lived at Çırağan could find no respite from the heat. They could not retreat to a summer villa on the Princes' Islands to benefit from the cool winds blowing across the Sea of Marmara, or hide away in a waterside mansion shaded by sweet-smelling forests of pine in the upper reaches of the Bosphorus.

Life in the household had regained a semblance of normality after all the scandal and distress of the foregoing weeks. It was laundry day, and the junior *kalfas* had collected the dirty laundry and linen from each suite in the main palace and the harem building. Giant samovars had been placed in the kitchen, and the harem eunuchs were continuously bringing in hot coals to heat the water. Seven large copper basins had been set on the floor, and three young maids were sitting around them. They chatted and giggled as they vigorously rubbed the soapsuds into the clothes and linen with their soft, supple hands. After the laundry had been washed in the first basin it was passed on to the next and washed again; then it went on to the next and the next again, until it had been washed in all seven basins. The Samovar Kalfa, a big, strong woman, was sweating from the effort of pouring stream after stream of freshly-heated water into the basins. The older *kalfas* took the clean laundry into the service garden, where they hung it out to dry. Following behind them came the junior *kalfas* – Nezihe and her younger sister Nevrestan; they were carrying woven baskets filled with wooden clothes pegs, and sang happily in their melodious voices as they handed them out. The warm sun dried the laundry quickly, so it was soon taken down, pressed, ironed and returned to the suites where it belonged.

Murad's laundry was carried out separately from the rest by the *Çamaşırcı Usta* – the Mistress of the Laundry – who washed the former Sultan's clothing with meticulous care in seven silver basins. Murad was very particular about his clothing and fastidious in the matter of his bed linen. It was changed every other day and aired each morning; rose-water would be sprinkled on his sheets before they were pressed, and again when they were replaced on his bed. In winter, rather than use the traditional feather quilts favoured by the rest of the household, he preferred thick wool blankets enveloped in soft linen sheets; in high summer, however, Murad used lighter blankets. Careful attention was paid to these sheets, which Mevhibe had embroidered with Murad's personal crest and name. They had to be laid out perfectly – Murad would notice if they were draped even slightly unevenly over his bed, or if they fell too near or too far from the floor.

❂ ❂ ❂ ❂ ❂

It was now late afternoon. While the *kalfas* had been busy with the laundry, the family had been relaxing in the gardens all day. Murad's consorts and *Gözdes* had spent most of the day sitting on low divans sheltered by a canopy, drinking iced sherbet and gossiping with Naziknaz and Jalefer. These ladies had been talking of their concern for Murad and Hadice, doing their needlework all the while. Selahaddin's five daughters, dressed in delicate white cotton lawn tea dresses trimmed with lace, had been lounging in the shade of the large oak tree reading novels, flicking through the pages of French fashion magazines and playing various musical instruments. Nihad and Safiru had been sitting with them: they had been entertaining little Vâsıb, delighting in the fact that the baby prince kept crawling towards his aunts – who would shower him with kisses and tickles the moment he came near them. Selahaddin had been tutoring Fuad in French and History for most of the day, and had rewarded his younger son for a rare display of concentration and diligence by playing backgammon with him on the terrace. Meanwhile, Fatma had persuaded her father to leave the solitude of his rooms and accompany her in a gentle stroll around the fruit gardens. They walked side by side, their arms lovingly entwined, as they discussed the themes of *The Cherry Orchard*, the most recent play by Anton Chekhov – whose death Murad had read about in the French newspapers that morning.

"I cried when I read the final act, where he describes the sound of the axes brutally chopping down the cherry trees in that orchard – the one that sounds so idyllic," Fatma said. "Can you imagine anyone ever being so horribly destructive as to do that here, in our beautiful garden?"

Murad reached up to an overhanging branch and picked a juicy, ripe peach from one of the trees. He gave it to his daughter, kissing her adoringly on the cheek as he did so, then smiled as she took a bite. He was pleased that he had agreed to the walk: he felt that the warmth of the sun combined with the warmth of his beloved daughter's love had rejuvenated him a little.

"Dear, sweet Fatma, you must try not to be like Chekhov's tragic heroine Madame Ranyevskaya, who is unable to cope with a changing society and insists on forever dwelling on the past," Murad said. "It is her inability to adapt that leads to her downfall, and it is exactly this that will lead to the downfall of the ruling class everywhere else unless they accept that change is inevitable." He had been an admirer of Chekhov's work for a number of years and had read French translations of most of his plays and short stories, so it had saddened him to learn that this literary genius had died of tuberculosis a few days earlier. Chekhov's complex characters, his elegant way of story-telling and his skilled use of bleak irony had kept Murad occupied for many hours, and for that he was grateful.

Murad went on to explain to his daughter the parallel in the play between the cherry trees and the old world order – both are being cut down by men from the lower echelons of society, and both will soon be replaced by modern alternatives based on Western values and ideas. "It is a highly perceptive play that contains stark and very pertinent warnings for us all," he said.

The day passed as many others had passed that summer, and many summers before that. Everyone was aware, however, that Murad had withdrawn into himself, having succumbed to the deep depression into which he had descended on learning of the scandal surrounding Hadice. Ever since that dreadful week in May a sense of foreboding had been hovering over the household like a dark cloud, but right now all were encouraged to see Murad enjoying the gardens with his youngest daughter.

After their walk, Murad and Fatma joined the wives, consorts and *Gözdes* under the canopy. Murad took a few sips of the iced cherry sherbet they offered him, but refused all food except for a single piece of orange-blossom Turkish Delight. They talked for a short time; then he stood up and graciously took his leave of the ladies. They all watched as he walked slowly away on the arm of his daughter, heading towards the large oak tree where his grandchildren were gathered. It greatly saddened Reftarıdil to see how her once handsome, vibrant and energetic prince now walked with a stoop, how his thick, shiny black hair had thinned and turned white, and how his large, chestnut-brown eyes were now sunken and dulled. Once he was far from sight, she resumed her needlework, thinking to herself.

The princesses were pleased to see their grandfather, and crowded round him as he sat on one of the wicker armchairs under the tree. Nihad put an extra cushion behind his back. Once he was comfortable, Murad suggested to the girls that they might like to sing to him; his granddaughters beamed with delight, and promptly went into a huddle to decide which song to perform. He then turned to Safiru: "My dear child, bring little Vâsıb Efendi to me, will you?" he said. "Let him sit on my knee for a while." Bowing, Safiru placed her son in Murad's arms. He kissed the baby prince gently on his forehead, and Vâsıb smiled up into the kind eyes of his great-grandfather. The baby sat there contentedly while his mother and his aunts performed the 'Humming Chorus' from Puccini's newly-reworked and recently-debuted opera 'Madame Butterfly'. Safiye delicately plucked the strings of her lute and Rukiye played softly on her flute as the others hummed the calm, peaceful melody. The three princes clapped enthusiastically when the princesses had finished – especially little Vâsıb! His chubby hands came together with unrestrained delight until Safiru came forward to take her son from Murad's lap.

"Wonderful! Wonderful!" Murad exclaimed. "That was absolutely beautiful. The reviews following the first perform-ance of this opera in Brescia were fabulous – but, my dear children, the best soprano singers in Italy could not have performed that chorus more exquisitely than you did. Thank you! Thank you for giving me such a beautiful gift."

"We have been practising with Dürrünab Kalfa for weeks, Grandfather," Atiye said excitedly. She and her sisters were now standing before Murad, their eyes gleaming with pride after the praise they had received.

"Well, it was very clever of Dürrünab Kalfa to get hold of a copy of the score of such a new opera. She has certainly excelled herself – and you, my precious ones, have brought me great joy. Having read the reviews back in May, I was eager to hear a piece from Puccini's most recent masterpiece. Thank you for making my wish come true." After kissing each of his granddaughters on the head, he took his daugh-ter's arm once more. "Come, Fatma, will you take me inside? I think I need to rest. Hearing that lullaby has made me feel quite sleepy!"

Slowly, Murad and Fatma headed back towards the harem building; before going inside, however, they paused for a while on the terrace where Selahaddin and Fuad were playing backgammon. They stood and watched a few throws of the dice; then Murad suggested a move to Fuad that his grandson had failed to see.

"You play very well, Fuad, but make sure you do not take

unnecessary risks that your opponent can then take advantage of," Murad said. "Always protect your pieces when you can, and do not risk losing them needlessly. A game of backgammon is like an encounter on the battlefield. It is a game of strategy as well as one of luck, and so like all good generals you must value every one of your men."

"Thank you, Grandfather. I will remember your advice – not just when I am playing backgammon, but when I am leading my men into battle, too," replied the young boy.

"I believe you will, Fuad, I really believe you will." Murad smiled back at his grandson, then turned to Fatma and asked her to escort him back to his rooms.

❁ ❁ ❁ ❁ ❁

That evening the Lady Şayan and Filizten, one of Murad's *Gözdes*, were attending their master as he performed his toilette before retiring to bed. The Mistress of the Ewer had filled his silver basin with warm water and left neatly-folded towels on a table next to the polished wooden case of his toilette set. The set had been a gift from his mother, commissioned for the state visit to Europe that had taken place when he was Crown Prince. Each ivory piece bore Murad's personal monogram boldly painted in blue; even after it had travelled so many kilometres and been taken to so many cities, and moreover after so many years had gone by since that time, not one single piece had been mislaid. The ladies waited outside the water closet while Murad was inside – until suddenly, they heard him cry out in agony. They raced to the closed door and called to him through the painted wooden panels. He did not reply; they could hear him groaning in pain. They tentatively pushed open the door.

Şayan gasped in horror: her husband's face was deathly

211

pale and contorted with pain. She rushed forward to help him. "My Lord, what has happened? Are you unwell?"

Murad's voice was barely audible as he whispered weakly: "Something has ruptured … and I am … haemorrhaging blood. My loyal wife, I am sorry … to alarm you, but please help me … to stand, and take me to my bed."

Şayan and Filizten supported Murad under the arms and gently guided him to his bed. As they did so, they both noticed how thin he had recently become: under his clothes, his body felt gaunt and skeletal. They undressed him and put on his nightshirt, then laid him down in his bed and tried to make him comfortable. Şayan held his hand while Filizten asked the attendants sitting in the corridor outside his bedchamber to go and find Selahaddin as quickly as they could, and inform him that his father had been taken ill.

Minutes later, Selahaddin burst into the room. As he looked upon his father, who lay semi-conscious on the bed, his eyes betrayed deep anxiety and fear. Şayan got up from Murad's bedside, bowed to Selahaddin and told him what had happened. He thanked her; then he went to the water closet to inspect it for himself. He saw that the commode was half-filled with blood. The colour drained from his face, and his heart began to pound with momentary panic.

Returning to the bedchamber, he bent over his father. He checked his pulse, and found it to be weak and rapid. "I am going back to my suite to collect my physician's bag and some medicines, but I will not be long," he said to Şayan reassuringly. "While I am gone, keep His Highness warm and raise his legs a little. He has lost a lot of blood, and I do not want him to go into shock."

As a young man, Selahaddin had been instructed in the science of medicine by Doctor Rifat Pasha, who had been appointed as doctor to the Çırağan Palace a few months after

Murad and his family had been sent to live there. He was a kind, compassionate man who was highly respected, and had remained loyal to Murad throughout his life. Rifat Pasha was aware that other doctors who were more opportunistic than he – such as Doctor Capoleone, who had treated Murad during his short reign and in the early months of his confinement – were in the pay of Abdülhamid and the ministers who had been responsible for the overthrow not only of Sultan Abdülaziz but also of Murad himself. It was in their interests to misdiagnose their patient's symptoms, and to ensure that he never recovered from his illness. As a result, the treatment Murad received from Doctor Capoleone and certain other doctors had been detrimental to his health, and this had greatly disturbed Rifat Pasha. Consequently, on his visits to the palace, Rifat Pasha had begun meeting Selahaddin on the pretext that he was treating him for some slight malady. Instead of doing this, however, he would spend hours teaching him about common afflictions and briefing him on diagnoses, treatments and cures for a wide variety of ailments and diseases.

Rifat Pasha knew that since he was an old man, he had to ensure that adequate provision was made for Murad's health care in the future: the kindly doctor needed to hand over this responsibility to someone he could trust – and with so many spies and enemies all around, that person could only be Selahaddin. During their clandestine meetings, Selahaddin would write down everything he had learnt from his mentor in his notebook, and would refer to it whenever the need arose. The devoted old doctor also helped Selahaddin establish his own small pharmacy and taught him about the healing properties of many different medicines and remedies; this knowledge would later prove to be invaluable.

It was not long before Selahaddin came back to Murad's

bedchamber. He was carrying the battered brown leather physician's bag that Rifat Pasha had given him many years previously, on his last visit to the palace before his death. Mevhibe, Reftarıdil and Resan were sitting with Şayan at Murad's bedside, but they all rose when Selahaddin entered the room. As Selahaddin examined his father, the look of concern on his face deepened. Murad's skin was cold and clammy, and it had become extremely pale. His breathing was irregular and he was drifting in and out of consciousness. Selahaddin politely dismissed the ladies, then set about trying to stem the flow of blood.

☻ ☻ ☻ ☻ ☻

Selahaddin had learnt a great deal from Rifat Pasha, and he treated his father competently for several days. He tried many different remedies and procedures to help his father, continually referring to his old notes and to the medical journals that he had collected over the years. Murad was no longer in pain, but the flow of blood would not stop and he was becoming weaker day by day. Again and again Selahaddin implored his father to allow him to send a message to Yıldız asking for a physician to be brought to examine him. However, Murad stubbornly refused. One afternoon Lady Reftarıdil was sitting with her husband reading *The Count of Monte Cristo*, one of his favourite books, to him. The misfortunes of Edmond Dantès, the innocent sailor who is imprisoned for life without trial owing to the intrigues and jealousies of others, clearly resonated with Murad.

"My Lord," Reftarıdil began a little hesitantly, having closed the book at the end of the chapter recounting Dantès' ingenious escape from imprisonment at the Château d'If, "please allow us to send for a physician, for I fear you grow weaker, my love."

But Murad rejected her plea. "My dearest wife, do you think that a man could really have swum to safety from the Château d'If after fourteen years of captivity? Would he not have been too weak to succeed in such an endeavour?"

"I do not know, Sir," she replied.

"I remember seeing the château when I arrived in Marseille with my uncle at the beginning of our visit to France," Murad replied. "It stands on a small island in the Bay of Marseille and has a very forbidding appearance. I think it highly unlikely that Edmond Dantès would have had the strength to swim such a distance, and indeed I feel that Alexandre Dumas' storytelling is a little unrealistic in this respect. Poor Dantès! Like Selahaddin, he was left to pine away his youth in a prison cell."

Seeing her opportunity, Reftarıdil said: "My Lord, Selahaddin has been taking care of you for the past few days, but he feels he is to blame for the fact that you are not recovering more quickly, and this worries me. His knowledge of medicine has greatly impressed me and I am proud of our son for all he has done, but I think that the time has come for a qualified physician to examine you." She laid her hands on his; then she lovingly stroked his hair. But her remarks had slightly irritated Murad, and he asked for a drink of water. Nefidem Kalfa, who had been sitting behind a folded screen in one corner of the room, immediately came forward with a goblet.

"I do not want to see any more doctors. Please understand this, my faithful wife. I have been subjected to so many of their examinations during my lifetime that I want no more of their intrusions now that I am nearing my end. Unlike Dantès, I cannot swim away from my jail, but I feel that the time will soon be here when I will be able to make my escape." A tear trickled down Reftarıdil's cheek. Over the years, she had come to accept her husband's fate, and knew that even if the doctors did come, there would probably be little they could do to help.

"Oh, my love!" Reftarıdil cried. She kissed Murad's hands. There was a long silence before she spoke again. Eventually, she said calmly: "I do understand your reluctance to see a doctor, my dear husband. Of course I do. However, I fear that the Padishah may be angry when he learns that we have kept the seriousness of your condition from him. He may even blame Selahaddin, seeing it as an affront to himself, and may hold him responsible if you do not recover."

Murad considered this as he drank his water. It was true that Abdülhamid was not to be trusted, and that in the past he had shown himself to be highly unpredictable. Fears raced through Murad's mind as he pictured his only son being accused by the Sultan of hindering his treatment – or worse still, of causing his death. "You are right, my dear," Murad said at last. "Nefidem Kalfa, please ask my son to come to me."

Within minutes, Selahaddin had entered the dark bedchamber. The heavy smell of incense filled his nostrils; meanwhile, the sight of his parents holding hands warmed his heart. Their union had always been a loving, affectionate one, unaltered by the passage of time.

Selahaddin kissed both his parents' hands. "My dear son," Murad began, "I have been speaking with your noble mother, and have come to a decision. I want you to ask Asım Ağa to send a message to Yıldız informing my brother of my illness and asking that Doctor Rıza Pasha should come to examine me." After Rifat Pasha's death, Doctor Rıza had assumed the duty of caring for Murad and his family. Doctor Rıza's father, who had been a respected field marshal during the reign of Sultan Abdülaziz, had been very fond of the young Prince

Murad, and the father's affection for him had been inherited by the son.

Doctor Rıza Pasha came to Çırağan straight away. Selahaddin described how his father had been taken ill, and told him of his symptoms. He also explained how he had been treating Murad during the last few days. The doctor then entered Murad's bedchamber; after examining his patient thoroughly, he inspected the blood, which had been collected in small silver bowls. Then he prescribed some medicines that it was hoped would stop the bleeding. Much to Reftarıdil's relief, the doctor applauded Selahaddin for his efforts and told him that there was little that he himself would have done differently.

However, within a few days it became clear that the new medicines were having little effect: the bleeding persisted. Doctor Rıza visited Murad every day for a month or so, but the prince's condition deteriorated and he gradually became weaker and weaker. The doctor recommended that Murad should not eat or drink anything hot, so he was given iced drinks and only allowed to eat cold dishes – but just as with the medicines, this new diet had no effect. Soon Murad refused to eat or drink anything, and the entire household was overcome by an all-consuming sadness, helpless in the grip of a deep sense of foreboding.

☻ ☻ ☻ ☻ ☻

August 1904

Murad sent for his son and his two grandsons. When they entered his suite, they came face to face with Mevhibe.

"How is my father today?" asked Selahaddin after greeting the First Consort.

217

"He seems a little better than yesterday," she replied, trying to smile. However, she was unable to disguise the anxiety she was feeling; even Fuad noticed it. "He has been very much looking forward to seeing you all." She handed Nihad the silver tray that she was holding. "Please try to encourage your grandfather to eat some of these grapes. He refuses them when I offer them to him, but he may eat some if you offer them." With that, she turned and left the room, leaving Selahaddin, Nihad and Fuad to make their way into Murad's bedchamber.

"My dear boys!" Murad exclaimed on seeing them. "Come and sit near me. There is much that I want to tell you." The princes greeted Murad and sat down on either side of his bed.

"Grandfather, would you like some grapes?" Nihad said, offering him the silver tray. The grapes lay on thin slivers of ice and had been cut in half, their seeds removed.

"For your sake, my dear Nihad, I will eat just a few. Thank you." Murad took some of the grapes, and seemed to enjoy their sweet, refreshing taste. Selahaddin and Nihad noticed how Murad's skin had become more ashen, and how his lips and fingernails had gone slightly blue.

After Murad had been offered more grapes and refused them, Fuad spoke up: "May I have some, too?" he asked. That brought a smile to Murad's face. His youngest grandson always had that effect on him.

"Of course you may. Nihad, give Fuad the tray so that he can enjoy these grapes while we talk." Nihad passed the platter to his little brother; then Murad fixed them all with a serious look. "I asked you to visit me this afternoon because I would like to share with you some wise counsel that my father once shared with me," he began. His voice sounded stronger than it had done in recent days. "He told me to pay heed to the words of the Prophet Isa: *Be wise as serpents and as harmless as doves.'* It is good advice for us all to follow, but I would like to take it one step further."

Murad began by telling them of his own father's plans to reform the Dynasty's laws of succession. He had wanted to change the current system of agnatic seniority to one of agnatic primogeniture, the intention being to give increased stability to the Dynasty and bring the Empire into line with the other ruling houses of Europe in this important matter. He added that Sultan Abdülmecid had asked if it had been mere coincidence that the Empire had been at its most powerful when the throne had passed from father to son, noting that decline had set in once this system had been changed. Sadly, Sultan Abdülmecid had died young, and so had been unable to introduce the dynastic reform that would have seen his eldest son Murad succeed him instead of Abdülaziz, his brother.

Murad reminded Selahaddin that had the proposed changes been implemented, Selahaddin would have become Crown Prince on his birth, which had taken place only a few weeks after Abdülmecid's death. As he listened, Nihad began to think about all the 'what ifs': for instance, what would have happened if Murad, instead of his uncle, had come to the throne in 1861? "Always remember that you are descended from the senior branch of our family. I am telling you this in case Hamid tries to alter the line of succession in favour of one of his sons, as my uncle Abdülaziz tried to do," Murad told them. "That would not be right. Although I think it unlikely that Hamid will attempt such a thing, I do believe he entertains the fantasy that his favourite son Mehmed Burhaneddin Efendi might succeed him. Remember, any amendment to the current system must have the consent of the majority of the family if it is to have legitimacy. Because my father was the eldest son of the last surviving Ottoman

Imperial Prince, he had the support of many members of the Dynasty, as well as of the government and the *ulema*; however, when Sultan Abdülaziz tried to name his own son as his heir, support from these quarters was not forthcoming owing to the fact that Aziz was a second son. This made the validity of a reform of that kind highly questionable. I am certain that if Hamid were to plan a similar move, it too would be thwarted as he himself is only a second son; however, you must be watchful, and be ready to act if necessary. If a change in the laws of succession is made in such a way as to exclude you, you must be sure to defend your rights – and therefore those of your future descendants as well. For the order of succession to follow agnatic primogeniture in any way that is legitimate, it can only pass from me to Selahaddin, then to Nihad then to Vâsıb. Do you understand all this?" As he spoke, Murad had become slightly agitated, but once he had finished he seemed to become calmer.

Before Fuad could fully grasp the reason why he had been excluded from this important-sounding list, Murad began to speak of the might of England. Selahaddin and his sons had previously heard him tell them many stories about the strength of the English navy and the wealth generated by England's industrialisation, but his intention on this occasion was to issue a strong warning. "The English are brazen opportunists. They fear our influence over their Moslem subjects in Africa and India, they worry about maintaining control of the Suez Canal, and they have their eye on our territories. It is therefore in their interests to see our Caliphate and our Sultanate fall. Today they are pretending to be our friends because they are desperate to secure concessions from our government; in particular, they need our authorisation to search for petroleum deposits in Mesopotamia – in the Tigris

Valley, I mean – but we must never grant them any such concessions. If we do, it will be the beginning of the end for us in those provinces, especially if petroleum is indeed discovered there. They will stop at nothing to control any new source of potential wealth, and if anything of that kind is found in our Empire the consequences for all our subjects will be dire."

"Grandfather, I thought you said that the English were amiable people, and that you liked everyone you met when you were in London," Fuad interjected.

"Yes, Fuad, that is true: I did like everyone I met, but I did not trust any of them, and that is a very different matter. If, when you are older, you ever become Padishah, you must always be suspicious of their motives. The British and the French have the same agenda, and that is to see our power diminished. This is what Lord Palmerston himself once said in a speech in the House of Commons: "We have no eternal allies and we have no perpetual enemies. Our interests are eternal and perpetual, and those interests it is our duty to follow." Make of that what you will, but I believe the English to be as cunning and Machiavellian as it is possible to be." Murad paused; then he asked for a small piece of ice to suck on. Selahaddin took a sliver from the gilded ice bucket standing on the bedside table and placed it on his father's tongue.

"I have three more warnings to give," Murad said once the ice had melted and moistened his mouth. "Firstly, should Allah see fit that you should rule over our empire one day, I advise you to be wary of your ministers, your generals and your advisors. Of course there are many good and competent men who will help you perform your duty, but do not give your trust too readily. Sadly, the Porte is like a fox's den: it has been infiltrated by cunning, self-serving officials who will never love our empire as we do – so you must be cautious. As you know, both my uncle and myself were deposed by ambitious men who had no more than a superficial respect for our dynasty and our traditions. In my case, it is partly my fault because I should have been stronger, but in that of my uncle they took advantage of unrest in the Balkans, a failed harvest and increasing public debt, using all these things as an excuse to overthrow him. They then had him murdered so that he could never be restored to the throne, and they staged it to look like suicide. Do not be fooled by the accounts of his death that would have you believe it was suicide, for it was most certainly cold-blooded murder. I believe that Avni Pasha and Midhat Pasha ordered my uncle's wrists to be cut with scissors, and that he should then be left to bleed to death. How anyone could be so ruthless and inhuman is quite beyond me. What a terrible fate! And what a pitiful end for such a strong and powerful man!" As he said this, Murad had tears in his eyes: although he had not been at all close to his uncle, and had moreover been treated unfairly by him, he was by nature forgiving and compassionate – in addition, he had admired and respected Abdülaziz for having instituted moves to modernise and westernise the Empire. In particular, he had given his uncle full credit for appreciating the importance of naval power, and for his determination to rebuild the Ottoman navy and make it one of the finest in the world.

"Those depraved ministers then had the shameless audacity to maintain that since my uncle had committed suicide, he must have been insane," he went on. "Therefore, in accordance with our custom, he should not be buried in the tomb of any former sultan. There is much that I have done in my life that I am not proud of, but I am at the very least proud of the fact that I stood up to their wicked demands. I commanded that Sultan Abdülaziz be laid to rest in his father's mausoleum, thus showing the people of our empire that I did not believe the false rumour that he had committed suicide. So I speak from my own experience, and from that of my uncle, when I tell you that you always need to be strong and decisive, have faith in your convictions, and most of all be careful who you trust."

Murad paused: he was tiring, but he was determined to continue. "If one of you does become Sultan one day, you must never ignore the need for continuous modernisation and reform. If the Empire's power and influence is to be maintained, and civil disorder and rebellion are to be averted, this is an absolute necessity. If a constitution has not already been introduced, you should grant one before it is demanded of you. Our people deserve to live under a progressive constitution, and we have many able and worthy men who are capable of serving in a liberal and reformist government. If we can succeed in establishing a constitutional monarchy along the lines of the British system, then I believe we will have secured the future of our empire and our dynasty."

Selahaddin and his sons, knowing that Murad was desperate to impart to them certain warnings and advice while he was still able to do so, were listening attentively to everything he was saying. After a brief pause, he now returned to the subject of England. "I admired much of what I saw in England during the time I spent there; that is true not just of its system of government, but of other things too." Murad's lips thinned to a faint smile, and he slowly closed his eyelids to hide the expression in his eyes. "I remember an evening in London – that evening when I first met Queen Victoria's beautiful but headstrong and rather rebellious daughter Princess Louise. Did you know that it was even suggested that I might consider making her my wife? I was offered a castle in Scotland and the hand of an English princess in marriage if I would only divorce the Lady Mevhibe and your mother, but of course I politely declined!" Murad fell silent for a while, lost in his musings, then opened his eyes again and looked up at his son. Selahaddin smiled back at him, knowing that two things would be going through his father's mind at this point, although he would very likely be hesitating to say them. Firstly, a rumour had reached Murad's ears that not long before the Ottoman state visit Princess Louise had given birth to an illegitimate child, thus making her totally unsuitable as a prospective bride; secondly, Abdülaziz's ambitions for his own son would in any case have made it quite impossible for him to entertain the idea of a union between the House of Osman and the House of Saxe-Coburg and Gotha.

"However, I did enjoy the many conversations I had with the delightfully charming Princess Louise, and during them I learned much about her strong desire to bring about the emancipation of women and introduce universal suffrage – that is, giving women the right to vote. She was a very liberal-minded woman, and she helped me see that as our world goes through a process of modernisation and social change we must accept that women have an important role to play." Selahaddin and Nihad exchanged looks: they were wondering if now that Murad's mind had begun to wander back to the past they should leave him to rest, but it soon became clear that his mental focus was undimmed. "After all, every child's first teacher is his or her mother," he went on, "so these teachers should enjoy increased rights and greater access to education so that they can be prepared for the vital role they play in society, and of course rewarded for it. I believe that as yet only New Zealand and Australia have granted female suffrage, and then only in a limited form, but when we finally reopen our parliament it is important that we should not lag too far behind them. I hope you will remember this, and that you will do all you can to ensure that it happens. It will not be easy, for you will have the conservative forces working against you, but if we are to build a modern progressive society in our empire, then this is a step we have to take." But before any of the princes at his bedside could respond, Murad went on speaking; it was as if he was conscious that time might run out before he had said everything he wished to say.

His voice now began to show real concern. "Finally, I am very much afraid that the Young Turk movement, which seems to have replaced the Young Ottoman opposition, is growing more popular every day, and I worry that it might ultimately destroy the Empire. As you know, I agree with many of their aims, especially with that of establishing a constitutional system and parliamentary government in place of what we currently have – absolute monarchy, which in practical terms means my brother's despotic rule. Whatever happens, however, our people should never abandon their sense of being 'Ottoman' rather than members of one particular race or religion. Ottomanism is a unique bond that for centuries has held the many different peoples of our Empire together. I fear that if Turkish nationalism, as advocated by the Young Turks, ever comes to replace Ottomanism, then our honoured tradition of mutual respect, tolerance and understanding for people of different races and creeds will be swept away. Heaven forbid that anything of this kind should happen, for it would have catastrophic consequences for all the people who live under our protection. It is true that our ancestors' original intention was to establish a safe homeland for the Turkic people they led, but you must never forget that our small, weak state expanded

225

and flourished until it became a huge, powerful empire only because we embraced everyone who was brought under our rule as a result of our glorious conquests. It is therefore our duty to protect and defend the descendants of those people of all races and faiths who in the past helped make our empire a great power." Selahaddin and his sons murmured their agreement: they concurred wholeheartedly with this sentiment.

Murad then added: "Perhaps you could correspond with your cousin Prince Sabahaddin while he is in exile. My sister Seniha will have her son's address – I think he is living in Switzerland or Paris. I know that he is a prominent member of the Young Turk movement, but unlike many of his colleagues he is convinced of the importance of maintaining an Ottoman identity. He believes in granting autonomy to our provinces and sees decentralisation as the only means of holding our empire together as a functioning unit. He is trying to influence the ideology of the movement, and I am certain that he would appreciate your help in working to further the interests of the Empire and our people."

By now Murad's breathing had slowed, and had become more shallow. "There is one last thing that I want to say to you all," he said. "Then I must rest. You have spent too many years imprisoned with me in this damp, secluded palace, and I do not want you to waste any more years of your lives. When you leave this place – and I believe that day will soon come – promise me that you will find a way to travel. See something of this beautiful world in which we live. Perform the *hajj*, travel through the Empire to meet our subjects and visit our historic cities. And while you are there, take time to pray at holy sites such as the Dome of the Rock in Jerusalem and the Umayyad Mosque in Damascus; visit the tombs of our early ancestors who are buried outside the city walls of İstanbul –

in Söğüt and Bursa; take part in the archaeological excavations in Babylon; explore the insides of the pyramids in Cairo – or if that is too ambitious for you, just read a book in the shade of an ancient cedar tree in Beirut. These are all things I dreamt of doing but have been unable to do, so I want you to do them in my stead. And remember, be merciful, be humble and above all be kind to all you meet. Remember to always be kind." With that, Murad relaxed into his cushions and closed his eyes. He smiled when he heard his son and grandsons make their promise to him, but he was already losing consciousness; soon he slipped into a peaceful sleep, the smile still on his lips. Who knows? Perhaps, in his mind, he was travelling to all those places he had so wanted to visit, or perhaps he was reading a book under a cedar tree ...

�'s ☪ ☪ ☪ ☪

Doctor Rıza had worked tirelessly to help Murad regain his strength, but had been unable to do so. On hearing of the seriousness of his brother's condition, Sultan Abdülhamid had summoned Doctor İbrahim Pasha, his own personal doctor, who worked at the new Hamidiye Etfal children's hospital. Following his audience with the Sultan, Doctor İbrahim immediately went to Çırağan with instructions to return with a full and clear diagnosis of Murad's illness. He duly returned to Yıldız later that day and reported to Abdül-hamid that Murad was suffering from the effects of diabetes and loss of blood; he explained that the former Sultan was very weak and had not spoken during the examination, although he had not lost consciousness. Doctor İbrahim added that Murad was unlikely to recover.

Abdülhamid was devastated. Throughout his entire reign, he had lived in fear that his brother might one day be restored to the throne, but now that this threat was about to be lifted from his shoulders he felt nothing but sadness. Despite being very different in character, the two brothers – who had been born on the same day just two years apart – had shared a happy childhood. Murad had always been thoughtful and sensitive, and in the brothers' younger days he had looked after Abdülhamid and defended him when he fell foul of their stern tutors and strict *kalfas*. Now Abdülhamid was racked with guilt, for in his heart he knew he had wronged his brother and treated him with excessive harshness. Something told him he should visit Murad before it was too late to express his regret and explain that everything he had done had been done solely for the good of the Empire. There was still time to beg Murad's forgiveness, or at least to ask him to show understanding. However, there was a louder voice inside his head that advised him not to go, and in the end it was this insistent voice that won the battle. Knowing full well that he had usurped the throne and imprisoned his kind, gentle elder brother and his family for nearly twenty-eight years, Abdülhamid decided that he simply could not face Murad.

Instead, he spent the next two days in fervent prayer, waiting all the while for news from Çırağan.

☻ ☻ ☻ ☻ ☻

Monday 29th August 1904

In the morning, Murad dictated certain wishes to his scribe, Asım Ağa, in the presence of Selahaddin and Nihad. He made provision for everyone in his household; he also asked that alms be distributed in his name to the poor and sent to the holy cities of Mecca and Medina. Throughout the course of

228

the rest of the day, his family and the members of his household visited him to kiss his hand one last time, and to pray for his soul. Selahaddin's letter to Yıldız imploring the Sultan to permit Hadice and Fehime to visit their father was ignored. It may be that Abdülhamid did not want to arouse suspicion in the minds of the people of İstanbul that their beloved former Sultan might be approaching his end by allowing Murad's daughters to visit Çırağan; then again, it may be that his Senior Equerry Cevher Ağa prevented Selahaddin's letter from ever reaching his master's eyes in a final act of underhandedness and spite.

By early evening it was clear that Murad was slipping away. Mevhibe raised a silver teaspoon to his lips and gave him some peach sherbet. Fatma, Reftarıdil, Şayan and Resan wept silently, while Selahaddin and Nihad recited verses from the Quran, whispering the words softly over Murad's face and body. Sheikh Abdullah, who had come from the Yahya Efendi Dervish Lodge nearby, quietly chanted the thirty-sixth *sura*, the Sura of Mourning, to soothe Murad's soul before it embarked on its journey to heaven. The Sheikh then spoke the words of the profession of faith, and was joined in this by Murad. "I bear witness that there is no God but Allah, and that Muhammed is His Messenger."

Just before 8.30 pm, Murad closed his eyes for the last time, and murmured "Allah, Allah" before letting out his final breath.

Once it was clear that his soul had departed, the ladies began to wail uncontrollably. Their lamentations would protect Murad's soul from demons as it set out on its final journey.

CHAPTER THIRTEEN

The Final Journey

Monday 29ᵗʰ August 1904

As the incense went on burning, Sheikh Abdullah continued to pray. He pressed Murad's eyelids shut, turned the dead man's head towards Mecca and straightened his arms so that they fell limply to his sides. He placed a strip of white linen around Murad's head and tied it under his chin to hold his mouth closed, then used another strip to bind his feet together. Finally, a linen shroud was placed over the lifeless body.

Selahaddin turned to console the grieving women and his son Nihad. "Allah has released His Imperial Highness Prince Murad from the torment of imprisonment, and has permitted him to fly away from this gilded cage," he said, tears streaming down his face.

As always when circumstances demanded it, Mevhibe remained calm and controlled; it was almost as if she was in a trance. "I will write to His Imperial Majesty and inform him that his brother has departed this world," she said. "I will also inform Aynifer Usta so that she can give the news to the whole household." Then she tenderly kissed Selahaddin's hand. Fighting back the tears, she said: "My dear Selahaddin, now you must be strong. You must ensure that your father's body is treated with the respect due to a former Sultan of the Imperial House of Osman. You know what your father's wishes were, and what must now be done. Write to your uncle, and God willing all will be done as our Lord and Master desired." Selahaddin, unable to speak, nodded gravely in assent. Mevhibe took Reftarıdil's arm; then the two elderly consorts left the room together, their heads bowed in grief. Both were eager to return to the privacy of their own suites so that the tears they could feel building up inside them could be shed without restraint.

Fatma kissed Selahaddin on the cheek. Her unwavering inner strength came to the fore as she tried to comfort him. "Do not be sad, dear brother. Baba is free at last," she said. "I will go and tell Fuad and your daughters, so you need not worry about them. I will also write to Hadice and Fehime, and ensure that the letters reach them this evening." She looked at her beloved father one last time; then she linked arms with Şayan and with her mother Resan, and together they followed Mevhibe and Reftarıdil out of her father's bedchamber.

After some time had gone by, Nihad gently led his father, who was bewildered and visibly distraught, back to his suite. Deciding to stay with him until he had recovered a little, he looked on as Selahaddin lowered himself into the chair at his large mahogany desk and sat there looking dazed and disoriented. Protocol demanded that he write a letter of condolence to Abdülhamid. This was no easy task at such a time, but nevertheless he slowly made ready his pen and some writing paper, and began to think of appropriate wordings for what he needed to say. In his letter, Selahaddin informed his uncle that the doctors and all the servants had performed their duties impeccably; he also expressed his thanks for all that the Sultan had done to help Murad in his final days. As his father had wished, Selahaddin also communicated Murad's gratitude for the kindness Abdülhamid had shown in sending his own doctor to minister to him, and for the treatment he had received.

In her suite of rooms, meanwhile, Mevhibe was writing a letter of her own to the Sultan. *'To the high office of the compassionate Caliph, hereby addressed by your humble and most lowly servant,'* she began. She first thanked Abdülhamid for his protection and for the mercy he had shown in allowing her husband to die a natural death. It had always been Murad's deepest fear that following his deposition he would be surreptitiously murdered, as his uncle had been: Mevhibe was thus grateful that he had not met his end in this way. No one at Çırağan knew how close Abdülhamid had actually come to acting on one of the *fatwas* he had received from the Sheikh ul-Islam giving him authorisation to execute Murad. *'Please excuse the mistakes I make while writing to you, but my heart is weeping blood. Always at your command, Mevhibe.'* Once the letter was firmly sealed, she at last allowed herself to cry for the man who had been the love of her life. She buried her head in the palms of her hands and sobbed until she had no more tears to shed.

Both letters were immediately delivered to Yıldız Palace by messengers. Although Sultan Abdülhamid had been expecting this news, he was unprepared for the mixture of emotions that assailed him as he read of his brother's death. How he wished that he had gone to visit Murad when he had had the opportunity! Aware that he was being closely scrutinised by all those present, Abdülhamid turned to look out of the window in order to hide the tears of grief and remorse that had begun to sting his eyes. With his face averted from the prying gaze of his attendants, he cleared his throat; then he ordered that Doctor Rıza, Doctor İbrahim,

232

Doctor Aleksandros of the German Hospital and two other doctors from the Imperial household go to Çırağan straight away to examine Prince Murad's body. Always the strategist – even at a time like this – Abdülhamid was thinking of his public image. He did not want to be accused of responsibility for his brother's death, or be the object of any other kind of suspicion, and he knew how important it was that these respected witnesses should go immediately to record the cause of Murad's death.

The doctors were ordered to send a report back to the Sultan as quickly as possible. Since Doctor Rıza had been treating Murad for over a month, and Doctor İbrahim had also been attending him for the last two days, this was easily done. Soon the report was in Abdülhamid's hands. It read as follows:

His Imperial Highness Sultan Murad Khan, the Former Sultan, had long been suffering from diabetes and from the effects of a haemorrhage and diarrhoea. All of these things, compounded by grief, led to his death. ... All possible medical treatment was given.

Abdülhamid's eyes scanned the rest of the report – but all he seemed able to fully take in was that his brother had died of grief.

❀ ❀ ❀ ❀ ❀

Arrangements were hurriedly made. Abdülhamid knew of his brother's wish to be buried in the Imperial mausoleum located within the cemetery surrounding the tomb of Yahya Efendi, which was in the wooded hills above the Bosphorus very close to Çırağan. Murad had always admired the teachings of this highly-respected Sufi scholar. Yahya Efendi had been the beloved *süt kardeş* – 'milk brother' – of Sultan Süleyman the Magnificent, and his mother had been the great Sultan's wetnurse. However, Abdülhamid was reluctant to have a former sultan buried outside the hallowed city walls: tradition dictated that all sultans subsequent to the conquest of İstanbul be buried within them, and so far there had been no exceptions. Alone in his study, Abdülhamid now considered the possibility that Murad might be laid to rest in the mausoleum that had been built for their father, Sultan Abdülmecid, or perhaps in the tomb of their grandfather, Sultan Mahmud. While he was deliberating, the Sheikh ul-Islam was announced. He had come to offer his condolences – and more importantly, his advice.

When the formalities were over, Sheikh Ebülhüda Efendi broached this sensitive subject with the Sultan, advising him that wherever he chose to bury his brother, it should not be done with the pomp and ceremony normally accorded to a former sultan. "Your Imperial Majesty, in my humble estimation your esteemed brother should be buried quietly and without fuss," said the Sheikh, his ingratiating manner hiding a scheming nature and a natural talent for calculation. "If I may be so bold as to make this observation, it seems to me that for obvious reasons" – here, Ebülhüda Efendi cleared his throat – "he should not be buried in the Imperial tomb of a former sultan. Consequently, I fear that the mausoleums of your esteemed grandfather Sultan Mahmud and your noble father Sultan Abdülmecid will not be suitable."

Abdülhamid instantly understood the Sheikh ul-Islam's inference, and chastised himself for having even considered either tomb as a possible alternative. He recalled that in the seventeenth century Sultan Mustafa and Sultan İbrahim, having been deemed unworthy of the Dynasty on account of their alleged madness, had not been buried alongside their forebears. If Abdülhamid permitted Murad to be interred in either their father's or their grandfather's tomb, it would be tantamount to an admission that Murad had in fact been sane, and therefore that he had been fit to rule – which meant that as soon as he had recovered from his temporary illness he should have been restored to the throne.

Abdülhamid was acutely aware that he had been invited to assume power only because the murder of their uncle had caused Murad to have a mental breakdown. The office of the Sheikh ul-Islam had been invested with the authority to restore Murad to the throne as soon as his mental condition stabilised; this, however, it had neglected to do, even though Murad had recovered within months. The religious elite preferred Abdülhamid's conservative, traditionalist attitudes to his elder brother's more liberal and reformist ideas, and thus they had maintained the pretence that Murad's nervous breakdown was an incurable mental illness. If the Sultan admitted, even indirectly, that his brother had been sane at the time of his death, it would cause some highly inconvenient questions to be asked: in fact, if Murad's speedy recovery from that temporary illness in 1876 were to come to light, it would delegitimise the whole of Abdülhamid's reign since the time when by rights he should have relinquished the throne.

It was therefore in the interests of both the Sultan and the Sheikh ul-Islam – even now – to keep the truth hidden from the world. Both men knew, though neither wished to put it into words, that Murad had been greatly loved by the people, and that on his accession to the throne he had been welcomed with great warmth and affection: his death might therefore ignite hostile feelings towards Abdülhamid, and perhaps even give rise to civil unrest. This warning from the Sheikh ul-Islam, though expressed only in hints and subtle suggestions, rekindled the paranoia that gnawed at Abdülhamid incessantly and was ever willing to come to the surface. He knew that his ultra-conservative policies and heavily author-itarian style of governance had made him deeply unpopular with many of his subjects, and he was likewise aware that he had many enemies who prayed for, and in some cases even plotted, his replacement on the throne by a liberal ruler such as his brother would certainly have been.

All in all, therefore, Abdülhamid was easily persuaded by the Sheikh ul-Islam's arguments. He gave orders for Murad to be buried near his mother, Şevkefzâ, in the Cedid Havatin Tomb, which was known in the city as the 'Mausoleum of Imperial Ladies' as it contained the graves of many female members of the Imperial family. This solution suited Abdül-hamid's agenda perfectly: no former sultan lay buried in this mausoleum, and it was within the city walls. Once the place of burial had been decided upon, Abdülhamid's Senior Equerry Cevher Ağa was ordered to go to Çırağan Palace with other high-ranking harem *ağas* and palace officials, accompanied by soldiers and a number of servants; they were to collect Murad's body and take it to Topkapı Palace, where it would be washed and prepared for burial.

۝ ۝ ۝ ۝ ۝

After dispatching his letter to the Sultan, Selahaddin had returned to his father's bedchamber and was now sitting there in quiet prayer with Sheikh Abdullah. He knew that as the sun had already set, his father could not be buried until the following day: Islamic custom dictates that burials can only take place in daylight. He was therefore startled and not a little alarmed when in the middle of the night, his prayers were interrupted by the arrival of Cevher Ağa and his

236

entourage, causing a great commotion. He had assumed that his father would not be disturbed until daybreak and had wanted to spend these last hours by his side; however, Abdülhamid had ordered Murad's body to be taken from the palace in secret, under cover of darkness.

"Prince Selahaddin, may I extend my condolences on the death of your esteemed father His Imperial Highness Prince Murad," Cevher Ağa began. Selahaddin thanked him politely, but thought he detected a note of sarcasm in his voice; although he was determined not to show it, he was angry at having been disturbed by this man who had been the cause of so much distress to his father. "It is the command of His Imperial Majesty Sultan Abdülhamid that we remove the body of Prince Murad immediately. He will be taken by boat to Topkapı Palace to be prepared for burial." Cevher Ağa then turned to the elderly holy man and said: "Sheikh Abdullah, His Majesty commands that you perform the washing and ablution ceremony for Prince Murad, so please accompany us to the quay." With that, he turned to leave.

"I have not yet dismissed you, Cevher Ağa," Selahaddin said sternly. He was shocked that the Senior Equerry was capable of behaving with such insolence even at a time like this. "I have some questions I would like answered before you leave."

Cevher Ağa looked uncomfortable. He detested being reprimanded by Selahaddin, but even he was forced to acknowledge – only to himself, of course – that his manner had perhaps been unduly brusque and insensitive. "Your Imperial Highness, I am at your service," he replied with a hasty bow. He then answered each of Selahaddin's questions; knowing how deeply his replies would wound the grieving prince, his face wore an expression of smug satisfaction.

Selahaddin was devastated to learn that his father would not be granted his final wish – that of being buried near the tomb of Yahya Efendi – and made a mental note to write to Abdülhamid and try to persuade him to change his mind. He was equally distressed to be informed that he, Nihad and Fuad would not be permitted to attend either his father's cleansing ceremony or his funeral. He could not comprehend what motives the Sultan could possibly have for such vindictiveness. The one small assurance Cevher Ağa gave was that certain special rituals followed when the bodies of deceased Ottoman sultans were interred would be performed.

Selahaddin had not expected Abdülhamid to permit a state funeral, which would of course involve a procession, so was not surprised to learn that the burial would take place quietly; he was, however, stunned to hear that the tomb chosen as his father's final resting place was the Mausoleum of Imperial Ladies. Was this a parting insult from Abdülhamid to his brother? But now that his questions – with the exception of this last one – had been answered, Selahaddin had no choice but to let his dear father go.

Murad's body was carried out to the quay in front of the Çırağan Palace by four of his most devoted servants. His coffin had been covered with a linen shroud, and an old and rather worn fez belonging to one of the palace cooks had been placed on the lid to prevent the identity of the casket's occupant from being detected by a passing fisherman or boatman. Abdülhamid wanted to delay the public announcement of his brother's death for as long as possible in order to ensure that large crowds did not gather at the funeral. Sheikh Abdullah and Cevher Ağa accompanied the coffin as it was taken aboard the waiting steamship. Fehim Pasha, who had been appointed by the Sultan to oversee the funeral, was directing the proceedings. The remaining palace officials, together with the guards and servants from Yıldız who had accompanied them on their visit to Çırağan, boarded three other steamships which had moored in front of the palace.

Selahaddin, Nihad and Fuad were numb with grief. Standing helplessly behind the carved balustrade at the top of the main central steps running down from the palace doors to the quayside, they were as silent and as motionless as statues. The princesses, consorts, wives and *Gözdes* had been informed of what was about to happen as soon as Cevher Ağa had arrived, and had gathered behind the lace curtains in one of the drawing rooms overlooking the Bosphorus. All were gazing down upon the scene through tear-filled eyes. No one moved, and no one spoke; slowly, the small flotilla pulled away from the pier and disappeared into the moonlight, heading towards Seraglio Point below Topkapı Palace.

ᛨ ᛨ ᛨ ᛨ ᛨ

The Chamberlain of the Treasury and a number of other officials – all men who enjoyed Abdülhamid's implicit trust – were on the quayside to meet the boats when, after the short journey down the Bosphorus to the mouth of the Golden Horn, they arrived at Seraglio Point. Hastily, before a crowd could gather, Murad's body was carried through the rear gardens and outer courtyards of Topkapı Palace into the Apartments of the Holy Mantle, which were located within the pavilion that was the inner sanctum of the old palace complex. Sultan Mehmed II had built this pavilion to serve as his private chambers soon after he had conquered İstanbul in 1453. However, now that the sultans no longer lived at Topkapı and had moved to their more modern, European-style palaces on the shores of the Bosphorus, the pavilion had been given a new purpose: it was now the sanctuary of the Holy Relics of Islam.

Many of these relics had been brought to İstanbul by Sultan Selim I in 1517 following the final defeat of the Mamluk

Sultanate, which ruled Egypt and the Levant, and the subsequent conquest of the holy cities of Mecca and Medina. It was at this time that the Caliphate had passed from the Abbasid Dynasty to the House of Osman, with the result that the victorious Sultan Selim and his descendants now assumed the role of custodians of the sacred cities, defenders of the faithful, protectors of the pilgrimage routes and guardians of the Holy Relics.

The Throne Room within these former private chambers now housed the most precious of all these relics: the Holy Mantle, a cloak that had once belonged to the Prophet Muhammed and now lay in a golden case adorned with rubies and emeralds. The case itself was wrapped in seven silk scarves, each embroidered with holy inscriptions in silver and gold. It sat in a gilded chest, inscribed with the words of the profession of faith, that rested on the dais where earlier Ottoman sultans had once sat on their throne, hidden behind an ornate silver-filigree grating. By an imposing Baroque-style marble fireplace to the side of the dais sat a learned *imam* reciting the Quran – a tradition that had been observed continuously ever since the mantle's arrival in İstanbul nearly four hundred years previously. Incense burned in many silver burners, filling the room with the soft scent of aloe and amber. An aura of peace and tranquillity permeated this sacred place, even radiating through the thick stone walls into the courtyard beyond.

Tuesday 30ᵗʰ August 1904

Murad had been laid on a simple wooden washing bench, known as the 'bed of comfort', that stood on the raised marble platform outside the entrance to the Pavilion of the

Holy Mantle and Holy Relics. Nearby, a plain casket of cypress wood rested on a wooden trellis, waiting to welcome the former sultan when he had been prepared for burial. For centuries, the washing ceremony for deceased Ottoman sultans had been performed on this marble platform, which stood in front of the tall marble columns and pointed stone arches of the pavilion's portico.

It was only right and proper that in accordance with the traditions of the Dynasty, Abdülhamid should grant this same privilege to his brother. In defiance of custom, however, the Sultan had forbidden members of the Imperial family to attend the ceremony. As a result of this act of blatant cold-heartedness, not only were Selahaddin and Nihad excluded, but so too were Murad's surviving younger brothers – Crown Prince Mehmed Reşad, Prince Ahmed Kemaleddin, Prince Selim Süleyman and Prince Mehmed Vahideddin. The Minister of Internal Affairs and the Minister of Police were in attendance, however, as were other senior civil and police officials from the local municipalities. Cevher Ağa and Fehim Pasha had ensured that the gates at all entrances to Topkapı Palace were safely locked, and the police had formed a wide cordon to keep people away – a duty that they were performing with exemplary vigilance.

The conduct of the ceremony was governed by strict rules sanctioned by time-honoured religious practice, and the pious Sheikh Abdullah followed this procedure to the letter. The washing of the body symbolised the cleansing of the soul from spiritual and material impurity. Murad's otherwise naked body was covered from below the chest to just above the knees by a linen cloth. His skin was so white and smooth that it looked almost luminescent in the soft light. The Sheikh began his task. Using pure warm water, he washed Murad with such gentleness that it was as though he believed the dead man could feel every stroke of the sponge. Powdered camphor was then mixed with water and the minty, woody blend was reverently rubbed into Murad's hands, knees, feet, nose and forehead to cleanse the areas of his body that had touched the ground when he was praying. Verses from the Quran were read throughout the ceremony, and prayers petitioning Allah to forgive Murad for his sins were recited silently by the onlookers. Light flickered over the 'bed of comfort' from the large bronze lanterns that hung outside the Fountain Gate – the heavy gilded door that led into the Apartments of the Holy Mantle.

Once the washing had been completed, Murad's body was dried with silk towels. Pieces of dampened cotton were placed in the seven orifices of his body, between each finger and toe, and under each armpit; following this, a white muslin handkerchief that had touched the Mantle of the Prophet was laid on his chest. Finally, he was wrapped in a white linen shroud, and this was then tied at the neck, waist and feet and sprinkled with rose-water.

Murad's face remained uncovered as he was gently placed in the coffin. The officials, who had come to bear witness to this moment, now came forward, their hands folded respect-fully in front of them.

Suddenly, Fehim Pasha reached inside the coffin and tugged at Murad's hair, twisting it roughly between his fingers. Everyone present was appalled by this brutal, shameless act of disrespect – none more so than the Chief of Police, who shouted at Fehim Pasha to let go immediately. It transpired that this was yet another insult perpetrated on Murad at Abdülhamid's behest, as if the humiliations already heaped on him had not already been enough: the Sultan, fearing that one of the opposition groups – such as the Young Turks – might have devised a plan to feign Murad's death and then liberate him from Çırağan so that he could be restored to the throne, had ordered Fehim Pasha to make sure his brother was safely dead before the casket was closed. Indeed, Abdülhamid's paranoia seemed to know no bounds.

Sheikh Abdullah glared disapprovingly at Fehim Pasha before resuming the ceremony. As is the custom, he called out to the congregation gathered in the courtyard: "How do you believe this man has lived his life?"

"With honour," they chorused in reply. More prayers were said, and the coffin was closed. A shroud was placed over it, and on this was laid a ruby-red satin sheet embroidered with silver thread. Then an emerald-green satin scarf was wrapped around the head of the casket, and Murad's fez placed on top. Precious covers that had once adorned the Kaaba had been taken out of the Holy Relics Treasury Room, and these were also draped over the coffin. It looked magnificent, and although the jewelled ornaments that had been placed on the coffins of previous sultans were lacking, the richly-decorated coverings formed a stark contrast with the casket of plain cypress wood into which Murad had been laid. He was now ready to set out on his final journey.

☾ ☾ ☾ ☾ ☾

Four of Murad's servants from the Çırağan Palace now approached their master's coffin and raised it onto their shoulders. They walked solemnly out of the Inner Courtyard, following Sheikh Abdullah and the other *imams* along the Marble Way that led past the library of Sultan Ahmed III and the Imperial Audience Hall. Meanwhile, the ministers, the officials and the other members of the assembled entourage followed respectfully behind. The small cortège then passed through the Gate of Felicity with its six towering white marble columns and its great domed canopy elaborately decorated with motifs and inscriptions in gold leaf. Until this time, funeral prayers for deceased sultans had always been performed by the Sheikh ul-Islam under this canopy, but in a final insult to his brother, Abdülhamid had ordered that in Murad's case this part of the ceremony should not take place here. Instead, the funeral prayers were to be conducted in the Hidayet Mosque, which was next to the Cedid Havatin Tomb – the place where Murad was to be laid to rest. This small mosque is situated behind Yeni Cami, the 'New Mosque', in Eminönü – the bustling market area at the entrance to the Golden Horn.

The procession now progressed slowly across the Second Courtyard and through the turreted stone walls that flanked the imposing iron gate – the Gate of Salutation. It then proceeded along the path through the Outer Courtyard, passing by the fourth-century Byzantine church of Hagia Irene. Following the conquest of the city this church had not been converted into a mosque, as had been done in the case of many other churches. Instead, it had been used initially as an arsenal, and more recently as a military museum; perhaps this was *kismet* for the first church to be built in Constantinople. Finally, the procession left Topkapı Palace, passing under the monumental marble archway of the Imperial Gate – the first of the three ceremonial gates that guarded the palace. The *tuğra* of Murad's ill-fated uncle Sultan Abdülaziz hung over this gate, overseeing the procession as it passed through the palace walls.

As a further precaution designed to ensure that the cortège did not attract attention, Fehim Pasha ordered that the procession turn left outside the Imperial Gate – so that instead of winding its way through the city's crowded streets it could take the deserted path that ran alongside the high palace walls down to the sea on the south side. It could then follow the coast, rounding Seraglio Point until it came within sight of the Galata Bridge, Eminönü and the Golden Horn.

At first, Fehim Pasha was delighted to see that the news of Murad's death had not yet reached the public. Abdülhamid had ordered the Minister of Internal Affairs to release a short statement to the press announcing the death of the former sultan. The Minister had also been tasked with ensuring that the press only printed the words of the authorised statement, and that no lengthy articles were published on the subject. The newspapers had done as they were bidden, and every one of them had printed the announcement that morning exactly as instructed.

His Imperial Highness the former Sultan Murad died of natural causes yesterday after having suffered for a long period of time from diabetes. His death has caused immense sorrow. Sultan Abdülhamid has declared that the body is to be buried in the tomb of his brother's respected mother, near to Yeni Cami (the 'New Mosque'). May Allah have mercy on his soul.

However, by the time the small procession had reached the Basketmakers' Kiosk, a summer pleasure palace on the waterfront below the gardens of Topkapı, it had become only too clear that a large number of people had seen the small announcement, and had come to pay their respects to their former sovereign. Some, thinking that the funeral prayers would be held at Yeni Cami, had gathered there, but the police had used rough measures to disperse them. Although the planned route through the market area was guarded by rows of policemen and soldiers, the nearer the cortège came to the tomb the more difficult it became for them to contain

245

the crowd. Despite this, the procession entered the Hidayet Mosque without incident, and after midday prayers Sheikh Abdullah of the Yahya Efendi Order conducted Murad's funeral prayers in front of a congregation of palace officials from Yıldız. No members of Murad's family were present, but his loyal scribe Asım Ağa had slipped inside unnoticed, and so was later able to recount everything in detail to Selahaddin and the rest of his family at Çırağan.

While the prayers were taking place, the crowd that stood outside the mosque and lined the streets leading to the Cedid Havatin Tomb grew considerably in size. Murad had been deeply loved by his subjects, and hundreds, if not thousands, had come to pray for his soul. At the beginning of his reign, some had believed that it would be the dawn of a new era; however, their dreams of long-awaited and much-needed reform and modernisation had been thwarted by a coterie of scheming ministers, as well as by the ruthlessly ambitious Abdülhamid. Many in the crowd pitied Murad for having had to endure twenty-eight years of confinement, while others harboured feelings of guilt and shame by reason of the fact that their fear of the regime had prevented them from taking up arms to restore the rightful Sultan to the throne. Their sorrow was not only for the death of a noble-hearted, liberal-minded prince but also for the loss of an opportunity for a thoroughgoing reform of the Empire.

At the conclusion of the prayer ceremony, the four pallbearers exited the mosque carrying the coffin. Moments later, a young man burst through the police cordon; squeezing between two of the palace servants who were carrying Murad aloft, he raised his hands to help them. He was immediately joined by another, more elderly man on the opposite side. At this point the police lost control of the situation, and the whole crowd surged forward to follow the cortège. After the

246

six men had taken forty paces, others came forward to relieve them, they too wishing to share in the honour of bearing Murad's body to its final resting place. This process continued for the rest of the short distance to the tomb. Cevher Ağa and Fehim Pasha were of course outraged, but could do little: they were forced to watch Murad's coffin being carried in silence over a sea of people. The other palace officials, meanwhile, seemed quietly pleased that Murad had received such an outpouring of love and respect from the people of İstanbul; Asım Ağa, for his part, wept as he witnessed this show of devotion to his prince.

As the constantly-swelling procession approached the Cedid Havatin Mausoleum, it was met by armed palace guards wearing full dress uniform and crimson fezzes. They stood to attention in the open doorway, their faces flushed from the hot afternoon sun. Now that the crowd had performed their duty towards their beloved former Padishah, they did not hesitate to pass the casket to the four palace servants when they came forward to receive it. Once their master was back in their care, the four men followed Sheikh Abdullah into the cool, dimly-lit mausoleum. A grave had been prepared for Murad in the crowded south-east corner, next to his mother's resting place and close to that of Princess Fatma, his beloved sister.

An atmosphere of quiet dignity now enveloped the mausoleum. Sheikh Abdullah, standing in front of the casket and facing away from the other mourners, led the prayers. As this was going on, the lid was removed and Murad's shrouded body was carefully lifted out using three long pieces of cloth that had been placed underneath it. The pallbearers slowly lowered him into the waiting grave, positioning him on his right side so that he faced the holy city of Mecca. The grave was then filled in, and the mourners walked solemnly round it three times, reciting prayers under their breath as they did so. Once the third circumambulation was completed they withdrew from the mausoleum, leaving Sheikh Abdullah alone with Murad's soul and the two angels Nekir and Münker, who guard the heavenly gates.

These two angels always appear to the dead to question them once they have entered the grave. They ask three simple questions, to which there are three simple answers; however, only a true believer – a person of good and noble character – will be able to remember the correct answers. A wrong answer condemns the soul to hell, but the giving of three correct answers is the key that unlocks the door to paradise. Sheikh Abdullah's final duty as the presiding *imam* was to help Murad answer these questions correctly so that he could enter heaven.

The first question asked was: "Who is your god?"

Murad's soul replied without hesitation: "Allah." His soul then took its first step across the slippery, narrow Bridge of Sirat, the precarious walkway that spans the fires of hell and leads on to paradise.

Now the angels asked their second question, which was: "What religion do you follow?"

"Islam" was the firm and resolute reply. A second step was taken.

The final question came: "Who is this man?" – and the angels revealed the Prophet Muhammed to Murad's soul.

Sheikh Abdullah smiled in relief as the third question was answered. The outcome of this battle between the angel of goodness and the angel of evil, both of whom had tried to influence Murad's answers, would forever remain a secret shared only by Allah, the pious *imam* and the departed soul.

248

At Çırağan it had of course been a day of all-consuming grief, but what had struck most of all at the hearts of the palace's inhabitants had been something they were largely unprepared for – a feeling of indescribable emptiness that was if anything worse than their aching sense of loss. Selahaddin had repeatedly petitioned Nadir Ağa, Abdülhamid's Third Equerry, with requests for him to ensure that the letters he had written reached the Sultan. He hoped and prayed that these letters would move Abdülhamid to listen to the voice of his conscience and reconsider his decision not to allow Murad to be buried in the Imperial mausoleum within the cemetery that surrounded Yahya Efendi's tomb, or to permit a bereaved son to attend his father's funeral. But inevitably, these letters had been ignored. Selahaddin had done all he could to ensure that his father's wishes were carried out, but in his position – cut off from the world behind the high walls of Çırağan – he was denied any real effectiveness. He had dutifully read the short official announcements of Murad's death that had been published in all the Ottoman newspapers that morning. Reports in the foreign press had cruelly, but predictably, alluded to his father's supposed insanity; this had added to his heartache and compounded his feelings of desperation.

Selahaddin had sadly reflected that no one outside the 'prison palace' possessed any knowledge of his father's almost feminine gentleness, and that no one gave him credit for his modern, liberal ideas. It was not generally understood that of all the members of his dynasty, Murad had been the most free-thinking proponent of reform, or that he had aspired to put an end to all dogmatism and despotism in the Empire. Murad's musical talent likewise went unrecorded, and his natural warmth, genuine kindness and effortless charm were forgotten. Reading these disparaging articles about his father in the foreign newspapers had angered Selahaddin, and he had resolved to make a promise that he would later ask Nihad to make, too – that they would endeavour to keep the memory of the real Murad alive, and that each would exhort his family to pass on this duty to the succeeding generation. In this way, the lies that had been persistently told about Murad might one day be discovered and ultimately corrected.

Selahaddin had spent most of the day in quiet contemplation and private prayer, and this had been of great help to him at this time of bitter loss. Maybe not everyone in the palace understood his need for solitude, but then perhaps not everyone had fully appreciated the unusual strength of the bond that had existed between Murad and his only son. On Asım Ağa's return, Selahaddin had been touched by the account of Murad's funeral, and had felt a little better on hearing how the people of the city had come in their thousands to pay their respects. He had also taken some comfort in the knowledge that his father was resting close to his devoted mother and to his beloved sister Princess Fatma. Selahaddin knew that if his father was not able to lie in the Imperial mausoleum near Yahya Efendi's tomb, he would not wish to lie anywhere other than near his mother and his sister. But most of all, he prayed constantly that his father's soul might be finally at peace.

The princesses, consorts and *Gözdes* did their best to comfort and console one another in their respective suites, weeping on one another's shoulders and mourning Murad's loss. Meanwhile, the *ustas*, the *kalfas*, the harem eunuchs and the rest of the household staff also mourned their master and prayed for his soul. He would be sorely missed; they all knew, however, that as a result of his passing their lives would soon change forever, so in between their tears they anxiously contemplated what the future might hold for them.

The majority of the members of the household maintained that it was the shame of the scandal involving Hadice, and the consequent grief it had caused him, that had brought about Murad's premature death after only sixty-three summers. As he lay in bed that night, however, Selahaddin wondered whether his father had actually wanted to depart this world the previous evening as he simply could not bear to live to see the next day. It had seemed strange at the time, but when one of Abdülhamid's equerries had enquired in Murad's final days whether there was anything he wanted or needed, all he had asked for was a calendar. Tomorrow would be 31st August – the twenty-eighth anniversary of his deposition from the Imperial throne – and thus the calendar would have shown him that yet another monotonous, frustrating and humiliating year as a prisoner of state had gone by. Now, Selahaddin thought, his father's request seemed to make sense: perhaps Murad had endured enough. Perhaps he simply could not tolerate the thought of living through another of those dreaded anniversaries, with the prospect of even more years in captivity ahead of him and his family; perhaps, in fact, it had been time …

PART III

CHAPTER FOURTEEN

Life Continues

February 1905

I T had been nearly six months since Murad's death, and as the sun continued to rise each morning, so too did the people who were still living in the Çırağan Palace. Once the prescribed forty-day period of mourning was over, life carried on much as before – although the household was much reduced in number, and the void left by Murad's passing continued to be keenly felt.

On the death of their husband, Murad's consorts had chosen to vacate their opulent suites, and as a result the main palace building was almost deserted: the family only rarely used its grand reception rooms. After obtaining permission from Abdülhamid to buy a modest house in the inexpensive neighbourhood of Tarlabaşı, in the Beyoğlu district of İstanbul, the Lady Mevhibe, Murad's First Consort, decided to leave Çırağan. She sold one or two pieces of jewellery in order to purchase the property she had found, and was planning to live off the small stipend she had been granted by the Sultan. When she came to Selahaddin to tell him what she had in mind, he had never seen her so nervous. She clearly felt that in abandoning the family she was being disloyal; at the same time, however, she was aware that now

255

that Murad was gone she was no longer actually needed, so the time had come for her to leave. Her usually porcelain-white skin had flushed rose-pink, betraying the feelings of guilt she was trying her best not to show, but she need not have worried: Selahaddin understood and sympathised with her wish to escape the confines of Çırağan. He knew that Mevhibe possessed a fiercely independent nature – and it was this, indeed, along with her bewitching hazel-coloured eyes, that had once made Murad fall hopelessly in love with her. He also knew that like his father, she had been shut up in the Çırağan 'palace prison' for far too long, and he was therefore happy to give his blessing to her plan. Her 'sisters' – her fellow consorts – had helped her pack her belongings in her old marriage chest, and one cold winter morning, after a series of long, tearful goodbyes, she had driven out of the gates of the palace without turning to look back.

Unlike Mevhibe, Murad's other consorts did not wish to leave the palace even though they were now permitted to do so. Reftarıdil moved into a suite of rooms that adjoined Selahaddin's in order to be closer to her son and her grandchildren; Resan also moved into the harem building to share an apartment with her daughter, Fatma. Everyone had assumed that Şayan would seek permission from Abdülhamid to live with her daughter, Hadice, in her *yalı* in Ortaköy. Instead, however, she asked if she might share the suite of rooms that was occupied by Jalefer and Fuad. Believing it to be her duty to show loyalty to her husband by suffering a life of confinement similar to that which he himself had been forced to endure, Şayan chose to remain within the palace walls, refusing to consider any other alternative.

The *Gözdes* – the Ladies Gevherriz, Nevdür, Remişnaz and Filizten – had also left Çırağan once the period of mourning had come to an end. Abdülhamid had ordered that a small pension be paid from the Privy Purse to his brother's Favourites, and that they should leave İstanbul for Bursa to live quiet, simple lives together in a house owned by the Sultan's personal treasury. There, they would be under the protection of the Governor of Bursa, Tevfik Pasha, and his wife, Meyyal Hanım. The ladies had left with heavy hearts, distraught at having to move away from the family of their beloved Murad.

Before taking her leave on that cold, frosty winter morning, Gevherriz had received two unexpected letters from Hadice. They had been delivered by Fevzi, the handsome young farmer who worked the lands of the Muradiye Estate and came daily to the palace with his produce, often smuggling in correspondence or gifts from Hadice or Fehime. One of the letters was addressed to her, and Gevherriz had read it through tear-filled eyes; she had then placed the second one, which was intended for Kemaleddin, safely at the bottom of her travelling chest. How could she possibly refuse Hadice's plea for help? Was it not her fault that Hadice had embarked on the reckless course that had eventually caused her father's heart to break, and which had so severely damaged her own reputation? Gevherriz was painfully aware that it had been she who had taught French to Hadice as a young child, and she too who had introduced the princess to those romantic French novels that had so radically – and in the end disastrously – influenced her view of life. As soon as she arrived in Bursa, she thought, she would most certainly ensure that Hadice's letter reached Kemaleddin.

As was customary on the death of a sultan, Murad's senior servants were also obliged to leave the palace. After spending their whole lives in devoted service to the Imperial family, Ali Ağa and Sadık Ağa – both eunuchs, and both now in their dotage – retired, feeling unable to continue at Çırağan now that their noble Lord and Master was no more. Ali Ağa, who had rented a house nearby, would occasionally visit the palace, always bringing gifts of *lokum* or flowers for those of Murad's consorts who were still living there. Sadık Ağa had wept bitterly for days following Murad's death, but he had eventually found solace by praying at his late master's tomb every Friday; in fact, he continued to do this until the very end of his days.

The households of princes and unmarried princesses were not entitled to enjoy the services of *ustas*; in consequence of this rule, those *ustas* whose high rank dictated that they should only serve sultans and married princesses had all been obliged to depart. Thus the Mistress of Laundry, the Mistress of Shaving, the Mistress of the Ewer, the Mistress of the Baths, the Mistress of the Pantry and the Mistress of Coffee had all said goodbye to Çırağan. Some of these ladies, along with *kalfas* such as Nefidem Kalfa and Ferengiz Kalfa who had served Murad loyally for decades, had accompanied the *Gözdes* to Bursa; others, such as Aynifer Usta, the High Hazinedar, had decided to stay in the Imperial capital and live off the meagre annuity that had been granted to them by the Sultan. Dürrünab Kalfa, the Palace Music Director, and Tarzınev Kalfa, who had spent so many hours helping Murad with his compositions and had taught his children and grandchildren to play the piano, had likewise been told to leave Çırağan at the end of the mourning period; the same was true of Lebriz Kalfa, also a member of the palace's musical ensemble, Desteriz Kalfa, the Palace Dance Director, and her prodigy Teranedil Kalfa. Abdülhamid had awarded each of them a pension, albeit a pitifully small one, and had found them accommodation in the city: now that the Çırağan Palace was no longer the home of a former sultan, the size of its household had to be dramatically reduced.

A few of the more junior members of Murad's staff had

joined the households of Hadice and Fehime in their respective *yalıs*, while some – such as the sisters Nezihe and Nevrestan – had remained in the palace under Selahaddin's and Fatma's protection. The Çırağan Palace felt very quiet and empty without them all. Only the eunuchs and *kalfas* attached to the households of Selahaddin and Nihad, and those who were in service to Fatma and to Murad's consorts, now remained at Çırağan, as did the ever-faithful Asım Ağa: Abdülhamid was still under the misguided impression that the elderly eunuch served his interests.

❋ ❋ ❋ ❋ ❋

Selahaddin missed his father desperately, and following his death he had initially been plunged into a dark abyss of inconsolable grief and anguish. He had spent these difficult months in relative seclusion, hiding himself away in his study with only his well-thumbed books for company. During this time he had re-read his favourite passages from the writings of Ibn Sina, Ibn Arabi, Rumi, Ibn Khaldun and Katib Çelebi, as well as selections from the major works of Descartes, Voltaire, Rousseau and John Stuart Mill. Selahaddin had always had a passion for philosophy, and his efforts to understand human behaviour and the true meaning of life provided him with the distraction he needed while he grieved. Murad had been everything to Selahaddin – far more than just a father: he had also been his tutor, friend and confidant. The fact was that during the twenty-eight years they had spent living in enforced isolation from the world, Selahaddin had had no male company to speak of apart from him. The only other people he had been able to converse with were the ladies and children of the harem, the household staff and the doctor who occasionally visited the palace; the loathsome

259

palace administrators, though constantly present, were hardly agreeable companions. Having to live under these highly restrictive circumstances had forged a strong bond of mutual dependence between father and son – one that few could truly understand or appreciate; it was therefore only natural that on Murad's death, Selahaddin should have been left feeling utterly bereft. For the first few months he had found life almost unbearable; as the winter snows thawed across İstanbul, however, the pain and grief in his heart had gradually begun to melt away.

After mulling over the issue that had been occupying his mind for a number of days, Selahaddin had finally reached a decision. Earlier, he had sent a message to Nihad asking him to come to his study before dinner as there was something important he wanted to discuss. At the appointed hour there was a gentle knock at the door, and his eldest son entered the room. Nihad kissed his father's hand; then, smiling, he sat down beside him in front of the stove. It was late afternoon on a cold, dark day. The fire in the stove was burning brightly and the gas lamps had already been lit, throwing a warm, welcoming glow over the whole room.

"My dear Nihad," began Selahaddin, "as you know, your grandfather loved you very much. He saw in you a piety, a nobility of spirit and a devotion to duty that is rarely seen." This praise patently made Nihad feel highly uncomfortable, but even so Selahaddin went on. "Before he died, he told me that once he was gone he wanted you and your family to move into his suite. Tirendaz Kalfa has made all the necessary arrangements and the apartment is now ready for your use. You can move your personal effects across tomorrow. Now that Vâsıb is running around everywhere I am sure that you, your mother and Safiru will enjoy having the extra space."

Nihad was at a loss to know how to respond. He felt

unworthy of the praise he had just heard from his father's lips, and equally unworthy of the privilege that was now being granted to him. "Your grandfather also wanted you to have his piano, so it has been left in the salon." Nihad was overawed. It took him some time to grasp the significance of the decision to allocate Murad's rooms to him, but once he had done so a feeling of immense relief washed over him: it meant that Selahaddin was finally ready to come out of mourning and begin living his normal life again. Nihad cleared his throat to hide the strong emotion he could feel welling up inside him; then he rose from his chair, fell to his knees before his father and reverently kissed his hand to show his gratitude. Words were not needed. Privately, meanwhile, Nihad was also celebrating the release of the anxiety over his father's state of mind that had been plaguing him in recent weeks.

As Selahaddin smiled down at his son, he was aware that something remarkable had taken place in his inner world: the constant pain he had carried with him since his father's death had evaporated, leaving him free to feel joy once again. He had the sudden realisation that this was the first time for many months that he had smiled not in a perfunctory way, out of a feeling of duty, but with a genuine sense of pleasure. He now understood that the love of his wives and children, and their enduring patience, had at last brought him out of his despair; he felt ready to face the future that lay before him, however uncertain that future might appear to be. In the morning, his first priority would be to write to Abdülhamid and request that his family should no longer be held in strict confinement, but should be allowed certain freedoms. After all, with Murad gone, what justification could he possibly have for continuing to imprison them?

☺ ☺ ☺ ☺ ☺

Everyone was delighted to see Selahaddin take such a big step towards recovery. By the following day, the atmosphere in the household had changed completely: the palace harem was once again filled with the sound of laughter and excited chatter as everyone rushed along the corridors between Suites Three and Five carrying bundles and chests overflowing with possessions of every kind. Despite their servants' protestations, Nihad's brother and his sisters eagerly set about the task of assisting the *kalfas* and eunuchs with their duties. Fuad happily carried Vâsıb's toys to his new bedroom – which as before, he shared with his grandmother, Naziknaz. She liked to be close to her baby grandson at all times; this was something that Safiru had graciously accepted months ago, after she had stopped breastfeeding. Nihad's sisters helped Safiru bring her ornaments and the few pieces of jewellery she possessed across to her new room, while Nihad collected together all the carpentry tools, sketches and designs that he so treasured, and that no one else was permitted to touch. By the end of the day, Nihad and his family were happily settled in their new quarters.

It had been an exhausting day, so everyone retired to bed at an early hour – everyone, that is, except Nihad. He sat at his grandfather's prized Erard piano playing a waltz entitled 'Apparitions in the Mind' that he had composed for Murad's sixty-second birthday. The piece had been written the year he had married Safiru; those were the days when Murad was still in good health, and he himself had been young and naïve enough to entertain the belief that fate would ultimately be kind to his grandfather. As he played, he closed his eyes and thought of the happy days they had spent together. After a minute or two, something seemed to disturb his concentration, and he opened his eyes – to see his father standing in the doorway. Although Selahaddin had not recognised the piece, he had been captivated by its appealing melody.

"Please do not stop playing, Nihad. Go on, I beg of you," he said.

Selahaddin walked over to the piano and stood behind his son, placing a hand on his shoulder. This calmed Nihad, and he resumed playing. As his son's fingers ran lightly over the keys, Selahaddin scanned the sheet of music that stood on the piano. His eyes finally came to rest at the top of the page, where he could see something written in Nihad's neat, regular handwriting:

Respectfully dedicated to my revered grandfather.
10th September 1902.

As he read and re-read the dedication, it dawned on Selahaddin that Nihad had loved Murad almost as much as he himself had, and that in his own all-consuming grief he had failed to help his son overcome the sorrow that he too was trying to deal with. Feeling a sudden, sharp pang of guilt, Selahaddin chastised himself for having been so taken up with his own concerns that he had ignored his family's needs.

Once Nihad had played the final note of the waltz, Selahaddin suggested that they sit in the armchairs on either side of the large brass brazier which occupied the centre of the Hereke carpet. This beautiful carpet in varying shades of blue, cinnamon, gold and red was decorated with intricate floral motifs representing the various different species of flower that grew on the seven hills of İstanbul. Woven from the finest lamb's wool and Bursa silk in the Imperial Factory that had been set up in Hereke by Murad's father, it had been a gift from Sultan Abdülmecid to his son on the occasion of his marriage to Mevhibe. Selahaddin had in fact offered to give this rug, along with other pieces of furniture and ornaments, to Mevhibe as a parting gift when she was leaving Çırağan; she, however, had politely declined, taking only some items from her suite and a few keepsakes – such as one of Murad's embroidered handkerchiefs, and the book she had been reading to him just before he died.

Just then Dilber Kalfa entered the salon, bowing gracefully as she did so. She carried a silver tray on which were two cups of hot, steaming coffee and two small crystal bowls filled with orange Turkish Delight and pistachio nuts. Placing the tray on the round ormolu table that stood between the two princes, she quickly backed out of the room, leaving father and son alone together. Each picked up a porcelain coffee cup in its silver gilt *zarf*; in between sips, Selahaddin spoke comforting words to Nihad and apologised for the fact that he had been so withdrawn and unapproachable of late.

The two men talked for hours. They spoke not just of Murad and the painful ordeal they had both gone through during the last few months, but of many other subjects that were of interest to them. Selahaddin was delighted to find that he could talk to his son in almost the same way as he had once been able to talk to his father – about the family and about religion, politics and philosophy. Their conversation touched on the Russian surrender to the Japanese at Port Arthur, the January uprising in St Petersburg and the assassination of the Tsar's uncle, Grand Duke Sergei Alexandrovich. Finding themselves once again absorbed in the politics of the day – just as they had been on many occasions before Murad's death – they became animated; soon they went on to discuss the many problems facing the Empire and the Dynasty, and the pressing need for constitutional and social reform.

"It seems to me that just as we are, the Russian Empire is at a crossroads; if they take the wrong path it could prove fatal for them," said Nihad, adding more charcoal to the brazier. "Their disastrous war with Japan in Manchuria and Korea must have left them feeling humiliated and embarrassed by their military weakness, and it has also highlighted the obvious flaws in their modernisation and industrialisation programmes. As if this were not enough, they are facing a financial crisis not dissimilar to our own: they have burdensome European loans that they are obliged to service. So I suppose it is only to be expected that the people should blame the Tsar and his autocratic government for all their troubles."

"I agree, Nihad. We will have to wait and see what terms the peace treaty between the Tsar and the Mikado will contain, but I think the British will be working hard to prevent the Japanese from being too harsh towards the Russians, in order to maintain the balance of power. As far as the simmering unrest in Russia is concerned, in my opinion the uprising might well have been unplanned – it seems to have been rather disorganised, so I think it was probably spontaneous. The ruthless retaliation by the government has simply played into the revolutionaries' hands: it has united the people against their Tsar in a way that was never the case before. From the little I have read in the opposition journals that Asım Ağa somehow manages to smuggle into my study, it appears that the people who took part in the uprising only wanted to present a list of demands to the Tsar – demands that do not seem wholly unreasonable to me. In fact, we ourselves would do well to consider making concessions of that kind to our own people, before such things are demanded of us."

"You mean you have read some of the opposition journals, Father?" asked Nihad, wide-eyed in astonishment. A worried look came over his face. "If Cevher Ağa ever finds them in your possession there will be dire consequences, as I am sure you know," he added.

"Do not fret, Nihad. I always burn the journals after reading them, so even if that odious man does search my rooms he will find nothing. Hamid has such a tight stranglehold on the press that if one wants to find out what is really happening in the world outside, one has no option but to search out the news for oneself," replied Selahaddin with a wry smile. "Father and I always kept abreast of developments in world affairs by reading these journals in secret, and frankly I would advise you to do the same. You will obviously need to ignore the ardent revolutionary rhetoric in them, but underneath it there is usually a detailed and comprehensive account of events, mainly gathered from reputable European news agencies. I never ask how our loyal Ağa comes by these journals and pamphlets, although I would guess that he probably goes to the foreign post offices; suffice it to say that he is a very resourceful man who seems to know everyone in İstanbul. I only wish they were larger – I find the small print terribly difficult to read, and have to rely on my magnifying glass. However, perhaps that is a good thing, in a way: the fact that they are so small makes them easier to conceal under your coat, and therefore more difficult for Hamid's vigilant spies to find!"

"So what exactly are the Russian people demanding, Father?" asked Nihad, not wishing to pursue the subject of the opposition journals any further as it alarmed him. "Nothing about the uprising has been reported in our newspapers. All that has reached my ear so far is whisperings among the guards – who I think hear rumours in their barracks."

"Actually, their demands are quite simple," Selahaddin replied. "They want to have their civil rights respected and their wages increased; they also want a shorter working day. One thing they are insisting on is universal education, which

266

is something I think can only benefit the state in the long term – and, of course, they are demanding that the Tsar grant a constitution, which I personally believe he has no alternative but to do. According to the articles I have read, a group of workers staged a peaceful march. They walked towards the Winter Palace carrying religious icons and portraits of the Tsar. But as they came nearer, the troops and police protecting the palace panicked. They opened fire, and hundreds of people, including women and children, were killed or wounded. Mass protests and strikes right across Russia have followed, and although I am certain that the Tsar did not give the order to shoot, his people seem to have turned against him."

Nihad paused to consider all this. Picking up a piece of Turkish Delight, he chewed it thoughtfully. Then he commented: "So it seems even the autocratic Tsar Nicholas is losing his grip on power. There are so many obvious parallels between their empire and ours, Father, that I think we will need to keep an eye on events in Russia over the coming months, so that we can learn whatever lessons there are to be learned. Both their dynasty and ours rule over large multi-faith, multi-ethnic and multi-lingual empires, yet we both remain so conservative and autocratic. These are dangerous times, and Sultan Abdülhamid must be made to realise that it is no longer possible to ignore the fact that drastic reform is inevitable."

Selahaddin was enjoying this discussion with his eldest son, and was impressed by his mature approach, his intelligence and his perception. It was just the tonic he needed. He gave his son a quizzical look that showed he was seeing him in a new light – and perhaps pondering something privately, to himself. "You are quite right, Nihad," he said, taking a handful of pistachios from the bowl and beginning to unshell them. "I am sure the palace is kept well informed, but I suspect that Hamid will pay scant attention, if any, to these warnings. What I am certain of, however, is that our Padishah feels extremely unnerved when he reads the reports he no doubt receives each day from his ambassador in St Petersburg. The recent assassination of Grand Duke Sergei Alexandrovich, in particular, will have alarmed him most severely. Hamid's fear of assassination is already extreme – obsessive, in fact – but the murder of the King and Queen of Serbia in their bedroom just over a year ago, and now the killing of such a senior member of the Romanov family, especially within the walls of the Kremlin, will have exacerbated his paranoia even further."

Nihad had not read anything of the assassination in St Petersburg as Abdülhamid's censors had imposed a complete ban on the reporting of the incident in the Ottoman press. Oblivious of the lateness of the hour and eager to hear all the details, he questioned Selahaddin further. His father, equally unaware that it was long past the hour when he usually retired to bed, and pleasurably absorbed in the conversation, told him all he knew of what had happened. He explained that Grand Duke Sergei Alexandrovich had been not only the Tsar's uncle but also his brother-in-law: he was married to Princess Elizabeth of the Grand Ducal House of Hesse-Darmstadt, the elder sister of Tsarina Alexandra. Princess Elizabeth had in fact helped arrange Alexandra's marriage to the Tsar. Selahaddin spoke of how the Grand Duke's assassination had created ripples of alarm in every court in Europe, and how accounts of it had filled the pages of the opposition journals in İstanbul.

He then went on to explain that the Grand Duke had fought in the Russo-Turkish Wars and had been decorated for bravery by his father, Tsar Alexander II; Sergei was thus

268

familiar to the Ottomans. He had even met Abdülhamid: this had happened in January 1888, during one of the many visits to İstanbul he had made at that time while travelling to and from Jerusalem. His brother, Tsar Alexander III, had appointed him President of the Imperial Russian Orthodox Palestine Society and had commissioned him to build a Russian Orthodox church, to be named the Church of Mary Magdalene, on the Mount of Olives. During his brief audience with the Sultan, Grand Duke Sergei had shown him the designs for this church, which was to be built in white limestone and was to have seven gilded onion domes in the traditional Russian style. He had also shown him the designs for two building projects in Jerusalem that he had personally funded – the St Alexander Nevsky Church and the luxurious Sergei Courtyard, which had been constructed from imported Russian stone to house wealthy Russian pilgrims visiting the Holy Land. Abdülhamid had admired this Romanov Grand Duke's obvious devotion to his faith, but had not warmed to his arrogant and slightly peculiar character. Nevertheless, he had praised him for his benevolence and congratulated him on the impressive architecture of the hospice, which was very much in keeping with the historic atmosphere of Jerusalem.

Selahaddin then told his son that prior to his resignation a month previously, Grand Duke Sergei had served as Governor of Moscow for many years, adding that it was because he was such a martinet, alienating every section of society with his harsh and uncompromising policies during his tenure of that office, that he had evoked widespread hatred and resentment. In addition, he was unfairly held responsible for what had happened at the fields of Khodynka a few years before, when over a thousand people had been killed in a stampede during celebrations for the coronation of his nephew, Nicholas II;

Sergei's failure to show any sympathy for the bereaved following the tragedy had not been forgotten.

Selahaddin then went on to explain that the radicals loathed him because of his belief in firm, authoritarian government and his reactionary policies that continually blocked reform and restricted the activities of the intelligentsia. The nobility and merchant classes hated him for his efforts to eliminate fraud and corruption among them, and because of his desire to address the problem of poverty and improve workers' living conditions. Consequently, he had become a focus for the hatred of all those who opposed the Tsar's regime. Nihad listened intently to his father, wishing all the while that as a prince of the blood he were permitted to serve his empire and his people in some active role, as the Romanov princes were allowed to do.

"One of the French newspapers I read reported that just before his death, Grand Duke Sergei had moved to a palace within the Kremlin, with its fortified walls," Selahaddin said. "Apparently, his attitude towards his personal safety was one of Oriental fatalism – quite similar to ours, in fact. He believed that if it was God's will that his life should end, then no matter what precautions he took he could not avoid the inevitable. He did want to protect his family, however. On the afternoon of 17th February, the Grand Duke left in a carriage on his way to his old office in the Governor General's mansion, but before he had passed through the gates of the Kremlin a Marxist revolutionary stepped forward and tossed a bomb into his lap. He died instantly – his body was blown into a hundred pieces. The coachman was also killed, and little was left of the carriage apart from its wheels. That is not a death I would wish upon anyone – even an enemy who had once fought against our empire. There was no honour in this killing: it was just brutal, cold-blooded murder."

Nihad was shocked to hear that a senior member of the Russian Imperial family could be assassinated with such apparent ease at the very gates of the Kremlin. Perhaps Abdülhamid was right to be so cautious about his security; maybe his paranoia was not so unfounded after all. "If that could happen in Moscow, do you think it could happen here in İstanbul, Father?" he asked.

"I suppose it could, dear boy," Selahaddin answered. "The Padishah ought to listen to the people before it is too late; he should learn from the events we are witnessing both within our borders and beyond them. There is an awakening among peasants and workers everywhere: they are fast becoming politicised, and are falling under the influence of the ideologies propagated by these radical organisations that are constantly springing up. We should acknowledge this fact, and respond while we are still able to do so. When I read of this sad affair, what I found particularly moving was the reaction of the Grand Duke's famously beautiful wife, who I understand is a granddaughter of Queen Victoria. Apparently, the explosion was so violent that it shook the windows of the palace. Sensing that something terrible had occurred, Grand Duchess Elizabeth rushed outside and ran towards the spot where the assassination had taken place, which was now a scene of appalling devastation. According to the reports I have read, she then knelt down in the blood-soaked snow and calmly gathered up the remains of her beloved husband, putting them on a stretcher. She then returned to the palace clutching the medals and decorations he had been wearing next to his heart only minutes before. What amazing strength and fortitude that woman must have!"

The two princes sat in silence for a moment, imagining what this horrendous ordeal must have been like for the brave

Grand Duchess. Nihad then asked what had happened to the assassin.

"He was injured in the blast, and was arrested immediately. I am sure the Russian police are interrogating him under torture to find out who his accomplices were, but he will certainly be hanged when they have finished with him," Selahaddin replied with a shudder. "Anyway, enough of these distressing topics. Let us change the subject," he said, clearing his throat. "I have something to show you," he announced with a mischievous smile. Nihad fidgeted uncomfortably in his armchair – he felt perturbed by the conspiratorial look in his father's eye.

When Selahaddin had heard Nihad's comments about the parallels between the Ottoman Empire and Imperial Russia, and the urgent need for reform in both, he had been greatly impressed – and a thought had suddenly occurred to him. Nihad should not have to find everything out either from his father or from the state-censored press. Was it not time to further his education by encouraging him to think for himself and form his own opinions? Selahaddin could see that Nihad was eager to know what was happening in the wider world outside their palace prison. The really important thing was, however, that he had the intelligence and the acumen to judge for himself, and not accept everything he was hearing or reading at face value: he was able to weigh things, and form his own conclusions. This was an invaluable asset in a prince of the Imperial House.

Selahaddin slipped his hand into his inside breast pocket and pulled out a neatly-folded pamphlet. "This is something that Asım Ağa brought to me earlier this evening. I believe it may be of interest to you," he said, holding it out towards his son. "It asks the question: 'Following the death of his brother Sultan Murad six months ago, can Sultan

Abdülhamid at last feel secure on the Ottoman throne now that he is finally ruling as the rightful Padishah?'" Nihad looked shocked. He had not yet fully digested the fact that his father and grandfather had regularly perused illegal opposition journals and pamphlets together. The idea of taking an illicit item from his father's hand filled him with horror, but at the same time he was fascinated to hear that there was an article in the pamphlet that blatantly questioned the legitimacy of Abdülhamid's entire reign. The knowledge that his father had such a dangerous publication on his person set the butterflies dancing in his stomach; however, Nihad could not ignore the fact that the hairs on the back of his neck had begun to tingle in anticipation of reading a contentious article of this nature.

Sensing that his son was wavering, Selahaddin encouraged him with these words: "There is no one here to see you read this pamphlet, Nihad – no one to report us to that despicable man Cevher Ağa. We are alone in this room, and once you have read it we can throw it into the brazier and watch it go up in flames." Nihad still looked hesitant; however, his father persisted. "If and when you are ever in a position of power, it will be vitally important for you to understand the opposition's views, and for you to be aware of what the people are thinking," he went on. "There lies what is perhaps Hamid's greatest fault: he arrogantly ignores and dismisses public opinion in the belief that he can always control and manipulate it by means of strict press censorship, and if this is not enough, through intimidation and force. In this he is not dissimilar to the Russian Tsar – and if things do not change very soon, it could be the undoing of them both. One day, if it is God's will, you may become the head of our noble family. If it is your wish to rule well, you must be fully prepared. Remember what Caliph Ali once said:

'Knowledge is power, and it can command obedience.' Never underestimate the importance of knowledge, and always look for ways of acquiring it – even if this means having the courage to flout suffocating restrictions such as those imposed on us all by the current Sultan."

Nihad held out his hand and took the pamphlet. His blue-grey eyes eagerly skimmed the headline. "Read it, think about it, and then we shall discuss it together," his father said. Selahaddin was delighted to see that Nihad had abandoned his habitual, overly-cautious attitude, and had at last succumbed to the temptation to go down a somewhat more adventurous path. As his son read, he ate the last few pieces of Turkish Delight that remained in the crystal bowl on the table, savouring the tangy orange flavour that filled his mouth with its sweetness.

It took Nihad nearly half an hour to finish the article. Selahaddin watched him closely as his eyes ran across the pages, devouring every word. When he came to the end, he looked up and met his father's gaze. Without speaking, Nihad crumpled the pamphlet into a tight ball and tossed it into the brazier – where it was instantly consumed by dancing ribbons of hungry flame, at last disappearing into the bed of coal and ash. The incriminating document was gone, but Nihad could not forget what he had read: it left so many unanswered questions. For the next few hours he and Selahaddin engaged in a long discussion about the injustices surrounding Murad's deposition and his subsequent confinement, the legality of Abdülhamid's reign and the viability or otherwise of liberal reform in the Empire.

As they neared the end of their discussion, Nihad made a reference to the English philosopher Thomas Hobbes. The previous year Selahaddin had suggested that he read *The Leviathan* as he was trying to introduce his son to the concept

274

of a 'social contract' between a sovereign and his people. Nihad had never spoken of the book, so Selahaddin had assumed that he had either not read it, or that it had not made much of an impression on him. In fact, it had set the young prince thinking very deeply, but what with his grandfather's illness and the tragedy of his subsequent death, Nihad had never had an opportunity to discuss the thoughts that were going through his mind with his father. Now, however, it was time to unburden himself.

"I believe that both Abdülhamid and the Tsar are failing to respect the sanctity of the 'social contract', and are thus rocking the foundations of the Ottoman and Romanov Empires," he began, speaking with a firm conviction that showed he had come to this opinion after much consideration. "I say this because they are not protecting the natural rights of their subjects or responding to the 'general will' of the people," he went on. "Because they have failed in this duty, and have violated these rights, it is permissible for the 'social contract' to be broken, for their divine right to rule to be called into question, and ultimately for their respective subjects to rebel against them. Unless immediate action is taken to rectify the mistakes they have made, I am very much afraid that revolution will sweep the old order away, bringing in its wake a chaos that will benefit no one."

Selahaddin was speechless. He was also immensely proud – it was clear that Nihad had read not only Hobbes, but also Locke and Rousseau. He need not worry any further about his son's education. Unbeknownst to him, much indeed had been going on during his father's illness and subsequent to his death, and not all of it had been negative. A feeling of relief and satisfaction washed over him.

At that moment, their conversation was suddenly interrupted by the soothing sound of the muezzin calling the faithful to prayer, heralding the arrival of morning. "I had no idea we had been talking for so long, Nihad. It seems we have been talking all night!" Selahaddin said with a laugh. "I do not feel the slightest bit tired, which is quite remarkable – in fact, I feel strangely rejuvenated! Come, my dear boy, let us perform our ablutions and pray together before breakfast."

The two men did not know it, but the new day, announced by the muezzin from the balcony of the minaret, would be the beginning of a new chapter in the lives of Murad's family, for later that morning a letter would arrive from Yıldız Palace.

CHAPTER FIFTEEN

Winds of Change

A FTER much deliberation and not a little soul-searching, Sultan Abdülhamid finally wrote a reply to Selahaddin's letter, and ordered his trusted equerry to deliver it to his nephew at Çırağan in person. Having taken it from Cevher Ağa's hand and scanned it quickly to comprehend the general gist, Selahaddin was struck dumb. His heart began to pound with alarming violence: to him it seemed like a kettledrum being vigorously beaten by a drummer of the Janissary Military Band, marching into battle. The tightness in his chest was so acute that he could scarcely breathe. He re-read the letter, this time rather more carefully, but even after he had finished it the feeling of shock was still undiminished. He stared blankly at Cevher Ağa.

Realising that it was unwise to display intense emotion in the presence of his jailer's much-detested henchman, he finally managed to pull himself together. "Please thank His Imperial Majesty for his benevolence, Cevher Ağa," he said at last. "Thank you, that will be all." The eunuch, who was rather stout, gave his usual curt bow and withdrew from Selahaddin's study. Before he had set out for Çırağan, Abdülhamid had informed him of the contents of the message of which he was to be the bearer, and had issued precise orders as to how the Çırağan Palace was to be administered henceforward. As might have been abundantly obvious from his facial expression (if Abdülhamid cared about such things, which he did not), inwardly Cevher Ağa found these new instructions intensely irritating.

However much Selahaddin might read and re-read the letter, the writing on the sheet of paper in front of him steadfastly refused to make any sense at all. For several minutes he sat at his desk staring at the black ink that ran from right to left across the page in neat, flowing lines, but his mind just could not engage with the message that was being communicated. Then a ray of bright sunlight broke through the clouds and beamed through the window onto the letter, illuminating the words with a soft golden glow; suddenly, everything seemed to gel, and the meaning of the words he had been reading became clear to him. His racing heartbeat gradually slowed, and after a few more minutes he had recovered sufficiently to call Tirendaz Kalfa and ask her to tell the family to come to his salon – immediately.

It was not long before everyone was assembled, sitting in a wide semicircle, and Selahaddin began to address them. "I have received some important news that I would like to share with you all," he began. "This morning I received a letter from the Padishah, in reply to one I sent to him yesterday." He paused to smile at the row of faces staring back at him in bewilderment. "He has graciously granted my request that we no longer be held in confinement. From this day forward we are permitted to send and receive written correspondence, invite people to call on us, visit other people and go on excursions around the city."

There were tears of joy from the Imperial consorts and wives, and excited gasps from Fuad and the princesses;

Nihad's reaction, by contrast, was remarkably restrained. "And what are his conditions, Father?" he asked, his eyes narrowing with suspicion.

"Nihad, this is a moment to rejoice – the moment we have all been longing for. Why can you not just accept it and be happy, like the rest of us?" his father retorted. There was no reply from Nihad, who looked a little downcast, so Selahaddin continued. "As Descartes observed, *'An optimist may see a light where there is none, but why must the pessimist always run to blow it out?'* Sometimes I simply do not understand you. Finally you will be able to make the acquaintance of the other members of our family, meet other liberal-minded young men who think as you do, and experience the unique beauty of İstanbul and the delights it offers. At long last, Nihad, you will be able to live your life to the full. I am happy for you, even if you are not."

"I am sorry, Father," Nihad answered, "but before I can allow myself to be happy, I need to know if there are conditions attached."

"Very well, Nihad. Yes, there are conditions," Selahaddin sighed. "We are required to obtain written permission from Yıldız every time we want to leave the palace, and are to be accompanied by palace guards on all excursions and visits. Our correspondence is to be subject to vetting, and we will also need to obtain consent before inviting guests to Çırağan. That is all."

"So I suppose that means we are still not completely free to come and go as we please, doesn't it, Baba?" said Fuad.

"Nihad and Fuad, my dear nephews, this is just the first step," Fatma interjected, seeing that her brother was becoming exasperated by his sons' attitude. "I am sure that *Inshallah* the time will soon come when we will be completely free. In the meantime, we just need to learn a little patience. Remember – although patience is bitter, its fruit is sweet."

"I think everyone here has already mastered the lesson of patience, Aunt Fatma," Nihad replied with uncharacteristic bluntness.

"Believe me, Nihad, I fully understand your frustration," Fatma answered, unperturbed. "You naturally want to be completely free, and not be hampered in any way. But even you must admit that this is a start – and that, surely, is cause for celebration. Like you, I have never seen what lies beyond these walls, and whilst I freely admit that I am extremely nervous about venturing outside, the idea also fills me with enormous excitement. And, dear Nihad, I am quite sure that whatever you may say, if you are honest with yourself you will acknowledge that you, too, can feel that excitement bubbling up inside you. We can all feel it." She paused for a second or two, as if wondering whether or not to give voice to her thoughts. Then she continued: "Speaking for myself, I am feeling quite overwhelmed. In fact … however strange it may seem, just this once I am grateful to Sultan Abdülhamid."

"Thank you, dearest Fatma. Let us not spoil this occasion with needless disputes," said Selahaddin, casting a disapproving glance at his two sons. "Today we have been given far greater liberty than we had only yesterday, and for that we should all be thankful. We must plan some excursions. Perhaps, to begin with, a visit to the homes of Hadice and Fehime?"

The thought of going out in a carriage and visiting their aunts, and in the process seeing all the sights that the bustling streets of the city might present to them, filled the young princesses with a sense of joy and wonderment that they could not conceal. Şayan, meanwhile, wept at the prospect of seeing her precious daughter Hadice once again after so many years, and after all the endless pain and heartache they had both gone through; she smiled up at Selahaddin in gratitude, thinking to herself how kind and thoughtful he was – just like his father had been.

Everyone now began to speak at the same time, pouring out idea after idea as to what outings they would like to go on. Suggestions varied from boat trips along the Golden Horn and picnics on the shores of the Bosphorus to summer visits to the Muradiye Estates in Kurbağalı Dere and voyages to the Princes' Islands. The ladies soon began to plan shopping excursions to the fashion boutiques in the Grande Rue de Péra and trips to attend concerts or to see plays; these ideas did not impress Fuad overmuch, but he brightened at the suggestion that they might watch a cinematographic moving picture. The excitement and gaiety was infectious, touching all but Nihad.

Adile, the sweetest-natured and most considerate of his sisters, noticed how he remained silent, unaffected and seemingly unimpressed by all the hubbub. "And where would you like to go, Nihad?" she enquired softly.

"I would like to go and pray at Grandfather's grave," he said. Safiru gazed affectionately at her husband. For him, duty would always come before pleasure.

"My dear Nihad, as always, you put us to shame," his father said. "I will write to Hamid immediately and request that we all be permitted to do as you say. In view of the fact that we were forbidden to attend the funeral ceremony, and have so far not been allowed to pray at the grave, I see no reason why he should not give his consent."

Everyone now began to make long mental lists of all the people they wanted to see and all the things they wanted to do. However, there were so many that no one could possibly remember them all, so Behiye, as the eldest of Selahaddin's daughters, was given the task of recording each and every idea. Sitting at the mahogany writing table beneath the window that overlooked the gardens, she hastily scribbled down each suggestion as it was put forward. When lunchtime came, the *kalfas* brought in large trays of food and set them on low, folding stands so that the mood of excited concentration would not be interrupted.

As the family sat together, happily absorbed in sharing their ideas, Selahaddin listened with pleasure to the buzz of conversation. Yes, he thought to himself, they seem to have taken in the fact that their long years of confinement are finally over. But then he returned to a disturbing thought that had been occupying him intermittently ever since Nihad and Fuad had spoken up to voice their doubts and suspicions. How would his children react to the outside world – the world they had never seen? Did they really have any idea what it was like, the ugliness as well as the beauty?

Selahaddin's excitement at his family's forthcoming liberation now gave way to anxiety. The Çırağan Palace was a silky cocoon that had guarded their innocence all their lives; now, however, an opening had appeared in that cocoon, and like hatching moths they were about to emerge and see the world, with all its suffering and all its cruelty, for the very first time. They had never set eyes on a beggar or a cripple, or on anyone who was destitute, starving or dressed in rags. They had not seen the fear and anguish in the faces of orphans forced to survive on the streets, the desperation in the faces of refugees stripped of all they possessed, or the hatred in the eyes of those who looked with envy on people of rank and privilege. How could he possibly prepare them for the upset that these sights would undoubtedly give rise to in them? How could they acquire a lifetime's experience and knowledge of the ways of the world in just a few short days?

⊛ ⊛ ⊛ ⊛ ⊛

March 1905

Over a week went by, but Abdülhamid still did not ratify Selahaddin's requests for the family to go on a visit to Ortaköy to see Hadice and Fehime, and for him and his two sons to visit Murad's grave. This was a worrying time for everyone at Çırağan: what if the Padishah decided not to allow them out, after all? They all knew he was perfectly capable of playing with their feelings in such a cruel manner – and if he did not wish to hurt them, Cevher Ağa certainly did. But then an equerry arrived from Yıldız bearing a letter, and Selahaddin was almost as nervous and excited as he had been on receiving Sultan Abdülhamid's reply to his own first petition.

He opened it gingerly, muttered a prayer – and was mightily relieved to see that the trip to see his two sisters had been approved! As Hadice was still under house arrest following the scandal of the previous year, their meeting was to take place at her *yalı*. Reading on, Selahaddin saw that Abdülhamid had refused his request to be allowed to go with his two sons to pray at Murad's grave. That piece of bad news had, of course, been saved till last. He could not understand what possible reason his uncle could have – other than pure malice – for arriving at such a decision. He resolved to ask again, and to keep on asking until permission was granted. Nihad would have to be told, of course; Selahaddin knew his son would be angry and bitterly disappointed, and in consequence he was not looking forward to that conversation one little bit.

He dismissed the equerry – which this time was not Cevher Ağa, but a lackey of considerably less seniority: Cevher Ağa had feigned illness in order to avoid having to deliver this particular missive to his captives. Sitting down at his desk, Selahaddin struggled to recover his composure. Previously, the idea of riding out of the gates of Çırağan into the wide world beyond had been no more than a beautiful fantasy, to be relished at his leisure, but now the shock hit him with force: this time it was real. That, in turn, meant that everything would now be moving quickly: there were practical matters to be attended to.

True enough, deliverance from their long captivity had arrived – but with it came the likelihood of new trials and tribulations. Certainly, there would be new responsibilities: he needed to make sure that his family's first tentative step into the real world went as smoothly as possible, and knew he had to be prepared to reassure them and calm their fears. He himself, however, felt by no means confident that he could withstand the double ordeal of having to perform with absolute confidence in circumstances that were now completely foreign to him while at the same time behaving as a perfect role model under the watchful eyes of his entire family. Which of them would cope best with the experience, he wondered – and more to the point, which of them would be likely to succumb to the shock?

❀ ❀ ❀ ❀ ❀

The first signs of spring were evident in every corner of the palace gardens. The winter cold was now banished, to be replaced by the warm crispness of the coming season. Morning dew, in place of icy frost, covered the carpets of bright green grass, and the air was permeated with the inebriating scent of freshness and new growth. The trees, whose branches had been bare during the harsh winter months, were now covered in swelling buds that were beginning to unfurl, revealing tight bunches of lush new leaves. The heads of the crocuses, shaped just like the *zarfs* that held the palace's coffee-cups, had already burst through the soft, damp earth, and their delicate lilac, mauve and deep purple petals were now visible, sparkling like scattered amethysts among the blades of grass. The flower beds were full of tall daffodils swaying their heavy, trumpet-like heads, and the birds sang with full-throated zest as they busied themselves collecting twigs and moss to build their nests.

Inside the palace all was commotion: the *kalfas* were helping the ladies to put on their new *feraces*, which were made of fine merino wool. The dressmakers had been instructed to make *feraces* for all the Imperial ladies, and to do so in haste: previously these ladies' wardrobes had not included garments for wear on the streets of the city as – for obvious reasons – they had not been required. The ladies' excitement mounted as they put on the long, loose coats, trimmed with ribbon and lace, that completely covered their cotton day-dresses. Meanwhile, attentive *kalfas* tied muslin *yashmaks* in place to cover their heads and faces, the translucent veils looking like wispy clouds trying unsuccessfully to conceal the sun.

Selahaddin, Nihad and Fuad were waiting outside the main door of the harem, trying to control mixed feelings of excitement and trepidation. Three carriages had been sent from Yıldız to take everyone to Hadice's *yalı*, and the coachmen and footmen in their smart liveries and scarlet fezzes were waiting for the party to assemble – with much greater patience than the three Imperial Princes, it has to be said. Selahaddin would have liked to pace up and down, but

285

knew he had to control this urge in the presence of so many onlookers. A small platoon of cavalry guards who were to accompany the family on the short journey to Ortaköy had also gathered in the courtyard. Finally, the ladies were ready.

They emerged from the harem into the bright sunlight, and looked (with more than a little nervousness in some cases) at the steps of the waiting carriages. The six Imperial Princesses – Murad's daughter Fatma and Selahaddin's five daughters – all climbed into the first carriage, while Selahaddin and Nihad helped Murad's consorts – the Ladies Reftarıdil, Şayan and Resan – to mount the rather wobbly steps of the second. The Ladies Naziknaz and Jalefer shared the third carriage with Safiru and Vâsıb. Once Selahaddin and Nihad had mounted their horses and Fuad had got astride his pony, the small procession headed out through the heavily-carved marble gateway with its towering gates of ornate, interlaced ironwork – gates which had kept the family imprisoned within them for so many years, but which now hung wide open, inviting them to pass through. As his horse turned the corner into the road outside, Selahaddin felt a jolt in his stomach – was it really as easy as that to leave Çırağan? It was as if the walls of his prison had suddenly collapsed around him – a most odd sensation that was rather like looking into what you thought was a mirror, and suddenly realising that it was not a mirror at all, but just a gap beyond which the real world extended without interruption. He looked around him briefly; soon, however, he realised that the motion of his horse was making him feel dizzy, and lowered his eyes to stabilise himself.

Selahaddin had not been out in the streets of İstanbul since he was fifteen years old. Furthermore, he had not ridden a horse since that time, so he felt tense and desperately nervous as he sat astride the tall, powerful mare that had been sent from Yıldız as his mount. His two sons had learned to ride on docile old ponies plodding along the winding pathways of the enclosed gardens at Çırağan, and as a result Nihad, too, was unused to riding horses as spritely as the one that had been sent for him from the Imperial stables; moreover, neither he nor Fuad had ever looked along a wide open road such as the one that now lay before them. They, like their father, felt a little unsure in their saddles, and they squeezed a little too hard with their legs and gripped the reins a little too tightly as they rode past the guards. Then, suddenly, they were out of their silken Bastille – that prison that had been their protective cocoon ever since they had first set eyes on the world. The carriages followed behind, the wheels making a metallic, grinding noise that their occupants found strange and unfamiliar.

After half a minute or so, Selahaddin began to trust his balance; he relaxed his legs, allowing his weight to fall onto his heels. Now he felt confident enough to loosen his grip on the reins. Glancing at the beautiful chestnut mare's soft mouth, he knew instinctively that he would not have to pull or tug. Both horse and man fell into a natural rhythm, and Selahaddin kicked her into a trot. He then looked across at his sons, anxious that they might be having trouble controlling their mounts, but he need not have worried: they were both sitting upright in perfect postures, their heels down in the stirrups and their eyes focused firmly ahead. They were Turks – and as such were able to master any horse they rode as it was in their blood, and like their ancestors before them, they did so instinctively.

The party progressed along Çırağan Road towards Ortaköy, passing Feriye Palace on the way. Here, Selahaddin bowed his head in remembrance of his great-uncle Sultan Abdülaziz, who had been murdered there at the command of duplicitous ministers all those years ago, in the first days of his father's ill-fated reign.

The sights and sounds of everyday life in a big city – all those sights and sounds that its ordinary inhabitants become fully accustomed to in childhood – were disconcerting to him: in fact, he found them more than a little intimidating. For nearly thirty years he had lived with his family in total seclusion, so it was only to be expected that the voices of street-traders yelling hoarsely as they peddled their wares, and the shrill cries of young shoe-shine boys trying to attract customers, should come together in a merciless cacophony that reverberated inside his head, setting his nerves on edge. The numerous grubby-faced strangers huddled together in irregular groups along the pavement – who knows for what reason? – also made him feel ill at ease.

Then he passed a street market, and the smell of the freshly-caught fish stacked high in baskets gave him a sudden pang of nausea. He could feel beads of sweat beginning to form beneath his crimson fez; his hands felt clammy inside his white leather riding gloves, and once again, much to his alarm, his heartbeat began to quicken. Selahaddin took three deep breaths in an effort to calm himself, and resolutely fixed his eyes on a spot between his horse's ears so that he saw neither the road ahead nor the disturbing sights all around him. He admitted to himself that at that moment, all he wanted to do was turn around and retreat to safety behind the iron gates of Çırağan. At the same time, however, he chastised himself for giving way to such weakness; suddenly, the shameful realisation came to him that perhaps Abdülhamid really had succeeded in breaking his spirit, after all. Spurred by self-disgust, he forced himself on. What a good thing it was that none of his womenfolk could see the nervousness and irresolution in his face! That thought made him smile wryly to himself, and he immediately began to feel a little better.

The young princesses at least had each other for company, and that – for most of them, at any rate – made all the difference. Besides, they had the protection of an enclosed carriage, and so were less exposed to the harsh realities of life in the city's streets. Eager for their first glimpse of the world that lay outside their prison, the more adventurous of them peered through the latticed screens that hung down over the carriage windows, shielding them from prying eyes and allowing them to exclude the outside world if the sights it presented to them should prove too harrowing.

"Adile, Safiye, look!" Atiye squealed in delight. "There is a man selling songbirds over there. How colourful they are! Aren't they pretty?"

Safiye clasped the hands of both her sisters. She, too, was tremendously excited. "And look over there, near the drinking fountain!" she exclaimed. She had noticed a young boy in a threadbare jacket smiling broadly as he held aloft a forked branch interwoven with thickly-plaited reeds that had syrup-coated apples stuck to them. "Those apples look delicious!" she said. "Imagine what they must taste like!" The three young princesses' heads darted this way and that as they tried to take in everything at once. Enthralled by all they saw, they pressed their faces against the grille of the carriage, determined not to miss a single detail.

Behiye and Rukiye, meanwhile, were intrigued by the sight of two unveiled women bartering with a fisherman who was carefully weighing his catch. The two women turned to watch the procession drive past, allowing the sisters a glimpse of their striking beauty – which they were making no attempt to conceal. Behiye and Rukiye wondered whether the women were Greek, or maybe Armenian, or Jewish. "How do you think those women feel, walking the streets like that – unchaperoned, and without veils?" Rukiye asked her sister, thinking to herself that it must feel very liberating.

But before Behiye had had a chance to answer, Fatma broke in: "I should think they feel utterly exposed and vulnerable," she said, running her fingers over her *yashmak* to make sure it was properly pinned in place. Unlike her nieces, Fatma had not leant forward to look out through the grilles at the carriage window: ever since they had driven out of the palace gates, she had been sitting bolt upright between Adile and Safiye, nervously twisting the folds of her *ferace* between her fingers.

Up ahead of the carriages, Fuad sat confidently astride his pony. Earlier he had been upset that he had not been given a fully-grown horse to ride: being treated like a child always irritated him. As he rode along drinking in all the sights, however, this initial disappointment was forgotten: he was so thrilled that he did not know which way to look. The air was filled with the sound of bird-song and loud, raucous human voices. Everywhere around him he could see tempting treats being offered for sale, and their enticing aroma wafted up to his nose. Pretty young women – unveiled – smiled in his direction; and now he was riding past a real-life war veteran with a long, white beard who was proudly wearing a row of shiny medals pinned to his chest. To Fuad's amazement, the man actually saluted him!

Nihad's emotions, meanwhile, were far less straightforward than those of his younger brother. He was, of course, excited to be riding in the streets of the Imperial capital for the very first time, and although he was finding the experience more than a little overwhelming, the prospect of being allowed – at long last – to engage with the people he might one day have the honour to rule appealed to his sense of responsibility, bringing with it a more acute awareness of his possible future role; moreover, he was very much looking forward to seeing his aunts. But as his intelligent eyes scanned the streets, he could not prevent himself from feeling shocked and horrified by much of what he saw. He, too, had noticed the caged songbirds, and had felt a pang of sadness at the thought of them being trapped behind bars when they should have been free, flying in the skies. Immediately afterwards he had seen a young boy, not much older than Fuad, selling apples drenched in syrup; the boy was not wearing shoes, and his feet were black with dirt.

Nihad also noticed the multitude of stray cats; some were looking longingly at the fish being weighed by fishermen at small seaside fish stalls, while others were perching on crumbling walls or prowling hungrily across the rooftops. He had seen cats in the gardens of Çırağan as they sometimes sneaked in when the gates were opened; never before, however, had he seen so many of them at one time. Then he passed an old war veteran dressed in rags and gave him a nod of respect, hoping in this way to be able to show his appreciation for the tremendous sacrifice the man had clearly made: he had lost his left leg fighting for the Empire – perhaps during the Crimean Campaign, or perhaps in the more recent Russo-Turkish War. Now the man was leaning against his wooden crutch, trying to salute his father.

Just then, he noticed a four-legged furry animal with floppy ears. Although obviously under-nourished, it was wagging its tail, clearly unaffected by its miserable condition. There seemed to be many more of these creatures – some lying in the middle of the street dozing in the early afternoon sunshine, and some ambling along between the groups of people. Some of them were large and quite forbidding in appearance, but all of them seemed friendly and perfectly

291

used to human company. "I wonder what those are?" he mused to himself.

In fact, the reason the old war veteran had tried to salute Selahaddin was that he had realised that the carriages, the three riders and the cavalry guards accompanying them must have come from the Çırağan Palace: that meant that the distinguished-looking man riding between his two handsome sons must be Prince Selahaddin, only son of the late Sultan Murad Khan. As if by telepathy, others now began to arrive at the same conclusion. More and more people stopped whatever they were doing and stood beside the road, bowing low in homage; some of them performed the *temenna*, the traditional gesture of willing subjection, lifting their right hand to their lips and then to their forehead as the three princes rode past. Nihad noticed an old *simit*-seller come forward and carefully place his large wicker basket, filled with rings of bread covered with sesame seeds, on the ground. Wondering what the man was about to do, Nihad felt a stab of nervousness, and held the reins of his horse more tightly. The old man then startled him by letting out a shout of "Long live Prince Selahaddin! Long live the Padishah! Long live Prince Selahaddin!" He was soon joined by others, and Nihad was amazed to see coffee-sellers, water-carriers, yoghurt-sellers and many others line the road, all chanting these same words.

In the midst of this impromptu display of loyalty, one person alone seemed unmoved. A lone fruit-seller balancing a tray on his head – a thin young man wearing a shabby fez and a pair of threadbare shalvar trousers tied with a bright green sash – remained conspicuously silent. His sly, watchful eyes surveyed the crowd as if taking note of who was cheering Murad's family as they passed by. No one noticed him, however, as everyone's attention was directed towards

292

the three princes and the carriages following behind them. By now the news that these people were the long-incarcerated family of the late Sultan seemed to have reached everyone's ears, having spread like wildfire throughout the neighbourhood: there was sympathy for their sufferings and joy at their release in the eyes of all those lining the road. Tears streamed down Selahaddin's cheeks, yet he made no attempt to hide them from these people who were welcoming him so warmly as he rode past. When at last the carriages drove in through the gates of Hadice's waterfront mansion, everyone in the party from Çırağan was feeling both moved and profoundly humbled by this outpouring of love and respect on the part of the loyal people of İstanbul.

❁ ❁ ❁ ❁ ❁

Hadice and Fehime were waiting expectantly – and in Hadice's case, with extreme agitation – in the elegant salon overlooking the Bosphorus. Fehime was sitting at the piano playing a restful Chopin nocturne to settle her sister's nerves, while Aslan, having sensed his mistress's disquiet, lay curled up in her lap. Murad's two eldest daughters had not seen the other members of their family for nearly six years – ever since that day when they had left the Çırağan Palace, hoping to find suitable husbands under the guidance and protection of the Sultan. How bitterly they both regretted that fateful decision! For both of them, it had resulted in disastrously unhappy marriages – and, in the case of Hadice, shame and disgrace into the bargain. The sisters were both wearing gauze dresses of embroidered white silk with high lace necks and lace-trimmed sleeves. Hadice was also wearing a long string of pearls that was wrapped tightly three times around her neck and then fell to her waist, plus a pair of small pearl earrings. Fehime, meanwhile, was wearing the pale pink enamel-and-diamond butterfly brooch that her father had given her, set off by her favourite diamond-drop earrings. Within the family, she was affectionately nicknamed 'Kelebek Sultan' – 'Butterfly Princess' – owing to her predilection for gaily fluttering about, taking an interest in the latest fashions and all things beautiful. Sometimes Fehime found this somewhat superficial estimate of her character a little frustrating: in reality, behind the frivolous exterior she was not only passionately progressive and intensely patriotic, but also intelligent, accomplished, and a talented musician.

At last, the sound of horses' hooves and carriage wheels on the cobbles outside reached the two sisters' ears, and they stared wide-eyed at one another. Every instinct prompted them to run down the staircase, dash through the hall and hurry breathlessly out into the courtyard to welcome their relatives, but custom and propriety dictated that they remain in the drawing room and wait for their visitors to be announced. Although the wait was only a short one, to them it seemed like an eternity before the handles of the gilt-edged double doors of the salon slowly turned, and Hadice's High Hazinedar entered the room. As she bowed and laboriously enunciated the name of every single member of the party from Çırağan, the two sisters' eyes scanned the space beyond her, desperate for a sight of the loved ones who they knew would be waiting outside. Then the High Hazinedar withdrew, and Selahaddin led the way into the salon; conscious that Şayan was longing to embrace her daughter, he escorted her in on his arm, followed by the rest of the family in order of seniority.

Many tears were shed as Hadice and Fehime found themselves enveloped in a series of warm embraces. Şayan, unable to speak, kissed her daughter and cradled her head against her heart, while Hadice sobbed almost uncontrollably as the anguish of months of pent-up anxiety was released. How she had longed for the comfort and reassurance of her mother during that terrible time! And how she had missed her mother's unconditional love during the long years of their separation! Fehime was showered with kisses by her doting stepmothers Reftarıdil and Resan, both of whom loved her and Hadice as if they were their own daughters. Fatma, meanwhile, hugged her sisters tightly, crying as if the tears would never stop. She had missed them both desperately, especially since Aliye's death.

Selahaddin's daughters kissed their aunts' hands and in return received kisses of genuine love and affection on their rosy cheeks, now dampened by salty tears. Seeing how their aunts' dresses were cut according to the latest Paris fashion, their eyes opened wide in admiration; they also marvelled at their aunt Hadice's exquisite taste, remarking on the way the interior of the *yalı*, with its elegant white lacquer-and-gilt tables and chairs, was furnished in the most modern style. Naziknaz and Jalefer bowed before embracing their sisters-in-law, then complimented them both on their appearance, remarking how beautiful and how well they looked; they were very fond of Hadice and Fehime and had greatly missed their lively, vivacious company.

Selahaddin, Nihad and Fuad had stepped back after entering the salon in order to allow the women some intimate time together: this was certainly not an occasion for strict observance of protocol. Once the initial whirlwind of tears and embraces had subsided, Selahaddin approached his sisters. They each performed a respectful *temenna*, kissing their elder brother's hand and raising it to their forehead while bowing before him. Then, with tears in his eyes, Selahaddin drew each of his sisters close to him and held her in a long embrace. He, too, was overcome by the tide of intense emotion that had flooded the room, sweeping away years of suppressed longing.

"My dear brother, you have been through so much, but now *Inshallah* happier times lie ahead of us all," Fehime said, staring into his kind eyes. "How you must miss Father! My heart still aches for him every day, and I am sure it is the same for you." Selahaddin kissed his sister tenderly on the cheek; meanwhile, he noticed that she was wearing her butterfly brooch.

"Dear Selahaddin, how I have missed you, and how I have longed to escape my life here and return to you at Çırağan!" Hadice said, the tears returning to her eyes. Then she kissed her brother's hand once again and whispered to him: "I am so sorry for causing Father such heartache and bringing shame on our family. I will always be grateful to you for never losing faith in me, and for defending me to Sultan Hamid during my troubles. Thank you, dear brother."

"You owe me nothing at all, Hadice," Selahaddin said softly. "It is all forgotten."

Nihad and Fuad now came forward and formally greeted their aunts, kissing their hands and raising them to their foreheads. Hadice and Fehime, in turn, kissed them on their cheeks and smiled at their nephews.

"Fuad, how tall you have grown!" Hadice exclaimed. "You have turned into a young man since I last saw you." Fuad stood taller and puffed out his chest with pride. He did not really remember his aunts, but now he decided that he liked them both very much. "Before long you will be training at the Military Academy and commanding the Sultan's finest troops." Fuad beamed up at his aunt. It was his dream to become a soldier, and he was delighted to hear that his aunt thought him capable of fulfilling it.

"Dear Nihad," said Fehime, gently stroking her nephew's handsome face. "You have a wife and child now, I hear. *Alhamdulillah*!"

"Yes, Aunt Fehime," he replied. "May I introduce my wife, the Lady Safiru, and my son, Ali Vâsıb Efendi?"

Safiru was standing just within the doorway, holding Vâsıb's hand. She was feeling extremely anxious about meeting Hadice and Fehime again: the last time she had seen the two princesses was when she was a novice *kalfa* in Fatma's household, long before Nihad had noticed her. Although Safiru doubted that they would remember her, she remained just as much in awe of the refined, elegant sisters as she had always been. She walked forward apprehensively with Vâsıb, keeping her eyes lowered as she bowed and kissed the princesses' hands.

"It is lovely to see you again, Lady Safiru," Hadice and Fehime said warmly, almost in unison.

"Your son is so beautiful, and he looks so strong!" said Fehime, smiling down at the fair-haired little boy.

"Thank you, Princess Fehime," Safiru replied, her eyes still respectfully lowered.

"He is indeed a very beautiful child," Hadice added. She bent down to kiss him, gazing with tenderness into his forget-me-not-blue eyes and running her fingers through his fine, blond curls. She yearned for a child of her own, but knew that as long as she remained married to her uncouth monster of a husband, her dream of becoming a mother would never come true. "I keep some toys in a chest for times when children come to visit, which sadly are so rare," she said. "I love to hear the sound of their laughter filling my house as they play. I will ask Fetânıfer Kalfa to bring it for Vâsıb." Hadice had originally bought the toys for Cahid and Adile, Kemaleddin and Naime's two young children; before news of the scandal broke, they had often visited her *yalı* with their mother. She missed their playful giggles, as indeed she missed their mother's friendship – and most of all, of course, their father's love for her.

Everybody sat down and was offered sherbets and an array of delicacies and fruits by the *kalfas*. Şayan sat next to Hadice, her eyes never leaving her daughter's face – a face that was now radiant with the happiness that only release from long torment can bestow. The chest of toys was brought in and Vâsıb sat with Fuad on the soft carpet, helping him build towers with brightly-coloured wooden blocks; Vâsıb let out a cry of delight each time one of the ungainly structures toppled over and crashed to the floor. Jalefer and Rukiye took it in turns to play pieces on the piano, while Hadice and Fehime asked Selahaddin to tell them about Murad's final weeks; after a tearful interlude during which Selahaddin described everything that had happened, they dried their eyes and enquired about the household staff at Çırağan.

Adile, Safiye and Atiye petted Aslan, who was loving all the attention. Meanwhile, Nihad watched them with interest from the other side of the room. Finally, he plucked up courage and came over to make the acquaintance of this strange creature which like its less privileged cousins on the road outside seemed to enjoy human contact. He soon discovered that it liked having its ears played with, and was shocked when it suddenly put out its tongue and licked his face. Nihad drew back in alarm, much to his sisters' amusement, and asked a *kalfa* to bring a bowl of water and a towel so that he could wash away the traces of the creature's saliva.

Aslan was returned to his basket, and Adile, Safiye and Atiye begged their aunts – in between sips of sherbet and bites of cake – to recount stories of their experiences at court. They were especially curious to hear about the moving pictures that they knew were occasionally shown in the theatre at Yıldız; Fuad, too, was interested, and for a moment stopped playing with the wooden blocks to listen. Then the sisters asked about the private performance of 'La Dame aux Camélias' that had taken place the year before – the leading role had been played by Sarah Bernhardt, the internationally-famous French stage actress. Behiye was eager to know about the occasion when Hadice and Fehime had met Empress Augusta Victoria of Germany during her visit to İstanbul with her husband, the Kaiser; this had happened soon after they had left Çırağan.

"So what was the Empress like?" Behiye asked.

"I do not think she is a very intelligent woman, although her manner seemed quite serious," Fehime replied. "She is neither beautiful nor ugly; however, she always has a kind, gentle expression on her face."

"We met her at a reception held in the Grand Salon of the Imperial Lodge at Yıldız Palace," Hadice broke in. "She entered the room on Sultan Hamid's arm, and his youngest daughter Princess Refia presented her with a beautiful bouquet of flowers. She then sat between the Sultan and Perestu Valide Sultan, his adoptive mother, on a large sofa in the centre of the room."

"We had been warned by Hamid to behave with the utmost decorum during the reception," said Fehime. "Actually, I think this warning was mainly directed at his sisters, Princess Seniha and Princess Mediha, both of whom can be a little unrestrained at times! They took no heed whatsoever of his warning, however, and chattered and giggled noisily through-out the proceedings. Afterwards Hamid felt the need to apologise to the Empress for his sisters' behaviour, making the excuse that they had been nervous, which was certainly not the case!" Everyone laughed: the two senior princesses' ebullience was well known!

"Does the Empress speak any Turkish?" Safiye enquired.

"No," said Fehime, "not one word. We spoke to her in French; as you know, Hadice and I learned French from Father and the Lady Gevherriz, so we were able to converse directly with the Empress, which I think rather irritated the Sultan. The Valide Sultan, Hamid's wives and most of the other princesses there had to speak to her through the medium of the daughter of Artin Dadyan Pasha, the Undersecretary of State for Foreign Affairs, who was acting as interpreter."

"She spoke mainly of her children," said Hadice. "She has seven children – six sons and one daughter. She has surely been blessed. I remember thinking how amazing it was that she did not look plumper than she did. She must take great care over what she eats in order to keep her figure – I say this because I saw her refuse all the sweetmeats she was offered."

"And what did you wear, Aunt Fehime?" asked Atiye.

"Sultan Hamid had instructed everyone to wear white dresses, our Imperial orders and decorations, and our finest jewels and tiaras," Fehime replied. "I think his intention was for us to dazzle the Empress."

"I think she really was dazzled, and also very surprised to see us wearing such fashionable French dresses," Hadice added. "She complimented the Valide Sultan on her gown, and also asked to look closer at the Senior Ustas' costume, which she greatly admired."

"I remember that she made a few disparaging remarks about the English, criticising their liberal politics and their lack of morality," said Fehime. "I found that surprising, but it amused the Sultan a great deal. She obviously dislikes the English almost as much as he does!"

300

"Kaiser Wilhelm detests the English, so perhaps she has adopted some of her husband's sentiments," said Selahaddin.

"But why should the Kaiser hate the English, Baba, when his own mother was an English princess?" asked Rukiye.

"His mother was not an English princess, Rukiye, but a German one from the House of Saxe-Coburg and Gotha. By a strange twist of fate, a German prince of this house now wears the English crown, which I believe irks the Kaiser somewhat," replied Selahaddin. "He thinks that since the House of Hohenzollern once ruled Prussia, the mightiest of the German states, and now rules the united Germany, it should be the most powerful of the German houses on the world stage. The reason for the Kaiser's feelings of jealousy towards his cousin King Edward is that he covets his vastly more extensive empire, and of course his larger and more powerful navy. This resentment has led both to Germany's current interest in North Africa and to her race to build up her fleet. The Kaiser's almost fanatical obsession with Empire-building is, I fear, a most dangerous thing."

"I have heard rumours that the Kaiser's hatred actually stems from a psychological complex that is due to his deformed arm – something he blames on the ineptitude of the English doctor who delivered him," Hadice said.

At that moment, the door opened and Hadice's High Hazinedar entered. "Forgive me for disturbing you, Princess Hadice, but the carriages have returned to take Prince Selahaddin and his family back to the Çırağan Palace."

"Already?" exclaimed Fatma.

Selahaddin looked at his gold pocket watch. He was wearing the Breguet watch that had once belonged to both his grandfather and his father, and was dismayed to see that it was already three o'clock. Cevher Ağa had told Selahaddin that Hamid insisted that they return to the palace before half past three.

"Yes, I am afraid it is time to go," he said, "but we will be back for another visit very soon. Maybe, Fehime, we can come to your *yalı* next week, and then we can all call on Hadice together?"

"That would be wonderful," his sister replied, her face lighting up at the prospect of hosting her family in the villa next door.

"That is settled, then. I will write to Hamid on our return to request the necessary permission. Come, everyone, we must take our leave: I do not want to anger the Sultan by returning late from our first excursion." Selahaddin then turned to Hadice. "My dear sister," he said, "I know that you forbid your husband to enter your quarters in the harem, and that he confines himself to the *selamlık*, but I would like to visit him there before I go."

"Why ever would you want to do that?" she replied, suddenly angry at her brother's suggestion.

"Because I have visited his house, and I feel it is my duty to pay my respects to him out of courtesy, since you have forbidden him to pay his to me," was the terse reply.

"It is my house, Selahaddin, not his," Hadice returned defiantly. "It is therefore not necessary for you to see him at all."

"I know it is not necessary that I visit him, my dear Hadice, but I am of the opinion that it is right and proper that I should do so," he answered with a firmness that showed he was not to be swayed from his resolve. Selahaddin kissed Hadice on the cheek and thanked her for her most generous hospitality. Turning to the rest of the family, he said: "I will meet you all at the carriages in ten minutes, after you have said your goodbyes." Then, after kissing Fehime, he left the room.

۞ ۞ ۞ ۞ ۞

Selahaddin followed a eunuch to the part of the house where the *selamlık* was located. When he entered Vasıf Pasha's study he was not at all sure what to expect, but even so he was completely unprepared for the sight that now met his eyes: a scrawny, unshaven, dishevelled-looking man lay slumped over some cushions with a narguile in his hand. Vasıf staggered to his feet, trying ineffectually to straighten his cravat and his jacket as he did so. He gave a bow that was quite obviously delivered with reluctance, and mumbled an apology for the state of his appearance.

"Vasıf Pasha, I am sorry to disturb you, but before taking my leave after visiting my sister I wanted to meet you."

Vasıf looked uncomfortable. Clearly, he had no intention of inviting Selahaddin to sit down or offering him a cup of coffee. Instead, he stood there playing with his thick, unkempt moustache in a vain attempt to make it appear a little more respectable. "So you must be Prince Selahaddin Efendi," he stuttered after a long pause. A lop-sided grimace now appeared on his face. "On the rare occasions when I am in the company of your sister, she speaks of you with an affection that she has always denied me."

Selahaddin was rendered speechless by the man's rudeness, and felt the anger bubbling up inside him. How could Abdülhamid possibly have been so brutally insensitive as to disgrace his sister and his family by marrying Hadice off to such a vulgar, surly, indolent buffoon? Having done his duty and paid his respects, he was desperate to get back to the carriages waiting outside before he said something that might provoke a most distressing altercation with a man who possessed no shame of any kind. "Unfortunately, I am obliged to return home straight away, so I bid you good day," was all he managed to blurt out. Vasıf had slumped back onto the cushions even before Selahaddin had turned to leave.

303

When he arrived in the courtyard, trying to restore himself to calmness and equanimity, he found everyone ready to depart. The ladies were waiting in the carriages, and Nihad and Fuad were sitting on their mounts. Hadice and Fehime, who had put on their *feraces* and *yashmaks*, had come down to wave goodbye. Selahaddin walked up to Hadice and said to her quietly: "I vow to you that I will set you free from that despicable man; I promise that I will obtain for you the annulment you seek." He then mounted his horse and rode out of the gates without looking behind him.

CHAPTER SIXTEEN

A Mysterious Death

April 1905

S PRING was proceeding apace; all over İstanbul tulips
were in bloom, nodding their curvaceous heads in the
breeze. For centuries the beauty and splendour of these
flowers, each one like a brightly-coloured miniature turban,
had inspired Ottoman art and design; images of them had
been woven into luxurious carpets, embroidered on fine
textiles in silk thread and reproduced on ceramic tiles. But
for all the elegance of these human imitations, nothing could
compare with the natural beauty of Allah's creation.

April had always been Selahaddin's favourite month. What
gave him the greatest pleasure this particular April was having
the freedom to take his children on the occasional carriage ride
and show them the splendour of the Imperial capital. Great
changes had taken place in the city during the years he had
spent languishing in captivity in the Çırağan Palace. He was
particularly dismayed to see the once mighty Ottoman fleet
lying at anchor in the Golden Horn, where Abdülhamid had
left it to rot; he was, however, excited to discover that the
Sultan had built a large number of modern schools and
institutions of higher learning in the city, as well as many
hospitals and factories. The Imperial capital appeared to

Selahaddin to be as cosmopolitan and diverse as it always had been, but far more populous: it was swarming with people – to a far greater extent than it had been before. He told himself, however, that the reason why he felt this way was that he had become unused to crowds.

A few days after their visit to Hadice's mansion, Selahaddin and Nihad had been invited to attend their first *Selamlık* ceremony – this being the Sultan's weekly procession to attend Friday prayers at the Hamidiye Mosque, just outside the gates of Yıldız Palace; it was always a grand occasion. Unlike the other senior Imperial princes, neither of them had yet been given an honorary military commission, so they had no squadrons of men to lead in the procession. Instead, when giving the traditional salute to the Sultan after prayers, they each rode alongside the prince immediately above them in the order of precedence – Selahaddin beside Mehmed Vahideddin and Nihad beside Mahmud Necmeddin, the Crown Prince's middle son. Also, Selahaddin had not yet been received in audience by the Sultan; outside the mosque that day, however, he had held Abdülhamid's eye for a moment, and thought he saw the Sultan give him a subtle nod and a slight smile. As a result, he now felt sure that an invitation to Court and the granting of a commission in the army would soon follow.

During the *Selamlık*, Selahaddin had particularly enjoyed seeing his uncles Ahmed Kemaleddin, Selim Süleyman and Mehmed Vahideddin, all of whom he remembered vividly from his childhood. While everyone was assembling for the procession in the courtyard at Yıldız Palace, Kemaleddin had been the first to approach him – ignoring the rules of protocol in doing so. He had dismounted and embraced his nephew, displaying genuine affection for him. Appreciating that Selahaddin and Nihad must be feeling apprehensive, Kemaleddin had then introduced them first to his younger brothers, then to the other princes who were attending the ceremony that day; these included Selahaddin's old playmates Prince Yusuf İzzeddin Efendi and Prince Abdülmecid Efendi, the two eldest sons of Sultan Abdülaziz. Mehmed Reşad, the Crown Prince, had not been present that day – in fact, he was rarely granted permission to attend – so Kemaleddin had been the most senior prince in the gathering as he was next in line for the throne. In spite of this, he had shown no trace of arrogance or pretension – only consideration for the difficult position his nephews found themselves in.

Kemaleddin had perhaps been Murad's favourite brother. Murad had admired his enthusiastic attitude towards life, and had shared his dream of creating a liberal, modern empire. Kemaleddin, in turn, had adored and respected his elder brother; he had devotedly followed him into the Brotherhood of Freemasons, and had never believed the propaganda to the effect that he had been unfit to rule. So great had been his conviction that Murad should be restored to the throne, in fact, that he had plotted with Ali Suavi, the notorious radical, to rescue him from Çırağan so that he could once again be Sultan. Although this attempt had been unsuccessful, by lending his support to it Kemaleddin had proved his unswerving loyalty to his brother – something that Murad never forgot, and that he took great pains to ensure that Selahaddin, too, remembered. Although Abdülhamid remained in ignorance of Kemaleddin's involvement in the plot, he was only too aware of his brother's dangerously liberal tendencies, and had therefore placed him under close surveillance.

Süleyman and Vahideddin were much closer in age to Selahaddin than they were to his father; in their youth, therefore, they had been more like brothers to him than uncles. Süleyman had been born the year before Selahaddin, and

Vahideddin was a mere seven months older than his nephew. Selahaddin had sorely missed them both during his years of confinement. On seeing them in the courtyard at Yıldız before the procession began, he had recognised them instantly; instead of seeing the middle-aged princes with greying hair and thick moustaches that they had actually become, however, he saw instead the carefree faces of the young men they had once been. For him it had been not only an emotional reunion but also a most happy and satisfying one.

☙ ☙ ☙ ☙ ☙

After the day when he had attended the *Selamlık*, Selahaddin was permitted to call on Kemaleddin at his suite within the Crown Prince's residence at Dolmabahçe. Being second in line for the throne, Kemaleddin shared this residence with his elder brother Reşad. On the occasions when he visited Dolmabahçe, Selahaddin always found his uncles Süleyman and Vahideddin there too: Süleyman lived with his family at the Feriye Palace, which stood next to Çırağan, while Vahideddin lived in a mansion on his personal estate in Çengelköy. This mansion, which he had had rebuilt to his own design, had previously belonged to Kemaleddin – who had, however, been forced to sell it to pay off his debts; Abdülhamid had bought it, and had given it to his youngest brother, who was also his favourite among them.

Nihad and Behiye usually accompanied Selahaddin on these weekly visits. Behiye was slightly younger than Princess Münire, Kemaleddin's only child, but she soon developed a close relationship with her cousin. While the princesses amused themselves, the princes generally discussed politics. So when Selahaddin, Kemaleddin, Süleyman and Vahideddin came together at Dolmabahçe towards the end of April, the topic of conversation was the one the whole of Europe was talking about – the precarious balance of power that they feared was being threatened by Germany's recent, and highly provocative, challenge to French interests in Morocco.

Morocco was the last independent country in North Africa, her independence having been assured by an international convention in 1880. However, following the signing in April 1904 of the Entente Cordiale, which settled – temporarily, at least – the imperialist rivalries that had resulted in the 'Scramble for Africa', France had contravened the convention by sending troops into Morocco from Algiers, thus expanding her sphere of influence westwards with the tacit support of Britain. The Sultan of Morocco had been powerless to stop the advance of the French forces, and had lost control of vast swathes of his territory.

At the end of March 1905 the Kaiser had landed in Tangiers, ostensibly in support of the Moroccan Sultan. He had given a speech in which he declared that he recognised Moroccan independence, promising German support; then, posing as the saviour of the Moroccan nation, he rode through the city on a white stallion amid great pomp and ceremony. Few, however, were fooled by his antics: it was generally understood that the Kaiser's real intention was to try to unsettle the Entente by driving a wedge between the French and the British – who were not pleased with their allies for giving Germany an excuse to move into Morocco.

"It looks as if he really believes he is a great emperor, just like Sultan Mehmed II, the Conqueror of İstanbul," Kemaleddin remarked. "As you know, after taking the city he entered Constantinople on a white stallion, but in his case there were valid reasons for him to make a statement of that kind. However, I fear the Kaiser's vanity is very much misplaced!" His brothers all nodded in agreement.

309

"The British will not want Germany to gain any influence in Morocco," Selahaddin commented. "These ill-conceived actions on the part of the Kaiser are bound to create further tensions, and will only serve to strengthen the alliance between Britain and France – the very alliance that Germany finds so threatening."

"Why is that, Father?" Nihad asked.

"Your father is quite right," Kemaleddin interjected. "Morocco is very close to Gibraltar, which is strategically a very important place – one that commands the entrance to the Mediterranean Sea – so the British will do everything in their power to prevent a German naval base being built so close to it. Britain is already wary of the German navy's growing strength, and the Kaiser's latest actions will only exacerbate that concern."

"What worries me is that now that Britain and France have forged their unlikely alliance, this shift in the European balance of power will have a devastating impact on us," said Vahideddin. "Once they have finished subjugating Africa, they will turn their avaricious eyes towards our lands."

"Do not worry, Vahideddin," Kemaleddin said. "You are too easily unnerved. There is no need to feel intimidated by the Western nations. They have always been too preoccupied quarrelling amongst themselves to be a serious threat to our empire. They are so consumed with jealousy and so suspicious of each other that as long as we do not get involved in their squabbles, they can do us little harm."

"I have heard it said that Germany will soon be more powerful than both Britain and France," Süleyman said. "The Kaiser is expanding and strengthening not only his navy but his army too; people say that German advances in military technology will eventually make her far stronger than any other nation in the world."

"That may be," replied Kemaleddin, "but do not be deceived by their much-vaunted claims of military might. Personally, I do not trust the Germans any more than I trust the British or the French. In my opinion, we should trust no one: we should concern ourselves exclusively with our own problems – which are many, and as we all know in urgent need of solution. We should certainly not allow ourselves to get mixed up in the politics of the West."

The discussion then turned to the question of constitutional and social reform. Kemaleddin was neither as philosophical in his attitude as Selahaddin nor as ideological as Nihad; he was, however, far more passionate and impulsive by nature than either of them. They reacted with alarm to his admission that he had surreptitiously met with members of secret opposition societies and warned him to take great care, saying that participating in such meetings could be extremely dangerous for him. Kemaleddin reassured them: he said he was aware that Abdülhamid's spies followed him everywhere, so he always took every necessary precaution. He added that he had no wish to see any more attempts to interfere with the order of succession, so he prayed that one day his brother would voluntarily agree to abandon absolute rule and introduce constitutional government as a means of revitalising the Empire. Nihad was deeply impressed by his great-uncle, and understood immediately the reasons why his father was so fond of him.

Selahaddin and his children were relaxing in the harem gardens, enjoying the warmth of the spring sunshine. That morning they had received a note from Kemaleddin saying that he intended to call at Çırağan that afternoon as he had a surprise for them. Everyone was very excited, and also mystified: they could not imagine what their impetuous, kind-hearted uncle had organised. While they were waiting for his arrival, Fuad and the princesses were playing a game of badminton on the lawn. There was not a breath of wind to disturb the flight of the shuttlecock, and its white goose feathers barely fluttered as it was hit over the net. Fuad was partnering his eldest sister Behiye; they had just beaten Rukiye and Atiye quite decisively, and were now ahead in their game against the 'twins', Adile and Safiye. Fatma had been appointed umpire in the hope that she would be able to avert the family disagreements that habitually accompanied their games!

Selahaddin and Nihad watched from the sidelines, drinking mandarin sherbets and clapping each time someone hit a winning shot. Although he was the youngest, Fuad was easily the most athletic of them all, and certainly the most competitive: he darted about the court, lunging energetically to reach every shot.

"It disappoints me that I have not yet been permitted to pay my respects to Prince Reşad," Selahaddin said to his son. "He is the most sweet-natured of my uncles, not to mention the most devout, and it saddens me greatly to think of him living in the Crown Prince's apartment like a recluse."

"It is a shame that Hamid is so suspicious of his brothers, Father. I cannot imagine ever mistrusting Fuad in that way," Nihad remarked. His father smiled at him.

"Power does strange things to men, my son," Selahaddin said, his manner becoming more serious. "You must promise me that if fate should ever confer great power on you, you will never allow it to alter your character."

"I certainly hope I never will, Father," Nihad replied. "I trust in Allah to guide me, and I pray that whatever my fate may be, He may bestow on me strength and wisdom." Then, after a moment's thought, he added: "It may well be that it is because Hamid showed himself capable of betraying his older brother and usurping his throne that he believes his younger brothers are capable of doing the same to him," Nihad mused.

"Thankfully, my other uncles are nothing like Hamid," his father replied. "There is not one among them who would even contemplate such a thing. These are dangerous times, as I have told you many times before. If the Sultan can go so far as to mistrust even Prince Reşad, then no one is safe from his paranoia."

While Selahaddin and Nihad were inwardly going over the implications of this disturbing statement, Fuad shouted out in triumph: he and Behiye had won their game. Now he ran over to his father and brother. "That was such fun!" he said, trying to catch his breath after his exertions. "Behiye and I now challenge you, Baba, and you, Nihad!"

Selahaddin laughed. "So you think you can beat us too, do you?" he asked.

"Perhaps! At any rate, we will try," answered Fuad with a rather cheeky grin. He took hold of his father's hand and led him eagerly onto the court. Nihad followed, taking off his jacket and rolling up his sleeves; he picked up a discarded racket that was lying on the ground and made himself ready to play. Meanwhile, his sisters sat on the grass to watch the fun, not caring that their white linen dresses might be ruined by grass stains, and Fatma resumed her position at the side of the net to umpire the game.

☹ ☹ ☹ ☹ ☹

Half an hour later the game had finished, and everyone was enjoying the cool refreshment of iced mandarin sherbets. The tightly-contested match had been won by Fuad and Behiye; unbeknownst to them, however, their father had purposely hit his last shot into the net in order to give them their much-desired victory!

Just then, Tirendaz Kalfa approached the family to announce the arrival of Kemaleddin, and Selahaddin asked her to show him into the garden. He appeared almost immediately – before Selahaddin and Nihad had even had time to unroll their sleeves and put on their jackets.

"There is no need for jackets," Kemaleddin said, seeing Selahaddin and Nihad reach for them. His handsome face, so similar to Murad's, wore a beaming smile as he walked through the harem parterre and strode across the lawn towards the family. "It is a warm day, and in fact it will be better if you do not wear them – as you will understand once you have seen the surprise I have for you." Selahaddin and Nihad looked at each other, perplexed.

"Welcome to Çırağan, Uncle," Selahaddin said with a bow. "You do us a great honour by visiting us today." Kemaleddin, not being one for strict protocol or formality, embraced his nephew affectionately, then turned towards the others. Having met Nihad and Behiye at the Dolmabahçe Palace during their visits with their father, he instantly recognised them, and greeted them first.

"And you must be Princess Fatma," he said, addressing his niece before Selahaddin had had chance to make the proper introductions. "I know how much my brother loved you," he continued, taking both her hands in his and kissing her gently on the forehead. "When he wrote to inform me of your birth, telling me that you were to be named after our dearest and most unfortunate sister, I knew immediately that you would be special to me, too. I see it as my duty to my brother, and as a matter of honour, to act as your father in his stead. Of course no one can ever replace Murad, but I would like you to know that should you ever have need of anything, you can always come to me." Fatma was genuinely touched by this speech, which had suddenly brought to mind her father's love for her, and for a time struggled to hold back the tears. Then she thanked her uncle, and assured him that she would do as he had asked.

Selahaddin chose this moment to introduce Kemaleddin first to Fuad, then to his four younger daughters. They all kissed their uncle's hand in greeting, and Fatma handed him a glass of sherbet. He accepted it gratefully, being parched with thirst after the ride along the dusty road to Ortaköy.

"You have your grandfather's eyes, Fuad," Kemaleddin said. "In fact, you look very much like him when he was a boy. *Mashallah!*" Fuad was delighted by this compliment. "Tell me, are you brave?"

"Certainly I am, Uncle. I want to be a soldier when I grow up. I want to fight our empire's enemies," Fuad replied boldly, puffing out his chest and drawing himself up to his full height.

Kemaleddin smiled at this display of youthful enthusiasm – it reminded him vividly of himself as a child. "As the great Aristotle once said, *'You will never achieve anything in this world without courage. Next to honour, it is the greatest quality of the mind.'* Remember that, and I am certain that one day you will be a brilliant, daring and talented officer. Our enemies will run from your blade," he said affectionately, ruffling the young boy's hair. "It is good that you are fearless, Fuad, for my surprise will require you to show great courage," Kemaleddin said. That remark made Fuad even more mystified than before, increasing his sense of anticipation.

Although Selahaddin had already formally introduced them to him, Kemaleddin now asked Behiye to introduce her sisters once again, more slowly this time. He spoke to each of them in turn, showing interest in all they said and delighting in their innocence and charm. Atiye told him all about the kitten she had recently rescued from the streets, and had named 'Kaplan' on account of his shiny ginger-and-black striped coat. When she had finished, Kemaleddin put down his empty sherbet glass, and a mischievous look stole across his face; addressing the whole gathering, he asked everyone to turn around and keep their eyes closed. "And that includes you, Selahaddin," he said, noticing that his nephew was under the impression that the request had been directed only to the younger family members.

Kemaleddin then beckoned to Zülüflü Ağa and Kasım Ağa, who were in attendance a little distance away. He whispered something to them, and they disappeared. Within a minute or two both eunuchs reappeared with the presents Kemaleddin had brought with him. This time they had with them the two young *kalfas* Nezihe and Nevrestan, who were holding neatly-wrapped packages in their arms. "You can turn around now!" Kemaleddin announced.

Selahaddin, his children and Fatma all swung round. It took a second or two for them to focus their eyes on the strange objects standing in front of them. Then there was a squeal of delight from Fuad, who was the first to realise what they were. "Please accept these small gifts as tokens of my love and affection," Kemaleddin said. He was generous by nature, a trait that a few years before had led to his financial ruin and the loss of his private estate.

He distributed the packages to the princesses first. Each one was tied with a different-coloured satin ribbon. The princesses eagerly untied the bows and unfolded the brown wrapping paper. Inside each parcel was a piece of Bursa silk; the texture was the finest they had ever run through their fingers, and the panels of lacework were the most intricate

316

they had ever seen. A feeling of warmth entered Kemaleddin's heart as he watched their reaction and saw the happiness spread across their faces. "I am told by my daughter's dressmaker that there is enough fabric here for each of you to commission a court dress. I am certain that you will soon be invited to Court, so I wanted you to have something suitable to wear." The princesses gasped in disbelief. They already had many beautiful dresses, but none made of such exquisite material. They thanked their uncle profusely; when they tried to kiss his hand, he pulled them into an embrace and kissed them on their foreheads.

"Come, this is for you, Selahaddin," Kemaleddin said, smiling as he indicated the largest of the three objects before them. Selahaddin still could not tell what it was, never having seen a device of this kind before; he hesitated before thanking his uncle. "Come and sit on the seat," Kemaleddin said, gesturing to him. Everyone watched in silence as Selahaddin walked towards the strange metal object and sat down on its leather saddle. "Now, hold on to these handle bars, put your feet on these pedals down here and just … push down on them!" Selahaddin looked bemused and rather sceptical, but he did as his uncle had instructed. The three wheels attached to the body of the contraption began to turn, and he started to move slowly forward.

"This thing is called a tricycle!" announced Kemaleddin excitedly. "It was manufactured in Paris, and is apparently the very latest model. Keep pedalling, Selahaddin. You can go much faster than that, actually, but do not forget to use the handle bars to steer yourself, or you will end up pedalling straight into the Bosphorus!" Everyone laughed. Seeing their father perched on the tricycle looking rather suspicious but at the same time fascinated by this unusual method of locomotion, the princesses erupted into fits of giggles.

"Now, Nihad and Fuad, these two bicycles are for you."
Fuad ran towards the smaller one, clambered onto the seat
and started pedalling furiously before Kemaleddin had had
chance to warn him to take care; within seconds, he had fallen
off. "These only have two wheels, Fuad, so you have to be
careful to keep your balance. It takes a lot of practice to
master them, so please take things slowly. If you are too
hasty, your mother will scold me for getting your knees
grazed and your clothes torn," Kemaleddin told him. "Come,
try again. You need to pedal and steer in the same way as
your father did, but you must try to maintain a perfect
balance. You will fall off many times before you learn, of
course, but if you persist I promise that you will find it highly
enjoyable."

"This is the most wonderful present anyone has ever given
me, Uncle Kemaleddin. Thank you … thank you very much,"
said Fuad, unable to contain his excitement and the sense of
wonder he was feeling. Kemaleddin then showed Zülüflü
Ağa how to help the young prince by holding the bicycle seat
steady as he climbed back on and began to pedal.

"All right, Nihad, now it is your turn. You saw what your
brother was doing – just try to do the same." Nihad looked
terrified. "Stay off the paths and keep to the lawns: then when
you fall off it will be less painful," said Kemaleddin, laughing.
Kasım Ağa came forward to help Nihad steady himself.

Turning to the princesses with a smile, Kemaleddin said:
"That will keep your father and your brothers busy for a
while. So which of my beautiful nieces would like to play
badminton with me?"

By the end of the afternoon Fuad was cycling unaided: he
was racing through the gardens weaving figures of eight
around each copse of trees with no thought whatever for his
safety. Nihad, meanwhile, was finding cycling much harder

318

to grasp, but he had still managed to complete a few unsteady laps around the gardens without falling off or crashing into a tree; his brow was furrowed with intense concentration as he wobbled forward at a slow and deliberate pace. He was, in fact, looking forward to examining the contraption later: the mechanics of the thing fascinated him. Selahaddin, for his part, was exhausted after his game of badminton and all the pedalling he had done. Unused to so much exercise, he had fallen asleep in his wicker chair while watching his uncle play badminton with his daughters.

It had been one of the most enjoyable afternoons anyone could remember. Unfortunately, Abdülhamid had granted permission for Selahaddin to receive his uncle at Çırağan for a duration of only two hours, so the time soon came when Kemaleddin was obliged to take his leave. Before going, however, he invited everyone to call on him at Dolmabahçe Palace the following Wednesday afternoon, saying that he wanted to introduce his daughter to the cousins she had not yet met.

❀ ❀ ❀ ❀ ❀

Wednesday 26th April 1905

When Tirendaz Kalfa entered Selahaddin's study, he was sitting at his desk writing in his journal, as he often did. Selahaddin had started consigning his thoughts and feelings to paper soon after coming to live at Çırağan, and had filled many leather-bound notebooks with his accounts of daily life and his philosophical reflections. On this occasion, he was so immersed in his work that he did not look up.

"I am sorry to disturb you, Sir, but there is someone here to see you."

"Someone to see me? Who is it, Tirendaz Kalfa? I have

no appointments today – not until my family and I visit my uncle this afternoon, anyway," he replied.

"An Ağa in the personal service of Prince Kemaleddin is requesting an audience with you, Sir. He says he has a message of the utmost importance to impart."

"Very well, then, you may show him in, I suppose," Selahaddin said, closing his journal. He put the silver lid over the lead nib of his pencil and replaced the monogrammed pencil holder on his desk.

A moment later, a tall, handsome Sudanese eunuch entered the room and bowed before him. Selahaddin recognised the man from the times when he had called on Kemaleddin at Dolmabahçe. The eunuch was one of his uncle's equerries, and had escorted him to Kemaleddin's private chambers on several occasions. He immediately noticed that the man's boots were dirty; his frock coat was splattered with mud, and his cravat was askew. Even though the morning was cool and wet, he looked hot and flustered; his dark eyes were blood-shot, and seemed filled with anguish. Selahaddin saw that beads of sweat were glistening on the man's brow beneath the crimson fez, and his hands were trembling with nervous-ness as he clasped and unclasped them. It was clear that in order to communicate his message as quickly as possible he had run along the muddy street that separated the Dolma-bahçe Palace from Çırağan.

"Whatever is the matter?" Selahaddin asked. "And how come I have received no notification of your visit?" On the surface Selahaddin appeared disgruntled, but inwardly he was gripped by a sudden sense of foreboding.

"Forgive the intrusion, Sir. I waited near the tradesmen's gate, and was able to slip past the guards when the butcher arrived to deliver his meat. I then followed him to the kitchens, where I asked to speak to your Senior Kalfa. I explained to her that I had been sent by Princess Münire to deliver an urgent message, and she brought me to your apartment," the equerry replied, keeping his eyes respectfully lowered all the while.

All this was highly irregular, and Selahaddin knew only too well that if Cevher Ağa were ever to hear about this illicit visit, the new privileges he and his family had recently been enjoying might well be withdrawn. However, he also knew that if Princess Münire had decided that the risk of discovery was worth taking, then the message must indeed be important. Unable to think of any reason why Kemaleddin's equerry should be carrying out such a strange errand, Selahaddin was becoming more and more confused. "Very well, then. What is this message?" he asked.

The eunuch took a deep breath before answering. Then he blurted out: "My master, His Imperial Highness Prince Ahmed Kemaleddin Efendi, died this morning. May his soul rest in peace."

Selahaddin could hardly breathe. He could feel his chest tightening; his heart was pounding at an alarming rate, and his stomach was beginning to churn. He briefly whispered a prayer for his uncle's soul. Then he asked: "But how can this be? When Prince Kemaleddin visited me a few days ago, he appeared to be in the very best of health and spirits. Has he been ill?" He was trying his best to keep his voice calm and steady – but without much success.

"No, Your Imperial Highness, he has not been ill – *Alhamdulillah* he always enjoyed good health." The distraught equerry stuttered and stammered as he recalled the events of that morning: he told Selahaddin how just after sunrise a Pasha had arrived at the Dolmabahçe Palace, accompanied by three men dressed in the uniform of the Sultan's personal guard. These men, he said, were impos-

321

ingly tall and looked violent and ferocious; he described how the Pasha, speaking in stern and authoritative tones, had demanded to be taken immediately to Prince Kemaleddin's private chambers, and had pushed past anyone who stood in his way. The eunuch then described how the Pasha had burst through the door of the prince's bedchamber without waiting to be announced.

"I tried to stop the guards from following the Pasha into my master's bedchamber, but one of them put his hand around my throat and squeezed until I could no longer breathe," the man continued. "He then tossed me against the wall of the corridor so that I hit my head, and I fell to the floor. I must have been unconscious for some time, because when I finally came round everything was quiet, and the Pasha and his soldiers were gone. I went into my master's bedchamber, but Prince Kemaleddin was not there. I searched every room in the apartment, but there was no trace of him, and none of the servants was able to tell me with any certainty what had happened to him."

Selahaddin was aghast; his mouth had gone dry, and the pounding in his heart was getting worse the more he heard of this terrible story. The eunuch went on: "I found that the household had been told that Prince Kemaleddin had died during the night, and that after receiving a message to this effect the Pasha had come to remove the body so that it could be prepared and taken for burial." Here he paused, and the look of anguish on his face deepened. "Your Imperial Highness, I have to tell you that some sinister rumours are already beginning to circulate. A long silk scarf was found lying crumpled up on the floor next to His Highness' bed, and this has led Princess Münire to fear that the prince may have been strangled in his chamber, and his body then carried from the palace."

Of the rest of the account Selahaddin heard but little. His mind had drifted back to that sunny afternoon only a few days before when Kemaleddin had visited Çırağan. He could still hear his uncle's raucous laughter as he watched his great-nephews learn how to ride the bicycles he had bought for them, and as he played badminton with his giggling great-nieces. The equerry had not noticed that Selahaddin's eyes had glazed over, however, and was waiting for a response.

"My uncle Prince Kemaleddin was a good and honourable man, and he will be greatly missed by us all. We should not, however, jump to any rash conclusions. Instead, we must pray that his soul may have a smooth transition to paradise." The equerry bowed.

Selahaddin removed his spectacles and pinched the bridge of his nose – in doing so shielding his eyes, which were full of tears, with his hand. "Please thank Princess Münire for informing me of this tragic affair. The poor, gentle creature – she must be utterly distraught at losing her father in such terrible circumstances," he said with a sad shake of the head. "But now you must return to her at once: she will have great need of you," he added, regaining something of his composure. "Please tell the princess that she may turn to me at any time if there is anything I can do for her. And remember to take the utmost care as you leave: you must not be seen by any of the Yıldız Palace spies."

The eunuch bowed again and backed out of the room – leaving Selahaddin to grieve in private. And as if this were not enough, he knew that he now had the task of informing all his family that the man who only a few days before had been happily playing badminton with them in their garden would be seeing them no more.

A few hours later, Tirendaz Kalfa came into Selahaddin's study bearing a letter on a silver platter. He was sitting alone in his armchair, staring out of the window. Bowing, she presented the tray to him, and he took the letter. The red wax on the back was imprinted with the Sultan's seal, so he knew it had come from Yıldız. Selahaddin broke open the seal, took out the letter and began to read it. It stated that the proposed visit to Prince Kemaleddin that afternoon could no longer take place, and went on to announce that Lieutenant-General Prince Ahmed Kemaleddin Efendi had died unexpectedly that morning, having long been suffering from an undiagnosed malady. His body had been taken to the Yahya Efendi cemetery, where it had been buried in the Imperial mausoleum. As he read these words, Selahaddin uttered a prayer under his breath.

Just as he was reading the last sentence, Nihad came into the room. Excited at the prospect of the visit to Dolmabahçe, he did not notice the expression on his father's face. "Father, when are we to assemble for our visit to Uncle Kemaleddin and cousin Münire?" he asked. "The carriages have not yet arrived, but Aunt Fatma and my sisters have finished dressing and are nearly ready to depart, and Fuad is waiting outside."

"Nihad – we ... we will not be going to visit them today," Selahaddin replied, still holding the letter in his hand. Then he asked his son to sit down and repeated to him everything the equerry had said, pausing occasionally to let Nihad take it all in. Too upset to face the task himself, Selahaddin asked him to give the news to the rest of the family, and to tell Tirendaz Kalfa to inform the household.

☻ ☻ ☻ ☻ ☻

Immediately after Kemaleddin's death, the Ottoman press published a short official statement released by the Palace in which a mysterious illness was cited as the reason for the prince's sudden and unexpected demise. After a month had gone by, however, articles began to appear in the foreign press in which a very different version of events was described – one that was not only slanderous and defamatory, but also totally unbelievable. Selahaddin was deeply shocked by the many intimate and detailed revelations that were being made by journalists reporting on his uncle's death. He was also outraged to discover that within the walls of the Imperial palaces there were clearly some loose-tongued gossips – even worse, there appeared to be quite a number of untrustworthy servants who were more than willing to concoct a ridiculous story in exchange for a foreign bribe: that was surely the only possible explanation for the despicable assertions that were being bandied about.

The headlines were outspoken in their condemnation of Abdülhamid: some went so far as to say things like *'Brother Murdered by Sultan of Turkey'*, *'Sultan in Fear, Slays Brother'*. The articles beneath them, meanwhile, dwelt on the mutual enmity that had existed between Kemaleddin and Fehim Pasha. Everyone at Court had of course been aware of Kemaleddin's intense dislike for Abdülhamid's trusted henchman, but Selahaddin was surprised to see how much importance foreign journalists were attributing to this fact. According to some reports, Kemaleddin had discovered that the Pasha had fabricated and falsified certain documents in order to bring about the banishment, imprisonment or execution of his enemies; not only this, but he had procured deceitful witnesses who were willing to commit perjury.

Fehim Pasha's success in the matter of uncovering

plots against the Sultan had earned him a great deal of esteem in the eyes of his master – who seemed totally blind to the blatant dishonesty that was constantly being practised under his very nose. There was speculation that the reason for this might be that Fehim Pasha was the grandson of Abdülhamid's wetnurse and the son of İsmet Bey, the Sultan's *süt kardeş* or 'milk brother'. Unlike his elder brother, however, Kemaleddin had seen Fehim Pasha for the cruel, ruthlessly ambitious man he really was, and had been revolted by the way he exploited the power and influence he was permitted to wield. At Court, therefore, he had studiously ignored the notorious Pasha, invariably treating him with the contempt he deserved; much to the man's irritation, Kemaleddin had often referred to him as 'the policeman'.

The newspapers elaborated on the story, describing how Fehim Pasha had publicly vowed to take revenge on Kemaleddin after the Prince had obtained a beautiful Circassian girl as his *kalfa* – one whom the Pasha himself had desired and wanted for his own harem. The articles claimed that the Pasha, by way of reprisal, had falsely implicated Kemaleddin in a plot to depose and assassinate Abdülhamid. They said that in order to convince the Sultan of his brother's guilt, he had forged letters purporting to have been written by the Prince, and had coerced witnesses into giving false statements under oath that confirmed his guilt. The articles also stated that when this concocted evidence had been placed before Abdülhamid, the Sultan had flown into a violent frenzy, and had supposedly declared: "My brother shall die on the very day on which he intended my assassination to take place. Instead of ascending the Ottoman throne, he shall descend into his own grave."

The articles even quoted Kemaleddin's supposed last words – "What is the meaning of this insolent intrusion?" –

which had apparently been spoken when Fehim Pasha appeared in his bedchamber. The Pasha had allegedly replied: "His Imperial Majesty the Sultan has sentenced Your Imperial Highness to death, and these soldiers have orders to carry out the execution immediately." This assertion on the part of the foreign newspapers was absolutely outrageous: they were blatantly accusing the Sultan of having commanded Fehim Pasha to execute his brother. There were even descriptions of how Prince Kemaleddin had cried out in horror, and had attempted to escape into the harem before being dragged back and held down by the Albanian guards, who had then strangled him with a silk scarf.

More and more of these reports appeared in the various foreign newspapers that Selahaddin succeeded in obtaining; he read and re-read them in utter disbelief at the shameless fictions they were printing with the intention of damaging the Sultan's reputation. The articles were very similar, and had obviously been taken from the same news agency. Selahaddin told himself over and over that these stories were preposterous, and must surely be complete fabrications: they were simply another attempt by the Western powers to discredit the Sultan in the eyes of his subjects, and of course in those of the world at large. However, as he read the slightly smudged print on the flimsy pages of the broadsheets, Selahaddin could not help but wonder; he felt obliged, out of a sense of loyalty, to dismiss the accusations out of hand, but at the same time he could not deny that they were difficult to ignore …

☪ ☪ ☪ ☪ ☪

One night not long after this, Selahaddin found himself unable to sleep. He tossed and turned as conversations,

327

rumours he had heard and recollections of recent events spun round and round in his head. It was common knowledge that Abdülhamid's health had deteriorated of late as he had been severely unnerved by the assassination of Grand Duke Sergei Alexandrovich in St Petersburg. Yıldız Palace had been transformed into an impenetrable fortress; inside it the Sultan cowered in fear, seeing assassins and conspirators in every shadow. Rarely leaving the palace grounds, he had become a prisoner of his own making, thus imposing on himself a similar fate to that which he had forced on his brother, Murad. Selahaddin pondered the bitter irony of this twist of fate: the jailer was now imprisoned by his own fears, becoming ever more tormented by paranoia.

Whispers had reached Selahaddin's ear to the effect that the Sultan, in a moment of panic, had recently shot an aide-de-camp, thinking that he was reaching inside his jacket for a dagger with which to stab him – when in reality the man was simply retrieving a document for his master to sign. It was also true that Abdülhamid had placed many members of the Imperial family under even closer surveillance than before; some, such as Prince Sabahaddin, had fled into exile as a result. All this had served to deepen suspicions as to what the circumstances surrounding Kemaleddin's death had actually been. For the first time, as he lay awake, Selahaddin allowed his troubled mind to consider the possibility that the foreign press might have been printing the truth, or at least a semblance of it, and that Abdülhamid might actually have committed fratricide.

The practice of fratricide had been introduced to the Ottoman Court by Mehmed the Conqueror in the fifteenth century, but it had now been obsolete for just over three hundred years. It had originally been conceived as a means of preventing a possible war of succession between the deceased Sultan's sons, and thus of ensuring a smooth transition whenever a new Sultan ascended the throne. The rationale behind it was that the members of the Dynasty had a duty to sacrifice themselves in order to assure the unity, and therefore the strength, of the Empire; it was thought necessary, for the good of the people as a whole, to avoid civil war at all costs at a time when the continuity of the administration was at risk. Although brutal, the policy had largely been successful: it had kept the Ottoman Empire strong and united, whereas in Europe there had regularly been crippling civil wars between rival claimants to the various thrones.

It was the custom in the Ottoman Dynasty that the blood of members of the Imperial family should never be spilled, and as a result executions of Imperial princes were carried out by strangling them with a silk scarf similar to the one that had been found on the floor of Kemaleddin's bedchamber. The murder of Sultan Abdülaziz – an extremely bloody affair – had been the first departure from this custom.

The practice of fratricide had been abolished when Ahmed I ascended the throne in 1603: he was appalled at how his father, on his own accession, had ordered the execution of nineteen of his brothers. Accordingly, Sultan Ahmed changed the law of succession; henceforward, on the death of a Sultan the Ottoman throne would no longer pass to his eldest son, but instead to the eldest prince of the Imperial blood. It was hoped that in this way factional rivalries over who was most fit to rule would be avoided. There was, however, one important disadvantage: previously, Imperial Princes had been sent to the provinces to be trained in the skills of governance, but now they were confined to their gilded cage in the palace in İstanbul, waiting idly for the day when they might succeed to the throne – an eventuality that was not, however, guaranteed. This practice ensured that any chance of rebellion on their part was nipped in the bud, but it also sapped the strength and vitality of the Dynasty.

As Selahaddin lay in his bed, contemplating the possibility that Abdülhamid might indeed have ordered the murder of his brother Kemaleddin, the tale of Cain and Abel came into his mind. He recalled how after the deed was done, Cain had instantly regretted killing his younger brother, feeling only shame and sorrow over the heinous crime he had committed. If Abdülhamid was really guilty of an act of this kind (Selahaddin reasoned to himself), he would definitely be feeling the same way – for despite his ruthlessness in matters of state, family ties had always been of great importance to him. The more Selahaddin thought about this, the more convinced he became that this fact would have prevented the Sultan from ordering such a savage murder to be carried out in his name. Had Abdülhamid not, at least to some extent, risked his throne – and perhaps his own life – by ignoring the recommendations of his advisers and choosing, after Murad's deposition, to let him live? Had he not shown compassion in deciding to confine his brother to a splendid palace in İstanbul rather than exiling him to some remote corner of the Empire where his death could easily have been orchestrated?

Abdülhamid had clearly not wanted Murad exiled or killed, even though either would have been an easy matter for him to arrange, and would moreover have ensured the security of his own position as Sultan. This thought gave Selahadddin renewed confidence in his uncle, and confirmed his belief that Abdülhamid would never have ordered Kemaleddin's execution. Now restored to peace of mind, Selahaddin thanked Allah for helping him to see this truth, and thanked Him once again for the mercy the Sultan had

330

shown to his father. He decided to ignore the lies printed in the foreign newspapers, and resolved to give them no more consideration. He then rolled over onto his side, and within minutes had fallen into a deep sleep.

CHAPTER SEVENTEEN

Anarchy and Quiet Rebellion

Tuesday 11ᵗʰ July 1905

"NİHAD, what on earth are you doing up there?" Selahaddin called out anxiously to his son. Nihad was working on the roof of the harem building, his sleeves rolled up and his carpentry apron tied about his waist. The hot summer sun was beating down on his back as he bent over the russet-coloured clay tiles.

Nihad turned round carefully and looked down, surprised to see his father. "Hello Father," he replied. "When I came into the garden earlier I noticed that some tiles had slipped off the roof, so I decided to come up here and replace the missing ones before any further damage is caused to the building."

"Nihad, if your mother saw you balancing on the roof like an acrobat from the travelling circus, you would cause her great distress. Come down this instant, before you hurt yourself!" Selahaddin said sternly. Nihad was irritated, but obeyed his father immediately. Anyway, he had all but finished.

Nihad's great passions in life were architectural design and carpentry, and his dream was to one day design and build his own mansion fitted with all the conveniences of the age such as electric lighting, a central heating system and a telephone. He kept himself fully informed about all the latest technological developments and followed the new styles in architectural design that were coming into fashion, researching the new materials that were being used in building construction. He often busied himself at Çırağan sanding down warped doors and stiff windows, fixing broken furniture and shutters, or working on his own designs and creations. No maintenance work of any substance had been carried out on the palace since Murad and his family had gone to live there, and it was showing signs of dilapidation after so many years of neglect. This worried Nihad, and he had expressed his concerns on numerous occasions to Cevher Ağa.

He had thought that his repeated warnings had gone unheeded – but then, a few months ago, the renowned Italian architect Antoine Perpignani had been commissioned by the relevant government ministry to prepare a full and detailed report on the state of the Çırağan Palace and its harem and gardens. While Perpignani's inspections were in progress, Nihad had taken the opportunity to learn from him. He knew that the eminent architect had been involved in the design and construction of many beautiful buildings in İstanbul, including the neo-Gothic Bulgarian Orthodox Church of St Stephen on the shores of the Golden Horn. Those four days in late March had been some of the most exciting and rewarding he had ever known; Perpignani, for his part, had been pleasantly surprised by the young prince's eagerness to assist his team in their work, and had been impressed by how much Nihad knew about architecture and structural engineering despite his lack of formal training. As a result of this experience, Nihad had become even more enthusiastic about carrying out such general maintenance work at the palace as lay within his capabilities.

By the time he eventually joined his father in the shade of the large oak tree in the *selamlık* gardens, Nihad had washed his hands and face in the silver washbowl that Dilber Kalfa had brought to him, removed his apron, unrolled his shirt-sleeves, and put his linen jacket back on.

"There are plenty of carpenters and workmen whose job it is to repair and maintain such things," his father told him as he sat down. "You really must not take such needless risks. Please, no more scaling of rooftops. Now, let that be an end to the matter." Nihad sat in silence in the wicker armchair until his father had finished reprimanding him, then apologised for his reckless behaviour. Meanwhile, Tirazan Kalfa poured him a glass of iced lemon sherbet; as Nihad had been working in the strong sun for most of the morning his throat was parched, so he reached for the glass and emptied it in one go. The attentive maid then refilled his glass and withdrew to stand a discreet distance away.

"The reason I came to find you, Nihad, is that I have heard some interesting news today. It seems that the revolt in the Russian Navy is over." Eager to hear more about the volatile situation that was developing on the far shores of the Black Sea, Nihad sat up in his chair. Selahaddin explained that earlier that day his tailor had visited him to take measurements for a new pair of trousers. Owing to his fondness for sweetmeats, his existing pairs had recently become a little too tight and uncomfortable! The tailor had remained fiercely loyal to Murad and his family throughout their confinement, and during his rare visits to the Çırağan Palace he had often smuggled in pieces of information or secret messages. Thanks to his talent for cutting cloth, he had obtained the custom of many high-ranking officials within the European diplomatic corps, and had consequently become a valued source of foreign intelligence for Murad and Selahaddin. That morning he had divulged the details of how the mutiny on the Russian battleship *Potemkin* had ended – details he had been apprised of the day before while carrying out a fitting for a new suit on an imprudent young Russian naval attaché.

For the past two weeks, rumours had been sweeping through İstanbul that a group of revolutionary sailors on the most modern ship in Russia's Black Sea fleet had killed many of their officers and shot the captain. They had apparently raised the flag of rebellion in the hope of encouraging the crews of other ships in the fleet to do the same. The *Potemkin* had been on manoeuvres off the coast of Odessa when a dispute had broken out, prompted by the sailors' refusal to eat the meat soup they had been served: they had claimed that it was infested with maggots, and was therefore unfit for human consumption. An unruly sailor who had voiced his objections to the food had threatened his senior officer, and been shot for his act of insubordination. This had led to instant retaliation: many of the officers on board had been attacked and killed by the crew, and the ship had been commandeered by them. Everyone understood that the cause of the dispute had not really been meat soup: what had actually sparked it off was the hatred felt towards the privileged officer class and the mounting revolutionary fervour. Morale within the fleet had in any case been at a dangerously low ebb following the defeats in the Russo-Japanese War, and had worsened even further with the civil unrest that was plaguing the Russian Empire.

The *Potemkin* had returned to the port of Odessa, which like most large towns and cities in Russia was paralysed by widespread strikes, revolutionary protests and violent disturbances. The mutineers had sent news of their success in their conflict with the establishment ahead of them; consequently, when their ship came in they found large crowds waiting on the quayside to congratulate them. Within hours, warehouses had been looted and the harbour was in flames; following the Tsar's demand for firm and decisive action, martial law was declared. That night, soldiers of the military garrison assembled at the top of the Richelieu Steps that overlooked the harbour, and opened fire on the rebellious crowd that had gathered below. Mounted Cossack horsemen wielding deadly sabres cut a bloodstained path through the mass of people, leaving carnage in their wake. These steps, designed to form an imposing gateway to the city of Odessa, now became the scene of a brutal massacre – one which the sailors aboard the *Potemkin* had done so much to cause, but were now powerless to prevent. By the time calm and order were restored to the city, thousands had been killed or wounded, and the *Potemkin* and her crew sailed out of port to avoid capture – their spirit no doubt broken.

The Sultan and many of the Ottoman ruling elite feared that the ship might try to sail into the Bosphorus and through the Straits to escape the pursuing Russian navy. Although no hint of these events had been given in the Ottoman press, Selahaddin and Nihad had read about them in the opposition journals, and they wondered what action Abdülhamid would take. It was obvious that the Sultan would do all he could to prevent the revolutionary sailors from influencing their Ottoman counterparts, so they were not surprised to learn that Abdülhamid had given the order that two ships which were about to sail to Yemen to suppress a rebellion should instead anchor at the entrance to the Bosphorus and block the *Potemkin's* path. Apparently, he had also ordered the strengthening of the artillery detachments guarding the Straits. Abdülhamid was aware that the Ottoman Navy was too weak to mount a coup against his regime; however, the army was a bubbling cauldron of revolutionary ferment, so it was wise to take precautions.

The interesting news that the tailor had shared with Selahaddin that morning was that after the *Potemkin* had prowled along the Black Sea coastline for over a week, trying in vain to procure coal and supplies to keep her at sea, she had finally sailed into the port of Constanta in Romania. There, the crew had surrendered the ship to the authorities and been granted political asylum.

"So what has happened to the mutineers?" asked Nihad.

"The Romanian government has refused to arrest and extradite them, although the Russians have been putting pressure on them to do so," Selahaddin replied. "I assume that the sailors are intending to seek refuge in Romania while at the same time plotting a secret return to their homeland. We must hope they do not attempt to come to İstanbul – we do not want their socialism and their violent, extremist ideas here!"

"Does your tailor know what has happened to the battleship?" Nihad enquired. "Has it been returned to Russia?"

"He told me that in a final act of rebellion, the murderous crew had opened the ship's seacocks, flooding the engine rooms and causing it to partially submerge. He said it has now been successfully refloated and is being towed to Sebastopol. As you know, until quite recently Constanta was an Ottoman port, so it seems we have escaped involvement in a very delicate diplomatic situation."

"Your tailor has done well to keep us informed about all this, Father. I am sure the Tsar will be happy to have his now infamous battleship returned to him, but he must be finding the whole affair utterly humiliating. Russia is clearly no longer the mighty force she once was if her ships can be taken over so easily. As for the young Russian naval attaché, he should learn to be more careful before revealing embarrassing state secrets to his tailor! Next time, there may be consequences: in his excitement, the tailor might swallow one of his pins!"

Both men laughed as they finished their sherbets in the sun. They knew there were few secrets in İstanbul, and reflected that they were lucky to have such staunch allies in unlikely places.

❀ ❀ ❀ ❀ ❀

Meanwhile, in Bursa, Kemaleddin reached up to pick a large, velvety peach from a tree in the corner of the garden and sat down on a rickety wooden bench beneath its boughs, taking advantage of the shade while he ate his juicy prize. It was just over a year since his marriage to Naime had been annulled, and he had been banished from the capital in disgrace. Life in Bursa had fortunately been made easier for him by the fact that his guards were ardent admirers of his father; as a result they, together with the servants who had been placed at his disposal, were intent on making his stay as comfortable as possible.

Now that the roses of summer were in full bloom, the long days were made even longer by the fact that he rarely ventured outside the house and its small garden. He hated the way people stared at him when he walked through the bazaars, whispered behind their cups on his rare visits to the city's coffee houses, and avoided speaking to him at the mosque; moreover, the social functions at the Governor's residence he attended were marred by a sense of awkwardness surrounding him. As a result, quite soon after his arrival Kemaleddin had withdrawn from society and become something of a recluse, with only Niko for companionship.

338

Occasionally, however, he would allow himself to go hunting in the mountains; there, he would feel the adrenaline rushing through his body and the buffeting of the fresh wind on his face as he rode across the open upland meadows and through the dense forests. Sometimes, he would dismount and plunge into the ice-cold waters of the glacial lakes, emerging invigorated. Such days were rare exceptions to the general rule, but they served to remind him that he was still alive despite being so far away from Hadice, and from his two young children.

The letter that Gevherriz had smuggled out of İstanbul in her travelling chest sat folded in the inside pocket of his linen jacket – next to his heart – as it had done since the day when he had first received it nearly six months previously. It was all he had to remind him of Hadice – that and the silk handkerchief that she had embroidered with his initials, and the lock of her hair concealed in a locket ring that Abdülhamid's agents had failed to find during their search of his rooms on that terrible night. He had read and re-read the letter so many times that the scent of fresh jasmine which had formerly announced its sweetness each time he opened it had long faded to nothing. And that, it seemed, was exactly what Hadice's love for him had done.

He could not fathom how her feelings towards him could possibly have changed so quickly, for his had certainly not altered in the slightest. Far from expressing her undying love for him, as he had expected, the letter instead pleaded with him to forget her, and never to think of her again. In her customary dark purple ink whose colour he had come to know so well during the months of their illicit correspondence, Hadice had written of her deep remorse at having brought hurt and shame to his family, as she had done to her own, and at being the cause of his ruin. The letter was short, yet its words pierced his heart deeper than the point of any sword could have done. Despite this, Kemaleddin clung to the hope that it was the shock and grief that Hadice must have been feeling over the sudden death of her beloved father that had caused her to act so irrationally: surely, he told himself, a love such as theirs could never be extinguished?

He bit into the juicy peach, praying that he might be right in his suppositions. He then flipped open the tiny hinge on his ring, and ran a finger over the small lock of hair that lay curled up inside it. He would find a way back to her.

ꙮ ꙮ ꙮ ꙮ ꙮ

Two months earlier, on the anniversary of the discovery of the scandal, Abdülhamid had forgiven Hadice for her past indiscretions – though he had not been so lenient towards Kemaleddin, whose repeated requests to be allowed to return to İstanbul had been ignored. Hadice was no longer under house arrest: she was once again free to visit Court, go on outings around the city and visit friends and relatives. Throughout her year-long confinement she had found solace in her collection of romantic French novels and in the steadfast devotion of Aslan, whose companionship had helped make her life at least bearable. She owed a great deal to her sister, too: without Fehime's help she would never have been able to keep Aslan, and without her sister's daily visits and constant support she would never have survived the miserable, endlessly frustrating and monotonously empty days.

Fehime had never reprimanded her sister for what she had done, and neither had she made her feel more ashamed of herself than she already was, yet Hadice knew that Fehime not only strongly disapproved of her behaviour but was incapable, however hard she might try, of understanding Hadice's consuming need to be loved, to be held, to be touched. Hadice grieved for her sister, for she was privy to the closely-guarded family secret regarding Fehime, who had been born with an unusual physical condition that precluded any form of intimacy with her husband, and ensured that she would always remain chaste. It was this fact that explained the difference in the attitudes of the two sisters towards love, and towards the male sex. Simply put, Hadice craved intimacy, while Fehime feared it.

For all that, it was with only the very best of intentions that Fehime had persuaded Hadice to write to Kemaleddin soon after his banishment and make it clear to him that they had no future together. It was Fehime, too, who had suggested that the letter be delivered through the good offices of Gevherriz, thus ensuring that it would reach him without being intercepted. Despite her feelings of longing and desperation, Hadice had suppressed her overwhelming urge to send a second letter – one that would reaffirm her love; instead, she had listened to her sister, who had told her that it would only cause more heartache. Hadice knew Fehime had been right to insist that the correspondence with Kemaleddin must come to an immediate end, and was grateful to her sister for giving her the inner strength to begin the slow and painful process of healing her shattered heart. It was these feelings of gratitude that had prompted Hadice, soon after receiving Abdülhamid's forgiveness, to risk angering him all over again by agreeing to accompany Fehime to Nigar Hanım's infamous literary salon, where the princesses hoped to meet the Empire's most celebrated writers, artists, musicians and intellectuals – as well as some of the most ardent critics of the Sultan's regime; the visit had in fact taken place earlier that day.

The sisters had waited a long time to attend one of these notorious Tuesday gatherings, having initially discussed the idea at the time of Vâsıb's birth. First they had waited for the warmer spring weather to arrive; then the scandal had broken and Hadice had been prohibited from leaving her house for a year – and finally, when the restrictions had been lifted, it had taken Fehime weeks to persuade her sister to join her in such a daring enterprise. Fehime had never contemplated going without her sister, so in the interim she had satisfied her burgeoning interest in political affairs by reading opposition publications and foreign newspapers, as she had once seen her father and brother do every day at Çırağan. Murad had always encouraged his daughters to be free and independent thinkers, but until now Fehime had taken little interest in the world outside the harem. However, she had felt her thirtieth birthday, which had taken place just a few days previously, to be a turning point in her life, and she now desperately wanted to find new purpose and fulfilment – everything up to that point having been centred around music, parties and fashion. The plight of the Empire and the need for liberal reform were topics that resonated strongly with her, and she was now eager to learn more and do more.

The day had certainly not been a disappointment. As the two audacious princesses were rowed back down the Bosphorus after their brief visit to Nigar Hanım's summer residence, hidden from view by the silk curtains of the ornately-decorated kiosk built into the stern of the slender caïque, they chatted animatedly about the thrilling events of the afternoon. Their simple ruse of an innocent excursion up the Bosphorus had met with complete success, and no one had become aware of the clever deception. The Sultan's spies, believing their presence to be undetected, had followed behind the caïque at a discreet distance in a small rowing boat, but had been unable to keep pace. They had therefore not seen the caïque pull in to shore and tie up briefly alongside a deserted dirt track that wound its way inland just a short distance from the Rumeli Hisarı – the imposing medieval castle that dominated a sweeping bend in the Bosphorus. No one had seen Fevzi, the young farmer on whose faithful services the members of the family so often relied, drive an old, inconspicuous carriage out from behind a clump of pine trees as the princesses disembarked; their hasty climb into the carriage as the caïque pulled away had likewise remained unobserved. The sisters had then been whisked away to Nigar Hanım's summer house nearby, where they had slipped inside, disguised by their *yashmaks*.

They had not stayed long for fear of discovery, and their return to the caïque less than an hour later had been carried out with equal circumspection. Zeynel Ağa, relieved that all had gone according to plan, now sat proudly on guard outside the gilded kiosk; he was scanning the waterway with watchful eyes as the six pairs of smartly-dressed oarsmen pulled together in efficient unison. Their complicity and their silence had been bought for a small consideration, and the eunuch's formidable reputation for exacting harsh retribution if anyone should be so unwise as to cross him ensured that that silence would not be broken. As the caïque glided through the glistening waters of the Bosphorus, people in passing boats looked on with curiosity, trying to ascertain who might be sitting within. Everyone knew that the occupants of the kiosk must be Imperial princesses of the House of Osman: only they were entitled to travel in an Imperial caïque, rowed by such a large number of oarsmen.

As she reclined against the pale blue embroidered cushions that covered the seats, Hadice thought to herself that this was by far the most pleasant and relaxing way to travel around

343

İstanbul. She found the crowded, bumpy, unpaved roads of the city – muddy in winter and dusty in summer – extremely disagreeable. The soothing sound of water dripping from the oarsmen's blades as they skimmed over the calm ripples, and the feeling of gentle forward propulsion as the oars pulled through the water in synchronised motion, combined to create a peaceful, restful atmosphere; meanwhile, the cool air floating above the surface of the Bosphorus provided a welcome respite from the unrelenting heat of the late after-noon sun. At first Hadice had been reluctant to brave a visit to Nigar Hanım's salon: her self-confidence and the imper-turbable aplomb for which she was well known had been severely dented by the scandal, and the rebellious nature that had formerly led her to disregard Court protocol appeared to have been tamed – but now she felt delighted that Fehime had persisted in her efforts to persuade her sister to join her.

"Do you think anyone recognised us?" she asked with a twinkle in her eye. The princesses had attended incognito, as had been previously arranged with their hostess, to obviate the risk of any gossip reaching the ears of their uncle. He would not have approved of them attending a reception attended by men as well as women, especially when the assembled guests included so many vehement critics of his regime. The truth was, however, that the Muradiye princesses had been motivated by a long-suppressed need to rebel against the tight control their uncle held over their lives. It was this that had finally swung the balance, giving them the courage to thwart him despite the dangers of the escapade; this small act of defiance was, for them, symbolic.

"I am not sure," replied Fehime. "I was speaking to Osman Hamdi Bey, and I think he may have suspected something – but thankfully, he was polite enough not to question me further." Osman Hamdi Bey was a famous artist and renowned archaeologist who had founded the Imperial Academy of Fine Art and the Imperial Museum, which housed many of the ancient artifacts that had been discovered in many places throughout the Empire, often through his own efforts. Fehime admired his dedication to the work of unearthing and preserving these treasures from the past, and had been particularly interested to hear about his attempts to prevent unauthorised excavations, which led to precious finds being smuggled abroad – where they found their way into the hands of foreign collectors or European museums.

"I nearly betrayed our identity, too," said Hadice. "I overheard a conversation among a group of writers in which they were speaking about Father. I heard Halid Ziya Bey and Mehmed Tevfik Bey mention his name, and I edged closer to them so that I could hear what was being said. Both of them were highly critical of the Sultan's absolutist government, and both were intensely frustrated by the strict censorship imposed on their work and on the Ottoman press."

"Oh? So what exactly were they saying?" her sister asked. That afternoon Fehime, too, had enjoyed a conversation with Mehmed Tevfik Bey, who had revealed to her that 'Tevfik Fikret', a name she had instantly recognised from the opposition journals she often read, was his pseudonym. He had also told her that he was designing a house for himself in the grounds of Robert College, where he taught, and that he hoped it would be ready for him to move in the following year. She knew that Selahaddin very much admired his fiery writings, and it had immediately occurred to her how well he and Nihad would enjoy this man's stimulating company.

"Oh, Fehime, I nearly wept!" Hadice exclaimed. "I could scarcely believe my ears – all those authors, poets and intellectuals were praising Father to the skies for his compassion and his liberalism. They were saying that had he

345

remained on the throne, our empire would not be in such a perilous position as it is now because his policy of Ottomanism would have united all its various peoples. They also said he would have staved off foreign interference by bringing in constitutional government. I have never heard anyone speak like that about Father before – other than members of our immediate family, of course. His name is not even mentioned at Court, so I had assumed that he had been forgotten by everyone else as well. In fact, it was all I could do to prevent anyone from seeing the effect all this was having on me. I admit that I was grateful to be able to hide behind my *yashmak*!"

"So it seems there really are people who believed in Father and appreciated his ideas. If only he had known!" Fehime remarked pensively. "We must tell Selahaddin – it will make him very happy … although he might get angry when he finds out that we attended a mixed gathering," she added with a mischievous laugh. Fehime enjoyed shocking her elder brother from time to time!

"Well, actually, I do not think Selahaddin will disapprove of our going to Nigar Hanım's salon," Hadice said. "On the contrary, I think he will be proud of us for taking such a daring step and for trying to educate ourselves. In fact, I am sure of it." Fehime thought this was rather naïve of her sister, but said nothing. Hadice continued: "Is Nigar Hanım not truly marvellous, Fehime?"

Fehime was happy to see something of the old sparkle come back into her sister's eyes. "Yes, absolutely. She is an inspiration," she replied. "I admire the way she views the world, and her optimism about the possibilities that await us women if only we can be brave enough to seize them. Her strength of character sits comfortably alongside her feminine sensibility, and that, I am sure, is something to be emulated.

Did you know that a few years ago Sultan Hamid awarded her the Order of Charity in recognition of her humanitarian work?" Fehime asked, looking across at her sister.

"No, I did not know that," Hadice replied. "But I am delighted to hear that our uncle had the good sense to acknowledge that amazing woman's extraordinary qualities. I must admit that I sometimes wonder how Nigar Hanım can possibly find time to write such beautiful, powerful poems, while at the same time organising gatherings in her salon each week and doing so much charity work. And in spite of all she does, she still manages to look so beautiful and so elegant," she added. "She puts us to shame!"

"Yes, she is a wonder, isn't she?" said Fehime. "Everyone I met there was very interesting to talk to – so different from the people we usually meet at Court." She leaned forward and peered out of the tiny gap in the silk curtains to see where they were. "And I very much enjoyed my brief conversation with Osman Hamdi Bey. He told me about a new painting he is working on. It is called 'A Young Emir', apparently, and it sounded beautiful. I also asked him about his discovery of Alexander the Great's sarcophagus in that ancient city – Sidon, I think it was. I asked him to describe how he felt when he first came across those perfectly preserved figures carved into the marble tomb. Hadice, just imagine finding something so beautiful that had been lost to mankind for over two thousand years!" She paused for a moment, then continued: "Why don't we go and see it in the Imperial Museum – that and all the other Hellenistic statues they have there? Would it not be thrilling to see all those wonderful things from the ancient world?"

"Yes, Fehime, I believe it would: once the weather begins to cool down we should certainly go to the old city and visit Osman Hamdi Bey's museum," Hadice said. Her enthusiasm

347

for life and her old ebullience seemed to have returned as a result of the visit to Nigar Hanım; inwardly, Fehime heaved a sigh of relief – she had waited a long time for this moment.

"Do you think Selahaddin, Nihad and Fatma would like to join us?" Fehime went on. "I am certain Osman Hamdi Bey would organise a private tour for us if Selahaddin asked him to do so, and I am also sure Sultan Hamid would grant his permission for the trip. After all, the museum was built under his patronage, supposedly for the enjoyment and education of his subjects. And are we not his subjects, too?" she said, beginning to sound a little rebellious – not for the first time that day!

A gentle jolt announced that they had reached the landing stage outside Hadice's *yalı*. The princesses adjusted their *feraces* and *yashmaks* and came out from beneath the canopy of the kiosk, taking care not to slip as they stepped ashore from the rocking caïque. Placing her hand on Zeynel Ağa's shoulder to steady her, Fehime watched as Hadice almost skipped towards the harem door of the *yalı*, her steps far lighter than they had been that morning. Yes, she said to herself, the visit to Nigar Hanım had definitely been a good idea.

PART IV

CHAPTER EIGHTEEN

Attempted Assassination

Friday 21st July 1905

ELAHADDİN and Nihad, accompanied by two bodyguards, rode out of the gates of Çırağan Palace and
headed up the dry, dusty slope towards Yıldız Palace.
They had received a summons to attend the *Selamlık*
ceremony that week, and were looking forward to the
occasion. Princes of the Imperial family were expected to
attend the weekly procession to the mosque for Friday
prayers, and in normal circumstances would ride proudly at
the head of a detachment of men from their regiments as they
travelled the short distance between Yıldız Palace and the
Hamidiye Mosque. Selahaddin and Nihad were exceptions
to the rule, however, and continued to live under certain
restrictions: the usual rules of Court protocol did not apply
to them. They had still not received honorary commissions
in the army from Abdülhamid, and could only attend the
ceremony when invited to do so.

Also in attendance that day were Selahaddin's three
sisters – Hadice, Fehime and Fatma. The ladies had gone
on ahead: the harem carriages always departed from Yıldız
Palace half an hour before the Sultan and the princes set
out. As Hadice had not visited Court since the scandal of

the previous spring, she was feeling apprehensive – she did not relish the prospect of meeting her cousin Naime there. Unlike the princes, the Imperial princesses were not obliged to attend the *Selamlık*; however, the sisters had requested permission to go that day – partly because they had decided that Hadice ought to accept the Sultan's invitation to return to Court before he began to feel snubbed by her absence, and partly because now that the regulations governing Fatma's confinement had been relaxed, they wanted to introduce her to the aunts and cousins she had not yet met. Moreover, Princess Emine Necibe, the mother of the Khedive of Egypt and the Sudan, had expressed a particular desire to be introduced to the elusive Fatma, who had been locked behind the gates of the Çırağan Palace since birth. In fact, as Fatma had not yet been presented at Court, everyone there was keen to meet the youngest of Murad's daughters for the first time, and the Sultan had graciously granted permission for this to happen.

Since the death of her husband, Princess Emine had spent more and more time in İstanbul, and had become known at Court and in the city as the 'Valide Pasha', having had the title 'Pasha' bestowed on her by Abdülhamid. No woman had held the rank of Pasha in the Empire before, so it was indeed a unique distinction. Emine was a deeply religious woman, and when she was in İstanbul she would attend the procession to Friday prayers fortnightly, without fail. She held a high rank at Court: Abdülhamid held her in high esteem on account of her piety and her intellect – and also, of course, in recognition of the fact that despite the establishment of the British Protectorate over Egypt and the Sudan Khedive Abbas Hilmi II, her son, continued to rule as a loyal vassal to the Ottoman Sultanate. Emine had also been the stepdaughter of Princess Münire, Murad's half sister and the full sister of the recently deceased Kemaleddin, who had chosen to name his only daughter after her.

Fatma was very much looking forward to meeting the famously beautiful and benevolent Egyptian princess, and was even more excited about meeting the other members of her family following prayers that afternoon. It had become a tradition for the Imperial princesses, Abdülhamid's consorts, the wives of the Imperial princes and the wives of senior ministers of state to gather either in one of the pavilions at Yıldız Palace or in the gardens to pass the afternoon together after their devotions. They would then dine at the palace, following which they would attend a performance at the palace theatre in the company of the Sultan. Since this was the first time Fatma had attended the *Selamlık* – and, of course, the first time in her life that she had been in the company of so many people, she, too, felt extremely nervous as she sat with her sisters in the carriage on the way to the Hamidiye Mosque. As the adrenaline raced through her body, she was conscious that her upper lip and neck had begun to perspire, while the gentle rocking motion of the carriage did nothing to calm the butterflies that were fluttering wildly in her stomach.

That day, their carriage was the first to pass through the tall wrought iron gates into the courtyard of the Hamidiye Mosque. Until Perestu Valide Sultan, Abdülhamid's adoptive mother, had died the previous December, it had invariably been her carriage that had led the harem procession each Friday; today, however, it was the Muradiye princesses who led the way. Since Perestu had had no children of her own, on the death of Abdülhamid's natural mother when he was only nine years old Sultan Abdülmecid had given the boy, his second son, into her care. Circassian by birth, she had originally come to İstanbul to enter the service of Esma Sultan, the favourite sister of Sultan Mahmud, Abdülmecid's father. In fact, Princess Esma had begun to treat Perestu more as a daughter than as a servant, and had chosen a most fitting name for her – 'Perestu', which meant 'swallow' in Persian. It was a perfect description of her charge's petite figure and delicate, graceful elegance. A young woman of unrivalled beauty with long blonde hair and iridescent turquoise-blue eyes, Perestu had captivated Sultan Abdülmecid the instant he set eyes on her in his aunt's gardens, and he had married her almost immediately. A deeply religious person of inherent goodness, Perestu had reigned over the harem as Valide Sultan with justice, never interfering in the politics of the Empire – something that many of her predecessors had been unwilling to do. Abdülhamid had adored his adopted mother, and she in turn had adored him; as a result, when she died the Sultan had been left feeling totally bereft.

Of all the princesses attending Friday prayers that day, Hadice was the most senior. Her three aunts – the Princesses Cemile, Seniha and Mediha – were not present, and neither were the two elder daughters of Sultan Abdülaziz, the Princesses Saliha and Nazime; it was, therefore, Hadice who led the harem procession. Great emphasis was placed on seniority in the Ottoman Court, and the order of precedence was strictly observed. As the carriage drove past the huge crowd that had gathered outside the gates, Fatma leaned forward to look through the lattice grills fixed at the windows. The onlookers had come to witness the splendour of the ceremony, hoping to catch a glimpse of their Sultan and members of the Imperial family. A young boy sitting on his father's shoulders near the gateway caught Fatma's attention: he was wearing a bright green jacket with shiny brass buttons, and Fatma noticed that his small red fez had slipped precariously to one side as he waved excitedly at the passing carriages. She smiled behind her veil, then sat back against the soft velvet cushions. Once the carriage had pulled to a halt behind the Imperial Lodge on the left hand side of the mosque, she followed her elder sisters as they descended the carriage steps and disappeared into the Ladies' Lodge. They were followed by Abdülhamid's six daughters, the Valide Pasha, a few of the Sultan's consorts, the wives of the Imperial princes and the ministers' wives, and finally the Sultan's High Hazinedar. The horses were detached from their carriages to allow them to rest, and the carriages were lined up in order of precedence, ready to return to Yıldız Palace when prayers were over.

As soon as she had entered the courtyard and passed the sentry box, Fatma was struck by the beauty of the mosque's exterior. It had been built on the orders of Abdülhamid twenty years previously, soon after the assassination of Tsar Alexander II, the grandfather of the current Tsar and the father of Grand Duke Sergei – the man who had recently been murdered. Like his son, Tsar Alexander had been killed by a bomb thrown at him by a revolutionary; this had happened during his weekly visit to the military roll-call in St Petersburg. This attack on the person of the Tsar had had a profound effect on Abdülhamid, shocking him deeply and filling him with terror, and he had resolved that henceforth, rather than taking the unnecessary risk of driving through his capital for the *Selamlık*, he would instead commission a mosque to be built close to Yıldız Palace. As was the custom of the Ottoman sultans, the project would be financed by his own personal funds.

The design of the mosque was the work of Sarkis Balyan, the Imperial Architect who had earlier built the Çırağan

Palace along with his brother Hagop. The Balyan family were a dynasty of highly accomplished and innovative court architects – Ottoman Armenians who for nearly a century had loyally served six sultans; during this time, five generations of their family had exercised a powerful influence over Ottoman architecture. They had created a unique style – a strikingly creative fusion of European baroque with Oriental and Islamic motifs, and this style was evident in the many palaces, kiosks, mosques and other grandiose public buildings that they had built, and that now adorned the capital; indeed, the Balyans had transformed the appearance of İstanbul and the shores of the Bosphorus, and as a result they were highly respected in Ottoman society. Not since the time of Mimar Sinan – the golden age of Süleyman the Magnificent – had the city seen such beauty and splendour rising out of its deep, ages-old foundations.

Fatma had followed her sisters up to the mezzanine gallery at the back of the mosque; it was here that the ladies would wait for the Sultan to arrive, after which prayers would begin. She knelt between Hadice and Fehime behind a low wall under the ornate canopy, facing the marble *mihrab*. It was the first time Fatma had ever been in a mosque, and she felt a calm, comforting sensation wash over her, as if a cloak of peace and love had wrapped itself about her shoulders. Soft whisperings among the ladies broke the silence, and Fatma was certain she heard both her name and that of Hadice mentioned several times. Looking to her left, she noticed a demure figure with exceptionally fair skin, and correctly assumed that this was Emine, the Valide Pasha. Her eyes were smiling kindly at Fatma from beneath thick, dark eyebrows, and she nodded a greeting. Fatma nodded in return, then nervously raised her hands to adjust her veil – despite the fact that it was perfectly positioned over her hair.

Hadice gently reprimanded her. "Stop fidgeting, Fatma," she said in a low voice. "Everyone is watching us to see how we behave, so try not to give them anything to criticise." Fatma placed a reassuring hand on Hadice's arm: she well understood that her sister felt unnerved at being in the same place as Naime – neither had acknowledged the other, and the Hamidiye princesses had all been rather cold in their greetings.

Just then, the stirring sound of the Imperial March reached their ears. Then they heard the first gun salute, accompanied by a stately fanfare of trumpets; this announced that the Sultan was passing through the Imperial Gate to commence the short journey from the palace to the Hamidiye Mosque. Cheers arose from the crowd, mingled with rousing hurrahs from the rows of soldiers lining the route. Those inside the mosque could hear the cheering becoming louder and louder as the Sultan drew near. A second salute was fired off, then a third.

"Sultan Abdülhamid will be here in a few moments," Fehime whispered to her sister. "That was the final gun salute: it means His Imperial Majesty has arrived at the mosque, and is being greeted by the Sheikh ul-Islam at the door to the Imperial Lodge."

Fatma raised her eyes to take in her surroundings. The Hamidiye Mosque had been built not in the traditional style, which incorporated elements of both Byzantine and Islamic architecture, but in the neo-Gothic. She noticed that by now the princes and the ministers of state had all but filled the large rectangular space beneath her. The princes had entered from the Princes' Lodge, which was on the opposite side of the building from the Imperial Lodge where the Sultan would soon be kneeling; the ministers, meanwhile, had arrived via the main door. Nihad was hard to spot among the many

357

young princes, but she immediately recognised her brother Selahaddin by his familiar gait as he walked beneath the large Bohemian crystal chandelier that hung from the starry central dome. This dome was supported by four towering octagonal wooden pillars, and Fatma marvelled at them: painted in soft hues of blue, green and ivory, and highlighted with red, they were decorated with intricately carved Islamic motifs covered in gold leaf. They stood tall and erect, as if they were giant guardians tasked with protecting the sanctity of this holy place. Between them hung a chandelier, and the light was reflected off its white and dark red crystal, twinkling and dancing against the painted walls. It had been a gift to Abdülhamid from the grand Prussian statesman Prince Otto von Bismarck, who was an admirer of his, and it harmonised perfectly with its surroundings.

The dome and the ceilings were painted a bright indigo blue on which thousands of gold leaf stars had been superimposed, forming a celestial canopy above the faithful gathered below. This was obviously a reference to the name of the Sultan's preferred palace, the Yıldız or 'Star' Palace. Sunlight flooded down onto the luxurious blood-red carpet from the many windows, each one an arch coming to a point at the top, that supported the dome and ran in double rows along the sides of the building. In an attempt to calm her nerves, Fatma now began to count these windows; in fact, she counted them three times, making sure that she came to the same total – thirty-six – each time. A lace-like stone carving dropped down over the apex of each window on the outside, partly concealing it, in the same way as a lace mask might teasingly conceal an identity at a masquerade ball. This detail reminded Fatma of the Çırağan Palace, where similar carvings formed dramatic frames for the windows, creating a Moorish effect. Between the windows were sumptuously decorated panels bearing circular plaques on which were inscribed the names of Allah, His Prophet Muhammed, and the first Caliphs of Islam. Gilded calligraphy and motifs also decorated the *mihrab* and the marble *minbar*, from which the Sheikh ul-Islam would soon be leading the prayers and delivering his sermon; he had just taken up his position.

Abdülhamid always prayed alone in the Imperial Lodge, set apart from his family and the rest of the congregation. Fatma half-turned her head in the direction of the highly-polished wooden lattice grill that protruded slightly from the side wall, screening off the private chamber in which the Sultan was now kneeling before his God. She could just make out the vague outline of the man who had tormented her father and her family for so long, and it sent a chill through her body. But then her mind was brought back to the prayer ceremony by the voice of Mehmed Cemaleddin Efendi, the Sheikh ul-Islam.

❂ ❂ ❂ ❂ ❂

"We must wait here for a couple of minutes until the Sultan departs," Hadice said to Fatma once prayers were completed. "Then we will ride in the carriage back to Yıldız Palace, following behind the Sultan and the Imperial princes in the return procession. As it is such a beautiful day, when we arrive I am sure we will have a picnic in the private gardens, and then I will introduce you to everyone." Fatma smiled at her sister, but she could already feel the butterflies inside her begin to flutter once again, and her heart begin to pound within her chest. It was difficult to get used to the company of strangers after being in confinement for so long, but in spite of this she yearned to meet her cousins – and, of course,

359

to see the famously beautiful gardens of Yıldız that lay tantalisingly close on the other side of the marble bridge linking them to the grounds of Çırağan.

"You have nothing to fear, dear sister, absolutely nothing," Fehime said kindly, placing her hand on the soft leather of her sister's cream-coloured kid gloves. Fehime clearly remembered her first visit to the Court of Yıldız, and knew that Fatma would be feeling both excited and extremely nervous. "All our cousins will adore you – how can they do otherwise? You are the most sweet-natured of us all."

The princesses stood up and began to descend the small staircase that led from the raised gallery back into the Ladies' Lodge. They adjusted their *feraces* and *yashmaks*; then the door opened, revealing the waiting eunuchs who had come to escort them to their carriages. Suddenly a deafeningly loud explosion, louder and deeper than any cannon blast, reverberated through the thick stone walls. The ground shuddered; the windows shook violently, and most shattered instantly. Some of the ladies, especially the younger ones, screamed in fright, while others who had been taught to keep their emotions under strict control struggled to remain silent, but were unable to prevent the blood draining from their faces: everyone could hear muffled yells of pain and terror coming from outside the building. Hadice and Fehime instinctively put their arms around their younger sister Fatma, closing their eyes as they hid their faces in the folds of her *ferace*. The High Hazinedar remained calm, however, and immediately took control of the situation, ordering the doors to be shut and bolted; then, turning to the ladies, she suggested that they return to the relative safety of the raised gallery. A footman was dispatched to find out what had happened.

Drifting up through the shattered windows came the cries and moans of agony of the wounded and the dying, the shrill whinnying of frightened horses, and the frantic orders being barked out amid the general chaos. Though the ladies could not see what had happened, it was obviously something terrible beyond imagination. Princess Refia, Abdülhamid's youngest daughter, fearing that her father had been the target of an assassination attempt, started to cry. Her eldest sister Princess Zekiye cradled her head, and her other sisters tried to console her, but everyone knew she was probably right. Hadice, Fehime and Fatma sat huddled together in silence, worried for the safety of Selahaddin and Nihad, who they knew would not have been far from the Sultan. Meanwhile, the Valide Pasha soothed the ministers' wives and suggested that prayers be said.

Outside, the scene was one of carnage; the air was filled with the pungent smell of gunpowder mingled with that of charred flesh. A thick dust hung in the air, and the taste of metal seemed to be on everyone's tongues. A large bomb loaded with thousands of small pieces of iron had detonated in a parked carriage just outside the gates of the mosque courtyard, killing or injuring many. Even those who had escaped comparatively unscathed had been shaken to the core of their being by the devastating blast. Fortunately, the Sultan had not been injured, as – contrary to his usual practice – he had not been in a hurry to depart for Yıldız, and had taken a minute or two to speak with the Sheikh ul-Islam before descending the crescent-shaped steps of the Imperial Lodge and proceeding towards his carriage. Had he left immediately, as he almost invariably did, there can be no doubt whatsoever that he would have been at the very epicentre of the blast. Immediately afterwards a cavalry squadron had charged into the courtyard with swords drawn; meanwhile, the Sultan's personal bodyguards had ushered him back up the steps and into the Imperial Lodge, barring the door behind them. The soldiers who earlier had proudly lined up along the proces-

361

sional route and in the courtyard to cheer their Sultan were now in complete disarray: some were trying to help the injured and the dying, or endeavouring to control the horses, while others were regrouping in preparation for a possible attack on the Sultan. A few lay dead, or were dying from horrific injuries.

It took Abdülhamid only a few seconds to comprehend what had just happened, and to react accordingly. The thirty-fourth Sultan of the Imperial House of Osman, he had the blood of great warrior Sultans flowing in his veins, and consequently was not one to cower behind locked doors while his people panicked outside. Notwithstanding the extreme concern for his personal safety that he always felt, when faced with real, tangible danger he behaved with courage and dignity. Turning to Tahsin Pasha, his Private Secretary, he asked him to ensure that his immediate family be escorted back to the palace with a double detachment of guards. Members of the Imperial family who did not live at Yıldız, meanwhile, were to be taken back to their homes under heavily armed military escort: there would be no picnics in the gardens that day. Armed escorts were also to be provided for the Valide Pasha and all the ministers' wives so that they could return to their mansions in safety; however, every Minister of State was expected to be present at Yıldız within the hour for a full debriefing. Finally, he gave orders for the immediate restoration of calm. The injured were to be cared for at nearby hospitals at his own expense, and a list of the dead compiled for his personal attention: in this way, he would be able to ensure that a pension was paid to any woman who had been made a widow that day. Abdülhamid then demanded that the door be unlocked; against the advice of those around him, he walked bravely out onto the steps, not knowing whether a second assassin lay in wait for him.

"Do not be afraid. Do not be afraid," Abdülhamid said,

addressing the disordered throng before him with calm authority. Everyone stopped what they were doing, overcome with awe: these words were being spoken directly to them by their Sultan and Caliph. "We must have calm and order, for I do not want any further injuries to result from this situation. You are not to fear for me, for as you can see I am unharmed. Allah has protected me and saved me from my enemies. Praise be to Allah!" A loud cheer of 'Long live the Padishah!' went up from the crowd, but Abdülhamid continued: "This is a time for tending to the injured and praying for the souls of the dead. Tomorrow will be time enough for the seeking of justice." The Sultan then said a short prayer for the innocent people who had been killed in his stead.

These stirring words had the desired effect on the Sultan's listeners, and calm and order slowly began to be restored.

    ☻ ☻ ☻ ☻ ☻

Abdülhamid then climbed into his open carriage, followed as always by his favourite son Prince Mehmed Burhaneddin, and made his way out of the courtyard with his personal bodyguards running alongside him. Tears came to his eyes as he passed the horrific scene of death and destruction caused by the bomb – a bomb that he knew had been intended to kill him. As the carriage climbed back up the hill to Yıldız Palace, Abdülhamid sat in stony silence opposite his son, his mind racing as he went through all the possibilities: who, he asked himself, could have been responsible for this act of savagery?

Could one of the major European Powers – Britain, France, Russia or Austro-Hungary – have been behind it? Abdülhamid was only too familiar with their never-ending plots and devilish schemes, all aimed at causing unrest and encouraging uprisings in his empire, and thus undermining his power.

He was also very much aware of their desire to increase their influence over his empire's highly-prized provinces, and their unquenchable appetite for territorial expansion: notwithstanding the fact that Egypt and Cyprus had been acquired by the British, Tunisia by the French, territories in the Caucasus by the Tsar, and Bosnia and Herzegovina by the House of Habsburg, that appetite was still far from satisfied. His political intelligence service had also warned him that following Italy's occupation of Eritrea and Somalia and her failed invasion of Ethiopia, she harboured ambitions with respect to Libya and to the Dodecanese Islands in the Aegean, both of which were Ottoman possessions; no doubt they would not be at all averse to the removal of the strong, unflinching hand at the helm of the Ottoman Empire. Although Germany was unquestionably the most supportive towards the Ottomans of the empires of Western Europe, Abdülhamid knew better than to trust the Kaiser and his Prussian government. However, he calculated that German influence over the Ottoman army and Berlin's support for the Baghdad Railway project, which was of great importance from both the political and economic points of view, would be sufficient to ensure the continuation – for the present – of his friendship with the German Empire.

To his great shame, Abdülhamid had suffered substantial territorial losses during the course of his reign – more so, in fact, than any other Ottoman Sultan before him; even so, he was absolutely determined to avert any further humiliations. He had learnt to play the European Powers off against each other, and had become adept at reaping advantage from their differences and profiting from their mutual jealousies. His policy of Pan-Islamism had also been a success: it had enhanced his standing in the international arena, and had effectively countered attempts by colonialist powers to stir up dissent in Moslem territories with a view to acquiring them for themselves. Abdülhamid had become an expert in the field of geopolitics and had made himself a highly-skilled statesman and strategist: indeed, the German Chancellor Otto von Bismarck had been prompted to remark that "Of all the intelligence in Europe, ninety percent is in Sultan Abdülhamid, five percent in myself and five percent in everyone else." Having a weaker, more malleable Sultan on the throne of the Ottoman Empire would suit the interests of all the European Powers, and Abdülhamid knew that they were working tirelessly to remove him from power.

Having given the matter a little more thought, however, Abdülhamid arrived at the conclusion that none of the European Powers was likely to instigate an attempt on his life as this might have dangerous repercussions for them. They would never plot the murder of a head of state, he reasoned, for fear of provoking unrest in their own countries – especially during volatile times such as these when attempts were being made to assassinate members of almost all the ruling houses of Europe. He knew of seven attempts on the life of Queen Victoria, for instance, and of many on that of the Kaiser's grandfather; the governments of both Britain and Germany were therefore fully conscious of the dangers that irresponsible acts of this kind could bring. As for the French, although it had to be borne in mind that over a century ago they had murdered their royal family, the period between that event and the establishment of the Third Republic had been a tumultuous and unsettling one, and consequently Abdülhamid reasoned that the French would have no wish to see the stability of a sovereign state threatened by acts of violence against its ruler. His mind now turned to Russia – there, both Tsar Alexander II and his son Grand Duke Sergei had been murdered in bomb attacks, and the country was heavily embroiled in the struggle to ward off revolution; as a result, he concluded, the Russians would think twice before fanning the flames of unrest and anarchy, and would thus refrain from lighting them so close to their borders.

Finally, he reviewed the case of two less likely candidates: Austria-Hungary and Italy. The Austro-Hungarian Emperor Franz Joseph I had survived an attempt on his own life in Trieste, but had suffered the loss of his beautiful wife the Empress Elizabeth to a brutal assassin; in Italy, meanwhile, Umberto I, the present king's father, had also been murdered – shot four times at close range. As both countries had witnessed the assassination of members of their respective royal houses, they would have learned their lesson, and therefore would not act in this way against the Ottoman Sultan. Having satisfied himself on this account, Abdülhamid therefore ruled out the possibility that any of the major European Powers might have been involved.

Maybe one of the troublesome Balkan States was respon- sible – Greece, Serbia, or perhaps Bulgaria? After a few seconds' consideration he dismissed that thought, too. For the time being, Greece seemed content with her recent annexation of much of Thessaly, and with the granting of autonomy to Crete. Serbia was comparatively subdued following the murder of her king and queen only a few years before, and was now focused on her efforts to create a strong, stable state under a new ruling dynasty. The Bulgarians had enjoyed de facto independence for nearly thirty years, and although Abdülhamid knew they wanted to be fully inde- pendent and expand their territory, he did not think Prince Ferdinand capable of ordering a cowardly attack on his person such as had just been experienced: waging war on the battlefield was more his style. Also, as Bulgaria, too, had a hereditary ruler, she would not contemplate the assassination of an Ottoman Sultan for the same reasons as would discourage the Western European Powers from doing so.

Could the Young Turks, perhaps, have orchestrated the attack, or maybe one of his liberal opponents – such as his nephew Prince Sabahaddin? Abdülhamid was not entirely sure, but nevertheless he did not think it likely that they would go to the extreme of committing an act of cold-blooded murder as this would alienate public opinion from their cause. It was true that they were his political opponents, but the Young Turks' organisation was made up of liberal-minded medical students, young military officers and civil servants who were pledged to restore the Ottoman constitution and reopen the parliament; as for Prince Sabahaddin, he was an honourable and highly principled man, and moreover a member of the Imperial family. No, Abdülhamid concluded, he could not visualise either the Young Turks or Sabahaddin as assassins: if they were ever to unite in a bid to overthrow his regime, they would take a far less violent approach – one based on appeasement rather than assassination.

Perhaps the people responsible for the outrage were members of a Marxist organisation, or a group of socialist revolutionaries? It had been a group of this kind that had assassinated the Russian Tsar and his son. Maybe it could even have been one of the sailors from the *Potemkin* who had come to İstanbul from Romania intent on inciting revolution in the Ottoman Empire, as was being done in Russia? The next possibility Abdülhamid considered was that it might have been someone acting alone, as had been the case in the assassinations of the Empress Elizabeth and King Umberto. He soon decided, however, that this, too, was improbable, as the attempt on his life appeared to have been far too meticulously planned: it would have required substantial funding, and must have involved a large number of people.

Yet another possible perpetrator was the international Zionist organisation: they certainly had the means to fund an attack of this kind. Following Abdülhamid's second firm refusal to sell Palestine to them, they might have felt that only if they brought about the removal of Abdülhamid from the throne would they ever have a chance of settling in what they regarded as their 'promised land'. Acting on their behalf, Theodor Herzl had twice offered to pay off the Ottoman Empire's crippling foreign debt and provide support for the Sultan by spreading favourable propaganda about him in all the capitals of Europe in exchange for the granting to Jewish people of the right to settle in Palestine and govern it for themselves. In fact, however, the assumption on the Zionists' part that their gold was capable of persuading him to abandon Palestine had made the Sultan extremely angry. As he himself had told Herzl, he would never consider such a thing: it would mean giving up a land that not only Moslems but people of many other faiths considered sacred. He believed that it belonged to Ottomans of all religions, and feared that if Palestine and the holy city of Jerusalem were ever to fall into Zionist hands, the peace and stability of the entire region would be threatened. Pursuing this line of thought, Abdülhamid now considered the question of whether the Jewish community would sanction an attack on the Ottoman state; in the end, he came to the conclusion that this theory, too, was implausible. After all, the Ottomans had for centuries offered sanctuary to the Jews, giving them the freedom to live and worship in accordance with their beliefs and customs at a time when they were being made the victims of pogroms in Europe; at the end of the fifteenth century many had been expelled from Spain, and those who remained had been persecuted by the Spanish Inquisition. He also knew that Britain had recently made the Jewish people an offer of land in Africa, and that this offer was due to be considered at the Seventh Zionist Conference, which was to take place in a few weeks' time; this fact alone argued against the making of an attempt on his life at this precise juncture.

A new thought then occurred to Abdülhamid: for a decade, he had been denounced for his merciless suppression of the Armenian uprisings. Burgeoning nationalist sentiment among the Armenians had led to the establishment of a revolutionary movement that threatened the security of the Empire's eastern provinces, and he would not – indeed, he felt he could not – tolerate such treacherous behaviour from any community living within his borders, no matter who they might be. It was not just Armenian men who had been attacking Ottoman garrisons, but women, too: Armenian women armed with rifles, daggers and axes had attacked Ottoman soldiers and poisoned the wells that supplied them with water. In response, Abdülhamid had decided to have this insurrection suppressed by detachments of irregulars – Kurdish tribesmen and Turkic and Circassian brigands who patrolled the Empire's dangerous and disorderly frontier with Russia. The brutal persecution of Armenians that followed had led to widespread condemnation of the Sultan, but Abdülhamid believed that he had been obliged to act in this way in order to protect his empire from a very real threat. At the time he had seen no alternative to the use of irregulars; now, however, he regretted some of the more ruthless tactics to which these undisciplined troops had resorted in their drive to restore order to the region. Living with the consequences of his decision had not been easy, but live with it he must. "The Armenians. Yes, it will most likely be the Armenians," he concluded as his carriage approached the gate of the palace.

A group of foreign dignitaries had witnessed the whole scene outside the mosque from behind the white wrought iron railings of the Ambassadors' Terrace outside Yıldız Palace, which gave them an elevated position. On Sultan Abdülhamid's arrival, Baron Heinrich von Calice, the Austrian Ambassador, called out: "Vive le Sultan!" in heartfelt admiration for his bravery and composure in the face of such mayhem. These words prompted loud cheers from the other foreign diplomats, as well as from the hitherto silent crowd, which had been observing events in stunned silence. Once again the air was rent by rousing hurrahs from the soldiers, just as had been the case during the procession to the mosque earlier that afternoon. The Sultan acknowledged his people and the assembled dignitaries with a salute; then his carriage passed under the imposing archway of the Imperial Gate and he disappeared from view.

۞ ۞ ۞ ۞ ۞

Prince Yusuf İzzeddin Efendi, the eldest son of Sultan Abdülaziz, who following Kemaleddin's death was now second in line to the throne, had taken charge of the business of caring for the injured and arranging their transportation to hospital. Aghast at the horrific injuries that had been inflicted on these innocent people, he tried hard not to weep at the sight of so many with missing or shredded limbs, extensive, life-changing burns, and deep lacerations inflicted by flying shrapnel; in many of those affected, nails, glass shards and fragments of metal deeply embedded in flesh and bone were causing dramatic loss of blood. Immediately after the explosion it had been hard to breathe as the air, scorched by the blast and full of the acrid stench of gunpowder, had been heated by the merciless afternoon sun to form a suffocating, toxic mix; now, however, the dust was settling and the air was becoming clearer. Yusuf İzzeddin instructed the soldiers

370

of his regiment to dress all wounds as best they could by tearing strips from their shirts and using them as bandages, and he also ordered them to make improvised stretchers from anything they could find. The bodies of the dead were respectfully covered, ready to be taken to the nearest hammam, where they would be washed; later, after being identified by their grieving families, they would be taken away for burial.

The two princes following him in the order of seniority – Abdülhamid's younger brothers Süleyman and Vahideddin – had also assumed responsibilities. Süleyman, mindful that nothing should be disturbed until the evidence could be examined, had astutely ordered his men to create a cordon around the area from which the explosion seemed to have emanated. Vahideddin, meanwhile, had spoken to the other princes who had been present at the ceremony, and had arranged for the men of their regiments to form large military escorts so that the ladies could be accompanied back to their respective residences in the harem carriages as soon as possible. He also suggested that any superfluous regiments return to barracks immediately as all leave would no doubt be cancelled, having realised that if there were a large number of people in the vicinity, evidence could easily be disturbed, and this might hinder the ensuing investigation. His own regiment would remain at the scene of the explosion until all the dead and wounded had been removed.

Since Selahaddin held no military commission, his first thought had been to find his sisters and escort them back to their homes in person. His eyes scanned the surrounding area for Nihad, who had been standing next to him only seconds before, but his son had disappeared. Then he saw him near the gate amongst the scattered debris of glass, metal, blood and flesh: he was kneeling beside a mortally wounded horse, gently stroking its neck as it writhed about in pain. The round lamps mounted on top of the pillars at either side of the gate had shattered, and a piece of glass from one of them had pierced the horse's eye. Its body, littered with pieces of shrapnel, was drenched in the warm, sticky blood that was oozing relentlessly into the dust around it, and that was already attracting swarms of flies. Nihad tried in vain to soothe the dying horse. Its rider, a cavalry officer who only minutes before had looked so dashing sitting astride this beautiful chestnut-brown mare, lay dead, the limbs torn from his mutilated body by the force of the explosion – and yet his unmarked face wore a peaceful expression, as if he were sleeping. Nihad pulled the officer's blood-soaked pistol from its holster and held it to the horse's head with a shaking hand. He knew what he had to do. He steeled himself; then, muttering a prayer, he pulled back the trigger. The horse gave a convulsive shiver, then lay still beside its rider.

Selahaddin picked his way through the human wreckage to where Nihad was still kneeling beside the horse's body with a blank expression on his face. "Come away, my son," he said gently. "There is nothing more for us to do here." Placing an arm around Nihad's trembling shoulders, he helped him to his feet. "We must find your aunts and take them home." Together they headed slowly towards the Ladies' Lodge of the mosque with bowed heads.

By this time, the gendarmerie and Abdülhamid's palace police had started to arrive on the scene; seeing them begin to take control of the situation, Yusuf İzzeddin, Süleyman and Vahideddin reluctantly stepped aside to allow them to carry out their duties. Among the palace officials Selahaddin recognised Fehim Pasha, and a cold shiver ran down his spine. This brought him to his senses with a jolt: he quickened his pace, and hurried to find his sisters.

Even amidst all this chaos, protocol was still very much in evidence: as Selahaddin and Nihad approached the Ladies' Lodge, they saw the cloaked figures of Hadice, Fehime and Fatma climbing into the first of the harem carriages. The eunuch in attendance was about to close the door when Selahaddin shouted: "Stop! Just a moment!"

Recognising his voice, the three princesses were overcome with joy and relief: ever since the bomb had gone off, they had been imagining all manner of horrors. Through the carriage door they could now see their brother hurrying towards them with Nihad just a few steps behind.

Selahaddin, by now rather out of breath, leaned into the carriage to speak to his sisters. "Are you alright?" he asked anxiously. But before any of them could reply, Hadice – always the impulsive one of the three – threw decorum to the wind: unable to contain her feelings, she moved forward until she was balancing on the very edge of her seat, and wrapped her arms around her brother's neck.

"Oh, Selahaddin, it was awful! We were so worried about you!" she said.

Once he had broken free of Hadice's tight embrace, he repeated his question: "Well, you are alright now, aren't you?" Fehime and Fatma nodded and murmured a positive response, but he noticed that their hands were shaking; Fatma's face was streaked with tears.

"*Alhamdulillah*!" he said. "Then we have much to be thankful for. Nihad and I will ride home with you. I thought it would be better if we all stayed together for the rest of the day, so when we arrive at Çırağan, if you agree, I will send a letter to Yıldız asking if this may be allowed."

"Thank you, Selahaddin," Hadice replied. "As always, you are the very soul of consideration. After what has happened today, I could not bear to be apart from you and my sisters, and have no wish to return to my own *yalı*. And I am sure Fehime feels the same."

Fehime, too, thanked Selahaddin – but before he had stepped back from the carriage door she asked a question that he wished he did not have to answer. "We have heard that His Imperial Majesty is unharmed, but have many people been hurt?" The eunuch, who was now waiting to close the door, had seen little from his post outside the Ladies' Lodge, and was thus as eager to hear the reply as the three princesses were.

"Many are dead, and even more are badly injured. Please, my dear sisters, please promise me that you will not look through the windows as we drive out of the courtyard. I do not want you to see what lies there." And with that, Selahaddin signalled to the eunuch to shut the door.

A groom then approached leading two stallions by their bridles. Selahaddin and Nihad smiled, relieved that they were both unharmed. As soon as the two men had mounted their horses, they saw riding towards them the three eldest sons of Sultan Abdülhamid – the Princes Mehmed Selim, Mehmed Abdülkadir and Ahmed Nuri, who had come to escort their sisters and wives back to Yıldız Palace. They each raised their right hand to their heart in greeting, and as they came to a halt beside Selahaddin they bowed their heads to their elder cousin.

"*Selam aleyküm*, cousin. I trust your sisters are safe?" asked Selim.

"*Aleyküm selam*. Thank you – they are, *Alhamdulillah*," Selahaddin replied. "I understand that the Ladies' Lodge was untouched by the explosion, so you will find that your sisters and your wives are safe, too, but they will naturally be frightened and shaken." The three brothers were obviously relieved to hear this piece of news. "It is a great mercy that His Imperial Majesty was also unharmed," Selahaddin added.

"*Alhamdulillah*," Abdülhamid's sons answered in unison.

"I know that he will ensure that those responsible for this attack are brought to justice with all speed," Selahaddin went on.

Then he bade farewell to his cousins: he could see that the heavily armed military escort that was to accompany him and his sisters back to their homes was now assembling.

Riding over to speak to the captain, he informed him that everyone would be going to the Çırağan Palace, adding that he himself would take full responsibility for this change of plan. The captain did not argue: in view of present circumstances, he was sure that no one at Yıldız would object – not even Cevher Ağa. His men surrounded the carriage, following behind Selahaddin and Nihad as the party rode out of the gates past the chestnut mare and its fallen rider, whose body now lay under a bloodstained cloth.

As the carriage drove through the gates, Fatma leaned forward, unable to contain her curiosity. She noticed how they were contorted and twisted, and how the lamps above them were shattered beyond repair – but then she noticed something else.

"Don't look," Hadice warned.

It was too late. What Fatma saw – briefly, but it was enough – was a man kneeling on the ground rocking backwards and forwards in inconsolable grief and anguish. He was holding in his arms the limp, blood-soaked body of a young child wearing a bright green jacket with shiny brass buttons. Close by, a small red fez lay among the debris.

CHAPTER NINETEEN

The Holy Land

Late Summer 1905

A MONTH had passed since that traumatic day at the Hamidiye Mosque when an attempt had been made on the life of the Sultan. That terrible carnage, which would have been disturbing enough on a battlefield, but which called forth deep feelings of horror and outrage when seen at a place of worship, had not been erased from anyone's memory; Fatma, in particular, was badly scarred by everything she had witnessed. On their return to the Çırağan Palace, Selahaddin had immediately despatched Zülüflü Ağa and Kasım Ağa to the scene of devastation to offer help to those who had been wounded in the explosion. They had taken with them baskets hurriedly filled with clean linen and bottles of carbolic acid so that they could clean and dress the wounds of the injured, and had returned a few hours later when the last of the wounded had been taken to hospital. Fatma had asked Kasım Ağa to keep a lookout for a boy in a green jacket with shiny brass buttons, but the dutiful eunuch had not been able to learn anything of his fate. The image of the little boy cradled in the arms of his father still haunted Fatma's dreams and tormented her long, restless nights.

The day after the explosion, the Armenian Revolutionary

Federation had delivered notes to the French, Russian and Austrian Embassies claiming responsibility for the atrocity: Abdülhamid had been right in his conclusion as to the identity of the perpetrators. Details of the attack had also been published in the various opposition journals, and sensational headlines had appeared in the foreign newspapers. The *New York Times* had printed the sensational headline: *'Bomb Misses Sultan: Missile Explodes Close to the Turkish Ruler.'* The local press, however, remained completely silent as – predictably – censorship had been imposed on all reporting of the incident, but most Ottoman citizens felt a strong sense of indignation, and even Abdülhamid's most virulent opponents condemned the outrage.

The Committee of Union and Progress, which was the umbrella organisation of the Young Turk movement, had set itself apart from the view of the majority: at the end of August it had issued a statement saying: *'We express our heartfelt regret for the deaths of the innocent – if any can be found amongst those who perished while guarding Abdülhamid.'* Selahaddin and his family had been appalled at the callousness of this statement, and the high regard in which he himself had previously held the Young Turk movement was greatly diminished. There could be no excuse for regicide, whatever the political motives might be, and there could certainly be no justification for the cold-blooded murder of innocent bystanders.

All European and many foreign heads of state had added their voices to the general condemnation, and had immediately telegraphed messages of solidarity and support to Yıldız. Sovereigns and presidents throughout the civilised world knew all too well that a current of revolutionary ferment was sweeping across the world with no respect for borders or geographical boundaries, and this development was of deep concern to the ruling elites of all nations. The foundations of the established order were trembling, as if a hidden hand was shaking them with ever-increasing violence.

Asım Ağa, Murad's devoted and resourceful scribe, had remained in the family's service after the death of the deposed Sultan, and a week after the attack he had managed to obtain for Selahaddin a copy of the report on the bombing drawn up by the Beşiktaş Police. It stated that twenty-six people had been killed in the explosion at the Yıldız Mosque – four journalists and three soldiers, the remainder being civilians and palace officials. In addition, fifty-eight people had been injured, including a lady who had been watching the ceremony from the Ambassador's Terrace – which went to show how immensely powerful the explosion had been. Fatma took some comfort in the fact that the report made no mention of a child, and her sisters tried to convince her that the little boy about whom she constantly fretted must surely have survived. Nihad, meanwhile, continued to have nightmares, and they grew worse than ever when he read that twenty horses had perished on that dreadful day.

Two commissions had been set up to investigate the incident, but very little of any consequence had been uncovered. Abdülhamid had then appointed Necib Melhame Pasha, a trusted confidant of his, to lead the investigation. A Maronite Christian from the Ottoman province of Lebanon and a devoted member of the Eastern Catholic Church, this man had a reputation for being an honest and extremely clever servant of the state who in addition possessed a charming manner. He was a brilliant lawyer committed to ensuring that justice prevailed: making no assumptions, he worked with diligence and efficiency, meticulously collecting evidence, punctiliously interviewing witnesses and relentlessly interrogating suspects. Necib Melhame Pasha had earned the Sultan's respect by successfully carrying out his duties at the posts he had previously held – first at the Ottoman Embassy in Paris, and subsequently as Imperial Commissioner to Sofia. Selahaddin remarked that his powers of observation and deduction were equal to those of Mr Sherlock Holmes, Abdülhamid's fictional hero. Within a week, Melhame Pasha had arrested many of those involved in the plot, including a Belgian anarchist by the name of Edouard Joris. Over seven hundred people had been detained during the course of his efforts to round up all the suspects, but those whose innocence had been established were quickly released and duly compensated, while those deemed likely to have played a part in the plot were held for trial.

Every development in the investigation was followed closely at the Çırağan Palace; Selahaddin and his family were shocked, intrigued and amazed by turns at the daily discoveries and revelations.

۞ ۞ ۞ ۞ ۞

In addition to following the investigation, during late July and early August Selahaddin and Nihad had spent many hours sitting in the shade of the trees in the palace gardens reading articles in the foreign press about the Seventh Zionist Congress, which was being held in Basle at that time. Calls for an independent Jewish state were being made with increasing vociferousness by the Zionist movement, and the recent death of its founder and leader Theodor Herzl had done nothing to reduce their insistence. What had prompted Herzl to start the movement was his feelings of revulsion at the wave of anti-Jewish sentiment that had been called forth by the trial in 1894 of Alfred Dreyfus, a young Jewish officer in a French artillery regiment. Dreyfus had been falsely accused of handing over military secrets to the German Military Attaché in Paris; the court had found him guilty, and he had been sentenced to life imprisonment on Devil's Island in French Guiana. Herzl had reported on the case for a Viennese newspaper at the time, and in doing so had been appalled by the virulent anti-Semitism aroused by the trial – so much so that he had become convinced that the full assimilation of Jewish people in Europe would never be achieved, as hatreds and prejudices ran too deep. The only solution, as far as he could see, was the setting up of an independent Jewish state. He had advocated the establishment of a state of this kind in Palestine, and as a result the Ottoman Empire had acquired yet another powerful enemy.

"There are few questions on which I agree wholeheartedly with Sultan Hamid, but I certainly admire his steadfast refusal to accept Zionist enticements to sell Jerusalem for a few gold pieces. It would be like selling our soul to the devil," Selahaddin told his children one afternoon while they were having a picnic on the lawns.

He had read that despite Herzl's recommendation that the Congress should accept the British government's offer of territory in British East Africa – a scheme that had become known as the 'Uganda Plan' – they had voted to reject it. Following the anti-Jewish pogroms in Russia, Joseph Chamberlain, the British Colonial Secretary, had proposed that an area of the Mau Plateau be assigned to the Jewish people, ignoring protests from the native tribes in Kenya, which was a British colony. Herzl believed that accepting this offer would enable a temporary refuge to be found for all those fleeing the pogroms – without in any way compromising the ultimate aim of all Zionists, which was the foundation of a Jewish state in Palestine, as promised in the Torah. The predominant opinion among Zionists, however, was that as they had at last obtained the support of the British government in the matter of setting up a Jewish homeland somewhere, albeit under British suzerainty, if they agreed to go anywhere other than Palestine it would prejudice their chances of realising their dream of a Jewish state in the Holy Land. It was this difference of opinion that had caused the recent schism in the Zionist movement.

"You talk of 'selling Jerusalem for a few gold pieces', Father," said Nihad, "but a lot more money than that was involved. From what I understand, the Zionists offered to pay off the outrageously high Ottoman foreign debt, and to lend us their support on the Armenian issue by organising a propaganda campaign in our favour throughout Europe, thus raising our empire's prestige."

"The Sanjak of Jerusalem, as we call Palestine, is worth more than all the gold in the world, and all the prestige," Selahaddin retorted in a tone that showed he had been vexed by Nihad's remark. "We must never agree to allow unrestricted Jewish settlement there, or willingly give autonomy to the Zionists. Jerusalem is not a commodity that can be haggled over. The Ottoman Empire is not something that can be bought and sold!" He always became impassioned when the subject of the Sanjak of Jerusalem was raised. "It is a holy place, sacred to us all, and it must never be allowed to become the property of the people of one faith to the exclusion of all others. Mark my words: that would be a recipe for catastrophe. I fear that it is only we Ottomans who understand this; indeed, it is our understanding of this fact that has enabled us to rule Palestine and the holy city successfully, ensuring that their peace is not disturbed, for the last four hundred years."

Selahaddin went on to explain to his children that in order to maintain stability in the Holy Land, Abdülhamid had felt the need to restrict Jewish settlement in Palestine and to personally acquire nearly eighty percent of the land there. "Hamid has been accused of being covetous and anti-Semitic, which is preposterous: there are more Jewish people living in freedom within our empire than anywhere else in the world. Many of them hold high office in our government or are prominent in commerce, and are well-respected subjects of the Sultan. Not only that, but our city of Salonica has the largest Jewish population of any city in the world, and is a thriving, prosperous place thanks to the freedoms enjoyed by its people. Hamid's policy is designed, purely and simply, to protect the integrity of our empire's borders: he fears the rapaciously acquisitive nature of European Jewry, and rightly so. In this matter, I am in complete agreement with him!"

"It is sad that the rest of the world, and even Jewish people themselves, often forget that it was we Turkish Moslems who welcomed the Jews to our state when they were expelled from the countries of Western Europe during the time of the Crusades, and later during that of the Inquisition," Nihad said, mindful of the need to say something that would appease his father rather than irritate him. Being extremely well versed in European and Middle Eastern history, he looked forward with eager anticipation to the day when he would be able to use his knowledge in the service of the Empire. "In fact, was it not the English – the new friends of the Zionists – who began the persecution by expelling the entire Jewish population of their country in 1290 after two hundred years of brutal and unjust treatment?"

Selahaddin raised his eyebrows slightly, impressed by his son's knowledge. Then he nodded; this encouraged Nihad to go on with his historical lecture. "I understand that the Edict of Expulsion remained in force for over three hundred and fifty years," he said, "and that the Jews were only permitted to return to England under the Protectorate of Oliver Cromwell. Given Britain's own shameful past misdeeds, and in particular her arrogant and ruthless treatment of the native peoples currently living under her rule in Africa and India, it is nothing short of laughable that the British government should now be trying to portray itself as the defender of the world's oppressed peoples." Everyone smiled at this perceptive remark. Nihad deeply mistrusted the British: having studied their Machiavellian foreign policy, he had a sense of foreboding that one day they would bring about the destruction of all he held dear.

Then Behiye spoke up for the first time since the discussion had begun. "Father," she said, "must it not have been extremely tempting to accept those Jewish offers of financial help? After all, it is our foreign debt that is crippling us and preventing us from carrying out the reforms we need in order to develop our empire. The money might have paid for a lot more railways, roads, schools and hospitals, and we could have used some of it to strengthen and modernise our army and navy."

"You are right, of course, Behiye," Selahaddin said wistfully. "It is true that the Empire would have benefited hugely from a substantial influx of capital, but some things are more important than money. We must admire the Sultan for acting in accordance with his principles and his sense of honour. The reply he gave to Theodor Herzl's proposal made such a profound impression on me that it has stuck in my memory. It goes like this: *'I cannot give away a handful of the soil of this land as it is not my own: it belongs to all those Ottomans who fought for its sake, and watered it with their blood. The Jews may keep their gold; if the Islamic Caliphate is one day destroyed, then they will be able to take Palestine for nothing. While I am alive I would rather push a sword into my body than see the land of Palestine taken away from the Ottoman Empire. I will not start cutting the limbs from the body of our empire while it still breathes.'"*

Selahaddin noted with satisfaction the way his two sons and his five daughters held their heads a little higher as he recounted the speech Abdülhamid had made to Herzl's diplomatic agent Philipp Newlinski, who had presented the Zionist offers to him. He was proud to see that this powerful rhetoric had touched their young Ottoman hearts, etching itself deeply into their trusting Moslem souls. Yes, he told himself – *Subhan'Allah!* They understand what is at stake.

☪ ☪ ☪ ☪ ☪

September 21ˢᵗ 1905

Fuad came running out into the gardens to join his father and his older siblings as they sat relaxing in the sun, sipping mandarin sherbet and watching the seagulls soar and hover above the Bosphorus. The wind that lifted the birds' wings carried with it a slight autumn chill, but nevertheless the mid-September sun was still pleasantly warm.

"Well, Fuad, and what did you learn today?" Selahaddin asked his son as he sat down and set about eating sugared almonds.

"In the morning I did some mathematics, Baba, followed by some writing practice. Hodja Efendi was very pleased with me because I did not need the abacus to help me with my mathematics, and because there were no blots or smudges in my writing, and I did not make any mistakes," he replied with obvious pride.

"That is excellent, Fuad," his father said appreciatively. "I am pleased to hear that you are doing so well in your lessons."

384

"Thank you, Baba," Fuad responded, pleased at the compliment. "Then, this afternoon, Hodja Efendi showed me a map of the Levant, and I had to point out the different *vilayets* and *sanjaks*, and all the important cities – places like Aleppo, Beirut, Damascus and Jerusalem. They all sound wonderful; I hope to be able to go to them all one day!" He sounded genuinely enthusiastic; it was a rare thing for him to be fully engaged with his studies, but on this occasion learning about these fascinating cities had triggered his ever-active imagination.

"Do you remember from your lessons why Jerusalem is so important?" Selahaddin asked: the Holy Land was still very much on his mind. Although Fuad was a bright boy, unlike his elder brother he was not a natural student. He found it hard to concentrate, and it was difficult for him to retain all the pieces of information his tutors imparted to him every day. Consequently, he now began to fidget in his chair, afraid of giving the wrong answer and thus disappointing his father – in fact, he began to wish that he had gone to see his mother in her rooms instead of coming outside.

Behiye, who was always very protective towards Fuad, saw his discomfort and tried to distract her father by offering him another glass of mandarin sherbet. At the same time, she attempted to change the subject to that of a piece of happy news they had received only a few days before – the birth of Prince Mehmed Abid, Abdülhamid's new son; everyone at Çırağan had heard the five-gun salute announcing the new prince's arrival, and the 'Ceremony of the Procession of the Cradle' was to be held in two days' time. As it was now a little over a year since Murad's death, Abdülhamid had finally decided to invite Selahaddin and his family to Court, and Behiye and her sisters were very much looking forward to their first formal visit to Yıldız. They had heard wonderful stories from their aunts of the pomp and circumstance that surrounded the birth of the sovereign's children, and were eager to witness it – and, of course, to meet their extended family.

"Father, shall I invite Aunt Hadice and Aunt Fehime to Çırağan before the ceremony for Prince Abid on Saturday, so that we can all arrive together as a family?" Behiye asked, trying to sound as nonchalant as possible. In actual fact, her original intention had been to suggest this as soon as the invitation arrived from Yıldız: she knew that Hadice would be feeling anxious about seeing her cousin Naime for the first time since the scandal – especially in the presence of all the ladies at Court. The two had still not spoken to one another; in the Ladies' Lodge at the Yıldız Mosque on that fateful day in July, they had exchanged no more than a sideways glance.

"That is an excellent idea, my dear Behiye," her father replied; her ploy had only delayed the inevitable, however, and Selahaddin now repeated his question to Fuad. He was quite accustomed to his daughter's well-meaning interventions, particularly where Fuad was concerned, and although he loved her for them he was not going to allow himself to become sidetracked.

To everyone's surprise, Fuad immediately gave a brisk, confident reply. "I do remember, Baba," he answered. "It is important because it is a sacred place for all three Abrahamic faiths – Islam, Christianity and Judaism." Privately, he blessed his sister for buying him enough time to recall what he had learned in his lessons that afternoon!

"Very good, my boy. Well done. Now, Adile, can you tell me why Jerusalem is important to people of the Jewish faith?"

Adile, who up to that point had been playing with her bracelet, looked up, somewhat startled to hear herself being singled out. But her father's choice of one of his daughters, rather than one of his sons, to answer the question was deliberate: Selahaddin attached great importance to education, and being something of a modernist – like his father before him – he believed that girls should receive a similar education to the one boys were given. His daughters, therefore, had been taught by the same tutors as his sons, and had studied many of the same subjects, though military history had remained outside their curriculum, being replaced by needlework.

Selahaddin felt that intelligent women could make an invaluable contribution to any society. The traditional role of an educated woman was to provide support for her husband, offer him informed advice and ensure that their children received a thorough and well-rounded education; in the new world that was currently emerging, however, it was his belief that women should play a more equal role with men. In 1893 New Zealand had become the first country in the world to give women the right to vote, and Selahaddin had welcomed this development: he thought it would not be long before other progressive nations followed her example. Hitherto only Australia, her neighbour, had done so – this had occurred in 1902 – but a precedent had been set that the liberal states of Europe would surely adopt in time. Selahaddin had resolved that if he ever became Sultan, he would introduce female suffrage in the Ottoman Empire, too; in fact, this was something his father had advised him to do. In short, he believed it to be imperative that women should be well educated, and thus adequately prepared for the greater freedom and equality that would inevitably come.

The eyes of all Adile's siblings were upon her as she turned to answer her father. She was the shyest of Selahaddin's daughters, and did not enjoy being the centre of attention; nevertheless, she plucked up courage and began. "Well,

Baba, the Jewish people believe that the world was created from the Foundation Stone, which lies under the Dome of the Rock in *al-Haram al-Sharif* – the Noble Sanctuary, or 'Temple Mount', as the Jews and the Christians call it – in Jerusalem," she said. "They also believe that Allah created Adam from dust that had been gathered from that holy place, and that Adam and his sons Cain and Abel, and later Noah, offered sacrifices to Him at that spot," she went on. "Er … isn't that right, Father?" she asked, all at once overcome by diffidence.

"Yes, yes, my beautiful daughter," Selahaddin replied. "But tell us more about Temple Mount."

"Temple Mount is also the place where Jewish people believe that the Prophet Abraham sacrificed his son Isaac, thus showing submission to the will of Allah. But then a ram appeared and was sacrificed in his stead."

"But Baba," Fuad interrupted, "I thought it was his first-born son Ishmael that Abraham offered as a sacrifice to Allah, not his second son Isaac. And I also thought the sacrifice was made on Mount Arafat, just outside Mecca."

"You are absolutely right, Fuad. Well done!" Selahaddin said, smiling at his youngest child; to tell the truth, he was more than a little surprised by the extent of his knowledge. "But your sister is right, too," he went on. "In fact, you have identified two of the differences in belief between Judaism and Islam."

Adile then continued where she had left off. "King David made Jerusalem the capital of the first Kingdom of Israel and Judea, and the centre of worship; then his son King Solomon built the First Temple on the site of the Foundation Stone. The inner chamber, known as the Holy of Holies, housed the sacred Ark of the Covenant, which contained the two stone tablets inscribed with the Ten Commandments that were received by the Prophet Moses. The First Temple was destroyed by the Babylonians, so King Herod built the Second Temple – but the Romans destroyed that, too, when they sacked the city in 70AD. All that is left of that temple is the Western Wall, which is where Jews pray today when they make their pilgrimage to Jerusalem to mourn the destruction of both temples. Have I said everything, Father?"

"Yes, I think you have mentioned all the most important facts about the city of Jerusalem. Very good! So tell me – is there anything you would like to add about the Sanjak of Jerusalem, or about Palestine as a whole?"

"Well, I think that the Sanjak of Jerusalem, and in fact Palestine as a whole, is important to them because in their eyes it is the 'promised land' – the land of Canaan that was promised by Allah to Abraham, his son Isaac and his grandson Jacob. After the Israelites had followed Moses out of Egypt, they occupied this land; the Zionists claim descent from these people, and thus claim the land for themselves. However, the Jewish people abandoned Palestine after the Romans had destroyed Jerusalem, so I would argue that in doing so they abandoned their rights to it. What do you think, Father?"

"We will discuss that later, Adile," Selahaddin replied. "But please go on."

"Well, for the most part, the Jewish people went to live in Europe and parts of North Africa. Only a few remained, so how can their descendants possibly lay claim to it after almost two thousand years have gone by?" Adile sat back in her chair and rested against the cushion, feeling relieved that she had remembered her history to her father's satisfaction.

"You are absolutely right, my sweet daughter," Selahaddin said proudly. "I can add nothing to what you have told us. You have given a very thorough answer to my question, and

I commend you for it. I also agree with you that the Zionists' belief that they have a legitimate claim to land they chose to abandon two millennia ago is absurd. Can you imagine our family returning to our Turkish homeland in the Altai Mountains and laying claim to tribal lands that we left a thousand years ago? It would be ridiculous. The whole world would laugh at us – but they do not laugh at the Zionists, so we must act with caution."

He then turned to Safiye, Adile's 'twin'. "My dear gentle Safiye," he said, "can you tell us why the Sanjak of Jerusalem and the city itself are so important to the Christians?"

"Yes, of course, Baba," Safiye said with a happy smile; she was always eager to please him, and now willingly recalled her lessons. "The land is important to every denomination of the Christian faith because it is the setting for the story of the Prophet Jesus," she began. "He was born in Bethlehem, and raised in Nazareth. He travelled all over the region and spent a lot of time by the Sea of Galilee, where he delivered many sermons. According to Christian beliefs, it is here that he healed people and performed miracles such as the feeding of the five thousand at Tabgha. Consequently, throughout the Holy Land there are a large number of Christian monasteries, shrines and pilgrimage sites belonging to the various branches of the Eastern and Western Christian churches. The city of Jerusalem, however, is the holiest place on earth for Christians. It is where Jesus drove the merchants and money-changers out of the courtyards of King Solomon's Temple. It is also where he shared a 'Last Supper' with his disciples, after which he prayed and meditated in the ancient olive groves of the Garden of Gethsemane, at the foot of the Mount of Olives. He was then arrested, put on trial by the Jewish elders and Pontius Pilate, the Roman governor, and condemned to death. Jesus was crucified on the hill of

Golgotha, just outside the city walls, and his body was then placed in a tomb. But perhaps the most important thing for adherents of the Christian faith is that according to their beliefs, it was in Jerusalem that his resurrection took place – followed forty days later by his ascension to heaven from the top of the Mount of Olives."

Safiye seemed to be enjoying her father's attention. She was a diligent student, and had read a great deal about the history of the holy city. Now she continued: "For Christians, the most sacred site of all is the Church of the Holy Sepulchre, which stands in the Christian quarter of the city. It was built over the site of the crucifixion and the rock tomb in which Jesus' body was placed, and has been a place of pilgrimage ever since the Emperor Constantine converted to Christianity and ordered its construction. Pilgrims come to walk the 'Way of Sorrows', which leads through the heart of old Jerusalem and up to the Church, following the path that Jesus would have taken as he carried the cross. Inside the Church are many holy relics, including part of what is believed to be the 'True Cross', and the 'Stone of Anointing', on which Jesus' body was anointed with oil by Joseph of Arimathea. The Church also encloses the 'Rock of Calvary', which has a deep cleft into which the cross is believed to have been placed. The Church of the Holy Sepulchre is the seat of the Greek Orthodox Patriarch of Jerusalem, who has the highest authority in the Church, but ownership is shared between the Greek Orthodox Church, the Roman Catholic Church and the Armenian Apostolic Church. The Orthodox Coptic, Syriac and Ethiopian Christians also have certain rights and privileges, which are jealously guarded. The main place of worship is owned by the Greek Orthodox Church, but there are over thirty small chapels and designated areas of worship within the Church that belong to the various other

391

denominations. These include the Armenian Chapel of the Division of Raiment, where the Roman soldiers divided Jesus' clothes among themselves after his crucifixion, and the Franciscan chapel that is believed to have been built over the place where Mary, Jesus' mother, and Mary Magdalene saw him after his supposed resurrection. So … for Christians, Jerusalem is a place that is associated not just with deep sorrow and pain, but also with hope – and that is why it is so important to them," she concluded.

At this point, Fuad broke in. "Baba, I do not believe that the Prophet Jesus rose from the dead," he said. Once more, Selahaddin was pleased that Fuad had been giving his full attention to what was being said. Now he turned to his youngest child.

"Neither do I, my dear boy," he replied. "There is much that we Moslems and our Christian brothers agree about, but on this point we differ completely. However, Fuad, we must respect others' beliefs." He held out his hands towards Safiye, and she got up and went to kneel at his feet. Selahaddin kissed her head and gently stroked her hair. "Your interest in things of this kind is admirable, my little yellow rose, and so is your knowledge of them. Your mother would have been proud of you. As you know, her dying wish was that you should become a scholar – and I believe that *Inshallah*, one day you will."

Selahaddin often called Safiye his 'Yellow Rose': she had been born at the end of June, when everything was in bloom, and every summer until her mother's death he had filled the vases in her rooms with yellow roses from the flower gardens. Now, he did the same for Safiye every year on her birthday.

Selahaddin then addressed all his children. "I would like to tell you something interesting about the Church of the Holy

Sepulchre – something that I believe illustrates the Islamic principle of mutual respect and religious toleration. As I am sure you will remember, Jerusalem surrendered to the Caliph Omar in 637, and after that an agreement was signed guaranteeing freedom of worship for all the city's Jewish and Christian inhabitants. The end of oppressive Roman, and subsequent Eastern Roman, rule over the Jews allowed them to live and worship freely in Jerusalem for the first time in nearly five hundred years. Take note, my children, that this happened thanks to the just and tolerant nature of Moslem rule. Also at this time, it was agreed that the ancient cast-iron key to the Church of the Holy Sepulchre would be given to a Moslem family; they would then become the custodians of the Church, and would pass this sacred duty down from father to son. This was done in order to avoid conflict between the many Christian denominations, all of whom wanted to possess the key. A descendant of this family still holds the key today, and is responsible for opening the door to the Church every morning and locking it again every night. This tradition has continued for over twelve hundred years, and has helped to ensure peaceful coexistence between the followers of the various religions in Jerusalem."

Selahaddin now took a few sugar-coated almonds in his palm and popped one in his mouth; falling silent, he gave his children some time to think over what he had just told them. Atiye, knowing that she was likely to be picked on to answer the next question, kept her head down in the forlorn hope that she would be overlooked; meanwhile, she went on stroking Kaplan, her pet kitten, who lay curled up on her lap and was purring loudly.

"Now, Atiye, I would like you to explain to us why Jerusalem is a sacred place for Moslems."

Atiye stopped stroking Kaplan and reluctantly began to

speak. She was the least studious of Selahaddin's daughters – indeed, her lack of interest in her studies was a source of constant frustration to her tutors.

"For us, Baba," she said, "Jerusalem is the third most sacred city after Mecca and Medina. It is important as it is from there that Muhammed, peace be upon him, ascended to the seven heavens and spoke to the prophets before receiving the Second Pillar of Islam from Allah." Atiye then went back to stroking Kaplan – who blinked slowly, flicked his tail and carried on purring. She had been more than a little bored by the conversation about Jerusalem, and wanted to continue chatting with her sisters about the dresses they were to wear to the Ceremony of the Cradle for Prince Abid, which was going to be held at Yıldız.

Selahaddin sighed. He had given the easiest task of all to Atiye, but even so she had not distinguished herself by her answer. "Atiye, your two sisters have given comprehensive and detailed answers, but I fear you have been much too concise. I hope it is not because you have forgotten what you have been taught," he said, giving his youngest daughter a disapproving look.

"I am sorry, Baba," she answered – though her tone betrayed more sullenness than contrition. "And I have not forgotten what I have been taught."

"That is something, I suppose, my beautiful daughter," her father said. "If only you could show more enthusiasm for what is truly important, and less for everything that is frivolous! Come now, restore my good humour: tell me what else you know about the subject."

Atiye obediently did as she was bidden. Ejecting Kaplan from her lap (with difficulty, as he tried to hang on with his claws), she put on her most serious expression. "One evening in the year 610, the Prophet Muhammed was resting at the

394

Kaaba in Mecca when the Angel Gabriel appeared before him and told him he was to go on a 'Night Journey'," she began. "Buraq, the heavenly steed, had accompanied the angel, and now stood before Muhammed, waiting for him to mount. When the Prophet did so the handsome, white-winged beast bucked at first, but was soon soothed by the archangel. They travelled swiftly to Jerusalem and landed at the Noble Sanctuary, which is called 'Temple Mount' by the Jews and the Christians. Muhammed first tethered Buraq to the Western Wall, then led the prophets and the angels in prayer."

"Hmm," Selahaddin said, trying not to show how pleased he was by Atiye's account and hoping she would continue as well as she had started. "So tell us what happened later."

"After the Caliph Omar had conquered Jerusalem, he had the first Al-Aqsa Mosque built on this site, but during the time of the Fatimid Caliphate it was replaced by the Al-Aqsa Mosque we see today – the one that was later restored under Ottoman rule. Its name actually means 'the Farthest Mosque', and it was called this because of all the places where Muhammed prayed, this was the furthest from Mecca. In a courtyard within the complex there is an octagonal marble structure that is known as 'the Dome of the Prophet' because this is believed to be the precise spot where he knelt in prayer."

"Well, that was much better, Atiye," Selahaddin responded. By now his good humour had returned, but his face still wore a stern expression – for his daughter's benefit. "Could you now please tell us what happened when the Prophet Muhammed, peace be upon him, had finished praying?"

"Very well, Baba," Atiye said. Then she continued: "Once Muhammed had finished praying, he remounted Buraq and ascended through the seven heavens, meeting and talking with the seven prophets – Adam, John the Baptist, Jesus, Joseph, Idris, Aaron, Moses and finally Abraham – as he passed through each of their domains."

"May I interrupt you for a moment?" Selahaddin interjected. "I would like to ask you a question about the prophets."

"Of course, Baba," said Atiye, rather nervously. She cast a quick glance at Safiye, who gave her an encouraging smile.

"Of all the prophets you have mentioned, which one is not acknowledged as such by the Christians?"

Atiye glanced once again at Safiye, who mouthed the answer to her.

"Idris, Baba," Atiye replied.

Selahaddin had in fact seen all that had happened, but in order to make it appear that he had not, he turned his head to one side, coughed, and cleared his throat. It would, he thought to himself, be churlish to reprimand his daughters for their collusion at this point – after they had both given such satisfying explanations. "Very good! The Bible makes no mention of Idris, although many scholars accept that Idris and Enoch, the Christian prophet, are in fact one and the same. Anyway, that was just an aside. Please continue."

"Very well, Baba. After Muhammed had met the prophets and talked with them, he came to the Abode of the Righteous – Paradise – and there Allah spoke to him: He said He wanted His followers to offer prayers to Him fifty times a day. Then Muhammed left His presence and began to descend to earth once more, but Moses stopped him and persuaded him to re-enter Allah's presence and ask for the number of times prayers were offered to be reduced, on the grounds that fifty times a day was too often to be practical. It is written that initially, Allah agreed that ten times a day would suffice, but later He decided that Muhammed's followers should pray five times a day – and in this way the Second Pillar of Islam was revealed. Muhammed then returned to Mecca on Buraq."

Here, Atiye paused. Kaplan was about to jump back onto her lap, so she bent down to gently shoo him away. Swishing his tail angrily, he went over to Fuad, who never refused his attentions. On this occasion, however, he was in for a surprise: Fuad, thinking that his father might be angry with him if he gave his attention to a cat when such serious matters were under discussion, turned him away. But at that point, his father intervened.

"Fuad, there is no need to make Kaplan feel rejected," he said. "The poor creature has no idea what we are talking about."

"Thank you, Baba," Fuad replied, and lifted Kaplan onto his lap, where he made himself deliciously comfortable – and promptly stuck his claws into Fuad's knee, which thin cotton summer trousers were powerless to protect. Selahaddin saw the grimace on his son's face as he suppressed a yelp of pain, but his own smile of amusement was brief enough to escape anyone's attention.

"My dear Atiye," he said, "I am sorry for the interruption. Please continue. Could you perhaps tell us a little about the Dome of the Rock?"

"Thank you, Baba, I will," said Atiye, grateful more for the breathing space than for the invitation to proceed. She glanced over at her brother, who was now lavishing attention on her cat, and felt a pang of jealousy. Kaplan was making it only too obvious that he was just as fond of Fuad as he was of her, and she could not prevent herself from feeling a pang of resentment. She soon collected herself, however, and began: "The Dome of the Rock was built inside the Al-Aqsa Mosque complex to mark the place where Muhammed ascended to heaven, and that is why it is regarded as extremely sacred in Islam. Also within the mosque complex is the Dome of the Chain. This is the place where humanity will be tested on the Day of Judgement: only those deemed by Allah to be righteous and just will be able to pass through the chain."

"That is excellent, Atiye!" said Selahaddin. "Well done!"

"Thank you, Baba," Atiye replied, mentally heaving a sigh of relief.

"Just one more thing, though."

At this, Atiye felt a sudden tightening in her stomach. Just as she had thought her ordeal was over …

"And what is that, Baba?"

"Could you say a few words about Jerusalem in connection with the *qibla*?"

Atiye felt relief wash over her once more: she had anticipated being asked a far more difficult question, and was only too aware that Safiye would be unable to prompt her if she was required to say more than a word or two.

"Certainly, Baba," she began – somewhat briskly, with what she hoped was an air of confidence. "Muhammed at first decreed that the *qibla* should point in the direction of Jerusalem, Islam being in some ways a continuation, and in other ways a renewal, of previous Abrahamic faiths. In fact, the first mosques built in Medina faced Jerusalem, not Mecca; later, however, Muhammed changed his mind and decreed that the direction of the *qibla* should be towards the Kaaba."

"Very good! Brief, but to the point! So you see, Atiye, there is no need to be afraid of knowledge and learning. You are every bit as intellectually capable as your sisters."

"Thank you, Baba," said Atiye, wondering if this time she would be allowed to return to her daydreams.

But Selahaddin had not quite finished. "I would be pleased, however, if you showed it more often."

At this, Atiye's face coloured slightly, and her gaze was turned downwards. Selahaddin then said: "Before we conclude our discussion on Jerusalem, I would like to add just one more thing, which is that many of the Prophet Muhammed's companions lived in Jerusalem and were buried there, and this increased the city's religious significance even further."

Selahaddin fell silent, wondering whether this was the moment to return to the subject of Zionist ambitions.

"Baba!" said Fuad, interrupting his father's train of thought. There was a note of urgency in his voice.

"Yes, my son?" Turning to look at him, Selahaddin was surprised to see an agonised expression on his face.

"Er … well, it's just that …" Fuad began hesitantly. "Would you mind if I took Kaplan off my lap? He has been digging his claws into me for the past ten minutes. If it goes on any longer, I am afraid he will draw blood." Atiye smiled secretly to herself. Perhaps Kaplan did favour her, after all!

"Of course, of course, my son. But you do not need to ask my permission for a thing like that. And anyway, if the cat is troubling you, why did you not tell me earlier?"

Fuad did not reply: he was too busy extricating himself from Kaplan, who was hanging on with grim determination.

Looking up, Selahaddin noticed that the shadows had lengthened: the warm afternoon was drawing to a close. He heaved a sigh. "Well, I think I will leave you now, and pay my respects to my mother before we dine this evening," he said. Selahaddin was a dutiful son to Reftarıdil: it was his custom to visit her in her rooms after breakfast, and again before dinner. The children stood as Selahaddin got up from his chair and made his way across the lawns to the palace harem.

As soon as their father had disappeared, Atiye thanked Safiye for her timely assistance, and Safiye, in turn, congratulated her sister on her feat of memory.

Nihad had been silent throughout the discussion, and now he got up to go inside. Fuad, however, had other plans. "Nihad," he said, "let's ride our bicycles until Mother calls me in to wash and dress for dinner."

But Nihad, as always, was unwilling to comply: he considered bicycle-riding not only dangerous, but also rather undignified. "Not now, Fuad," he replied. "I would like to spend some time with Vâsıb in the nursery. Last week he said his first word – 'Anne' – so I am trying to teach him to say 'Baba' as well; he seems rather reluctant, however!" Smiling in the hope of appeasing his younger brother, he made for the harem building.

Disappointment was etched into every line of Fuad's face. Noticing this, Behiye felt a little irritated with Nihad – but said nothing. "I will ride with you, Fuad, if you will teach me how," she said.

Fuad's eyes lit up. He adored his eldest sister. "Will you really, Behiye? But what about your skirts? Will they not get caught in the chain?"

"Well, I will do my best. I can always hitch up my skirts a little. Bicycles are not just meant for boys, you know!"

Laughing, he took her hand and began to lead her towards the outbuilding where the bicycles were stored.

"Can I come too?" Rukiye put in. "Maybe I could ride Father's tricycle."

"Of course! Come on!" Behiye replied. Rukiye put down the novel she had been about to read and ran off to join her siblings in their search for the wheeled contraptions. Meanwhile, Adile, Safiye and Atiye stared at each other in astonishment, feeling more than a little concern for their sisters' safety.

✸ ✸ ✸ ✸ ✸

As Selahaddin walked slowly through the corridors towards his mother's suite, he reflected with satisfaction on what had just occurred. He felt proud of his three youngest daughters, and was pleased to see that they understood the importance to the three monotheistic religions of the city of Jerusalem and the Holy Land. They had touched on the various problems associated with Jerusalem – problems that did much to explain why so much blood had been spilled in the rocky, dusty land of Palestine. It was true that the region had been in the hands of Islamic rulers for nearly twelve centuries now, and that this was far longer than the rule of any other power – be it the Israelites, the Romans, the Persians or the Christians – had lasted. Selahaddin had an uneasy feeling, however, that Ottoman rule would soon be under threat – this time not from a crusade by Christian knights, but from a Zionist invasion.

He reflected on what his Ottoman forebears had done for the region. Since the conquest of Jerusalem by the Ottoman Sultan Selim I in 1516, the area had enjoyed a period of peace and stability; a *firman* – an Imperial decree – on this subject had been issued by Sultan Osman III in the mid-eighteenth century, and further decrees confirming the provisions of the first had been promulgated by Sultan Abülmecid. These decrees ensured the continuance of the Status Quo in the Holy Land and the city of Jerusalem. The old walled city remained divided into four quarters, the Moslem quarter being the largest: situated in the north east of the city, it contained the Al-Aqsa Mosque complex. The Christian quarter, in the north west, was where the Church of the Holy Sepulchre was to be found, while in the south west was the small Armenian quarter, dominated by the Monastery of St James. The Jewish quarter, which included the Western Wall, was in the south east of the city. The people of each quarter enjoyed special rights and privileges, and all the various Christian denominations were represented in the Church of the Holy Sepulchre. Everyone's rights had always been respected, and this had ensured that peaceful coexistence was maintained in what was potentially an extremely volatile environment. Selahaddin feared that if this delicate balance were ever to be disturbed, blood would once again flow in the Holy Land – something he prayed he would never see.

Just then, the happy, excited voices of Fuad, Behiye and Rukiye came from the garden. "I hope my children never have to experience a war of that kind in their lifetime – or indeed, any war at all," he said to himself. Suddenly, he felt a shiver go down his spine, and this perturbed him somewhat as he approached his mother's door. Stopping outside it to regain his composure, he told himself that such feelings were no more than foolishness. Then he knocked on the door and went in.

CHAPTER TWENTY

The Imperial Court of Yıldız

Saturday September 23ʳᵈ 1905

T HE Ceremony of the Procession of the Cradle had been a wondrous occasion at which the Court had displayed all its Imperial splendour. It had been the first time that Fatma and Selahaddin's sons and daughters had witnessed the full magnificence of the Ottoman Court, and they had been dazzled by all the pomp and ceremony. The Muradiye princesses had understandably felt apprehensive about attending their first official ceremony at Yıldız, but in the end their excitement had overcome their nerves, and they had taken delight in everything.

They had worn beautiful court dresses made from the things their uncle Kemaleddin had given them only a few months before – the sumptuous silks and satins, and the delicate lace. Hadice and Fehime had wisely sent their own dressmakers to the Çırağan Palace with instructions to create dresses that would take everyone's breath away. The dressmakers had duly obliged, conscious of the fact that as the princesses had lived their entire lives in confinement at Çırağan, they would be objects of intense fascination for the other princesses and ladies at Court: they were certain to be closely scrutinised, so they needed to be dressed faultlessly

403

– in accordance both with the fashions of the day and with their rank. Yet even the princesses themselves had been struck by how magnificent they looked when dressed in all their finery.

Fatma had worn her spectacular diamond crescent brooch across her heart, while Selahaddin's daughters had put on some pieces of jewellery from their great-aunt Fatma's collection that he had presented to them that morning, in addition to their finest pearls. As Murad's sister Fatma had died childless, she had bequeathed all her jewellery to Selahaddin with instructions that it should be shared among his daughters in whatever way he saw fit – and this had seemed the perfect occasion to distribute some of it to them. Behiye and Rukiye had received matching diamond bracelets that their great-aunt had once worn as a pair. Each one had a large diamond flower worked into the filigree; they certainly caught everyone's eye. The younger princesses, meanwhile, had been given exquisite drop earrings made from coloured diamonds, and matching jewelled hairpins; Adile's hair had been held in place by a pin decorated with a tulip head made of violet-coloured diamonds, while Atiye's hairpin had borne a carnation encrusted with pink diamonds. For Safiye, Selahaddin had asked Margos Bey, his father's old Armenian jeweller, to use some yellow diamonds taken from one of his aunt's brooches to create a hairpin in the shape of a rose. When it was ready, he had placed it in her hair himself, and she had wept with joy.

Murad's consorts had decided not to attend the ceremony, but Selahaddin's wives Naziknaz and Jalefer had gone to Yıldız along with the Muradiye princesses, as had Nihad's wife Safiru. Safiru had wanted to stay behind, but Nihad had insisted that she come to pay her respects to the Lady Naciye, Abdülhamid's young wife, and to the newborn prince. The truth was that as Safiru had once been a novice *kalfa* at Yıldız, she dreaded returning there, and hoped that no one from her old life would recognise her.

In this she was immediately disappointed, since when the ladies from Çırağan entered the harem at Yıldız, the *kalfa* who had so often scolded her as a young girl immediately acknowledged her presence with a condescending nod. Safiru felt uncomfortable and unnerved, and instantly recalled the harsh treatment and the constant, biting criticism to which she had been subjected on a daily basis by this most severe woman. She had never spoken to anyone at Çırağan about her unhappy days at Yıldız, not even to Nihad. Instead, she had shut away her feelings – not just those arising from the time when she had been a humble servant in the Imperial Harem, but also the even deeper hurt and feelings of unworthiness imprinted on her as a result of having been abandoned by her parents as a small child. Safiru thought she detected a look of disdain and mockery in the old *kalfa's* cold, dark eyes as they bored into her, and she trembled beneath her tightly-laced corset. It was not in her nature to gloat over the fact that she had risen to become the wife of a prince of the Imperial House; modest by nature, and always preferring to remain inconspicuous, she simply lowered her eyes and walked past.

The Imperial ladies had gathered in the Grand Salon of the harem. The Lady Naciye, who had given birth to the Ottoman Dynasty's newest prince, sat glowing with pride in her lying-in bed, which was draped in soft satin the colour of red poppies and was richly embroidered with rubies, emeralds, sapphires and pearls. As the princesses from Çırağan entered the imposing salon, they greeted the *loğusa* – the new mother – by kissing the coverlet of her bed; then, after presenting their gifts, they took their places to her right. Meanwhile,

Abid suckled contentedly at the breast of his wet nurse, who sat at the foot of the bed.

Safiru was reminded of her own accouchement; although Vâsıb was now nearly two years old, it seemed to her like only yesterday. Abid looked so tiny – just like Vâsıb once did, she thought to herself. Then came the moment she had dreaded: doing her best to appear calm and collected, she took her place among the other Imperial wives, hoping against hope that no one would address her. On that score, at least, she need not have worried: as everyone waited for the arrival of the wives of the high-ranking government officials who had been invited to attend, the mother and her newborn baby were very much the focus of attention.

Princess Cemile was the most senior princess in the Imperial family, and she therefore took precedence at the ceremony. Like Abdülhamid, her elder brother, she had lost her birth mother to tuberculosis when still a young child; as a result, the Lady Perestu had become her adoptive mother – as indeed she was to become Abdülhamid's a few years later. This shared experience of loss in early childhood had created a close relationship between brother and sister, and it was the strength of this bond that had led Cemile and her husband to endorse Abdülhamid's accession to the throne when Murad was deposed. She had been the only one of his siblings to offer him her support: the others had either actively tried to help Murad, or had remained silent. Her loyalty to her brother had been severely tested, however, when Abdülhamid began to mistrust her husband – as he mistrusted most men – and exiled him to Taif, where soon afterwards he was found strangled. Heartbroken, Cemile had immediately withdrew from Court life, living as a recluse for close on twenty years – until Perestu's illness and death the previous year had brought her to her brother's side once more. She now officiated at all Court ceremonies, taking the place of the deceased Valide Sultan; today, she sat immediately to Naciye's right. Her sisters Seniha and Mediha, being next in order of rank, sat next to her in the Grand Salon, and they were followed by Saliha and Nazime, the two elder daughters of Sultan Abdülaziz; Hadice, meanwhile, sat next to Nazime.

Safiru's eyes scanned the row of Imperial princesses sitting straight-backed on their chairs, which were upholstered in red silk. Their beauty, grace and elegance overwhelmed her, increasing her own sense of unworthiness and insignificance. She had never been able to understand how she had caught the eye of the handsome, dashing Prince Nihad: she knew that she was plain, simple and in every way unremarkable. The princesses were all dressed in the most fashionable pastel- and ivory-coloured silks and satins, their hair loosely piled up in the high, swirling pompadour style that was favoured in Paris and London; jewels sparkled at their throats, on the lobes of their ears and on their wrists. Only Cemile was dressed in the traditional Turkish style, as was her custom. She invariably wore exquisite robes with long flowing trains in varying shades of brown, made from the finest Bursa silks. Spurning the enticements of Western fashions, Cemile would only purchase fabrics that had been woven within the Empire. Today she was dressed in a beautiful robe of light taupe silk with a matching *hotoz* – a traditional Turkish headdress from which a long lace veil hung down her back and rested on her train. Ever since her husband's death she had worn no jewellery; despite this, as Safiru's eyes passed over her she thought Abdülhamid's younger sister looked neither plain nor austere. Quite the opposite, in fact: she was the most regal of them all. To Safiru she was the very epitome of an Ottoman princess, having intellect and graciousness of manner in addition to her imperial bearing.

Everyone was now awaiting the arrival of the Grand Vizier's cradle, which was certain to be lavishly ornamented with jewels, a noble aigrette at its head. The cradle given by the Chamberlain of the Imperial Treasury, which would have followed the Grand Vizier's cradle in the procession, would enter more discreetly, and would be placed without fuss in the middle of the room – where it would join the Valide cradle, which had been presented by Cemile and had already been received by the harem. The sound of the Imperial band was soon heard drifting into the Grand Salon. Silence followed: this meant that the procession had arrived at the entrance to the harem, where Abdülhamid would be greeting it and bestowing gifts on all those who had accompanied the cradles along their route.

The door to the harem was then opened by the Chief Eunuch, and all the ladies stood as the cradles were carried inside by the High Hazinedar and other senior *kalfas*. As the Grand Vizier's cradle passed in front of her, Cemile tossed some gold coins into it, and the other guests did the same. When their turn came, Murad's and Selahaddin's daughters threw into it some gold coins minted during the short reign of Murad V; this was in fact a show of defiance – a subtle reminder that his reign would not be forgotten. The Midwife to the Imperial House then prayed before the cradle, placed Abid inside it and rocked it three times before returning him to the arms of his wet nurse. The cradle now passed in front of all the guests a second time, allowing them to place in it their gifts of fine silks and embroidered linens for the midwife. Safiru did not recognise the midwife: she was not Hayriye, the midwife who had attended her after Vâsıb's birth. Watching as the cradle began to overflow with fabrics,

408

she wondered to herself if this woman might perhaps be Hayriye's daughter. But soon the midwife withdrew carrying her coins and her gifts, and the entertainments began.

⊕ ⊕ ⊕ ⊕ ⊕

There was beautiful music and graceful dancing, interrupted from time to time by extraordinary performances from contortionists and acrobats. The food was sublime, every mouthful tasting as if it had been prepared in paradise. Safiru, however, was only remotely aware of all this: her attention was fixed on Hadice, who was sitting next to Princess Zekiye, Abdülhamid's eldest and most dignified daughter. Zekiye was married to Ali Nureddin Pasha, the elder brother of Kemaleddin Pasha – the mere mention of whose name still sent Hadice's heart into a flutter.

Safiye was perturbed to see that things were not going well between the two cousins: Zekiye was behaving with a harshness that was quite uncharacteristic of her. Indeed, although she was the younger of the two – and despite the fact, moreover, that Hadice was a guest in her father's harem – she seemed to be taking the opportunity presented by her cousin's return to Court to chastise her. It was understandable that she should blame Hadice for causing Naime so much heartache, and for bringing shame to her own husband's family; none the less, as she usually acted with the utmost grace and decorum, her behaviour on this occasion was all the more upsetting for being completely unexpected. There was no doubt, of course, that the circumstances were not conducive to peace and harmony: Hadice and Naime had yet to be reconciled, Kemaleddin still languished in exile, and the whole sordid affair continued to be a favourite topic of Court gossip. It was hardly to be wondered at, therefore, that

409

Safiru should not be the only person staring at Hadice, whose return to Court had aroused a great deal of interest among the assembled ladies; regrettably, however, not all the indiscreet whispers were hidden behind raised fans.

Safiru's eyes ran along the row of princesses, all seated in order of seniority, until they fell upon Naime, who was sitting uncomfortably between Fehime and Fatma. Sweet, gentle Fatma was obviously trying to engage her in conversation, but Naime was not making this easy for her: Fatma was, after all, the sister of her tormentor. It pained Safiru to see Fatma, who had been so excited about meeting her cousins, being cold-shouldered in this way. But worse was to follow: Princess Emine, the youngest daughter of Sultan Abdülaziz, was sitting between Fehime and Zekiye, and now Fehime – always the most hot-headed of her sisters – leant across Emine to come to Hadice's defence.

"I think you have said quite enough, Princess Zekiye," she said, slightly louder than she had intended. Zekiye ignored her; she did, however, turn away from Hadice and begin speaking to Emine, who was clearly embarrassed by the altercation. Hadice glared at her sister disapprovingly for having made a scene in front of all the Court ladies at a time when above all else, tact was required. The truth was that Hadice felt she fully deserved all the rebukes Zekiye had delivered, and that in consequence she had no right to defend herself against them. Every day, she had to live with bitter feelings of remorse at having caused so much hurt and shame, and had no desire to see her sister risk her reputation to salvage what was left of her own.

After that, conversation languished. Nothing Fatma could do succeeded in breaking through Naime's icy reserve, and Emine's generous attempts to engage Hadice in conversation likewise fell flat: Hadice was tense and reserved, and Emine

410

could not be expected to maintain a conversation in which the other party hardly ventured more than a monosyllable. For Safiru, therefore, the meal was a most unpleasant occasion, but not in the way she had expected: having dreaded the mortification of being singled out as an upstart who had risen above her station, she had instead had to endure the distress of witnessing an angry scene in which she had no power to intervene.

❋ ❋ ❋ ❋ ❋

Not for nothing did Cemile occupy her prominent position at Court: there was very little that escaped her attention. Once the celebrations were over and everyone had begun to take their leave, she sent a *kalfa* to ask Murad's three daughters to join her in a small antechamber before they went on their way. Abdülhamid's two eldest daughters were also summoned. The five princesses now stood nervously before their aunt – wondering what would transpire, but at the same time having more than an inkling of what it might be.

"Princess Fatma, it has been wonderful to meet you today. I sincerely hope that from now on we will see you more often at Court," she began. Fatma bowed her head respectfully. "I was very fond of your father, but now that he is gone I want you to know that if there is anything you or your sisters need, you must come to me: I will do my utmost to help." Fatma kissed her aunt's hand and raised it to her forehead in gratitude. She had been rather afraid of her formidable aunt when she had first seen her in the Grand Salon, but here, in more informal surroundings, she found her to be most considerate and kind-hearted.

"I have been admiring your brooch – it is quite exquisite, and reminds me of one my sister used to own," Cemile said,

411

giving the faintest of smiles and raising an eyebrow. Fatma did not know how to reply. She knew there would be terrible recriminations if it were ever to be discovered that her Aunt Fatma had contrived to send gifts to the Çırağan Palace. She had imagined it would be safe to wear the brooch at Court, not expecting that it would be recognised after so many years – but then, she had not accounted for her aunt Cemile's perspicacity.

Cemile, of course, had no intention of alerting Abdülhamid to the fact that Murad and his sister Fatma had clearly maintained some form of correspondence during their respective confinements. A part of her was pleased that her two sweetest and most gentle siblings had had at least some form of solace in their isolation. Since they had both departed this world, little good would come of betraying their secret: it would only cause distress to her innocent niece. "It greatly becomes you, my dear, and I hope to see you wearing it again at Court," she added.

Even after the revelation that her aunt had recognised the brooch, Fatma had not been expecting this, and now she blushed very slightly. "My dear, you really must come to visit me at Fındıklı Palace with your sisters and your nieces," Cemile continued. "Or perhaps, when the spring arrives, you might take a caïque and visit me at Kandilli Köşk, where I sometimes take up residence with my son and his family."

"Thank you, Aunt Cemile. That is very kind. I would like that very much," Fatma replied, unable to restrain a smile. Relieved that her aunt had asked no awkward questions and overcome by the genuine warmth and affection she had shown to her, Fatma mourned the fact that they had been strangers until now. Tears pricked her eyes at the thought of how long so many simple pleasures, such as time spent with family, had been denied her.

Cemile then turned to the four older princesses, and the change in her tone took Fatima aback and unsettled her, even though it was not she who was being addressed.

"I will not tolerate dissension between the ladies in this family. We have enemies enough without making enemies amongst ourselves." They hung their heads in shame, each knowing that she had done wrong.

"Princess Hadice, by returning to Court today you have shown courage and great strength of character. While I do not condone your past behaviour, it now lies in the past. If His Imperial Majesty my brother has granted you his forgiveness, then it is for no other to hold a grudge. Princess Zekiye, you will apologise to your cousin for the way in which you spoke to her today, and you will never behave in that manner again." Zekiye's face flushed. She knew her aunt was right to scold her, and immediately did as she was told. Though Cemile had said nothing about the subject, they both fully understood the reason why Abdülhamid had forgiven Hadice so readily – which was also the reason why Zekiye must now try to do the same. It was simple: Hadice reminded him of his first child, Princess Ulviye, who had died as a little girl many years before, when Abdülaziz was still on the throne. Her clothes had caught fire in a horrific accident, and she had died in excruciating pain. Ulviye and Hadice had often played together in the Crown Prince's apartments, and had been as close as sisters. Everyone in Abdülhamid's family knew that it was only when he saw Hadice that he was able to hear the sound of his little sunbeam's laughter once again as the image of her face reappeared in his mind. It was for this reason that Hadice would always be forgiven, whatever she did.

"Princess Fehime, you are impulsive, and must learn to control your emotions. While your wish to defend your sister

413

is admirable, you made a scene in front of the wives of state officials, and they will no doubt recount what they saw to their husbands. Family matters must always be dealt with discreetly and behind closed doors. I hope you will learn from this and heed my advice."

"Yes, Aunt. Please forgive me," Fehime said, and kissed her aunt's hand.

"Princess Naime, I understand better than most how deeply you have suffered in the past year as a result of losing your husband, but the time for mourning and self-pity is over," Cemile said. "I would like you to call upon Princess Hadice before the holy month of Ramadan begins, and I would like you to sit together and resolve the differences that exist between you. I know that at one time you were close, and I would like to see that friendship restored."

"I will do as you say, Aunt," Naime replied with a bow, her normally pale, indeed almost translucent, complexion colouring pink with remorse.

"Good. As for your behaviour today towards Princess Fatma, it was inexcusable. She has never done you any harm, or wished you ill. Today was her first visit to Court, and you should have welcomed her in a spirit of warmth and friendship. You are aware of what she has suffered, and you should feel ashamed of your lack of compassion towards your cousin. I fear your thoughtless and unkind behaviour will have spoiled her day."

"Really, Aunt, Princess Naime was most welcoming, and I have very much enjoyed my first visit to Yıldız," Fatma said.

"You are obviously as kind and gentle as your sweet-natured father was, Princess Fatma," Cemile replied, smiling. "However, I know what I saw in the Grand Salon."

"Princess Fatma, please forgive me," Naime said. "I can

offer no excuse for the way in which I behaved towards you. Perhaps, with my father's permission, we will be able to go for a walk together in the palace gardens after the *Selamlık* one Friday – if the weather is fine, of course."

"That is a lovely idea. Now, let this be an end to the discord between you all. I see no need to speak of this to my brother the Padishah, or to my nephew Prince Selahaddin," Cemile said, looking intently at her nieces. "However, if you disappoint me by not becoming reconciled with one another, I may have to discuss it with them after all." She then dismissed the five princesses with a cursory wave of the hand and an attendant opened the door, allowing them to depart.

Selahaddin was standing by his sisters' carriage, accompanied by his daughters and Nihad. The other carriages had already left, and they were beginning to wonder what had become of Hadice, Fehime and Fatma.

Earlier, Selahaddin, Nihad and the other princes had gathered in the Little Salon of the state apartments to offer Abdülhamid their congratulations on the birth of his most recent son. Selahaddin had been unsure as to what kind of reception he and Nihad would receive from the Sultan on this, their first official visit to the Court of Yıldız; he need not have fretted, however, as Abdülhamid had greeted his nephew with a display of affection, and had spent a considerable amount of time speaking with them both. He had been informed of Nihad's act of mercy towards the dying horse on the day of the explosion at the Hamidiye Mosque, and had praised him for this action. Abdülhamid had, in fact, seemed impressed by Nihad, and had promised that he would soon award both him and his father regimental commissions

– something that was not only deserved, but also long overdue. Nihad had thanked him profusely: there was nothing he wanted more – he saw it as the first step towards achieving his long-held ambition of serving the Empire in some capacity. Selahaddin, on the other hand, had been somewhat less effusive in his expressions of gratitude: he remained wary of Abdülhamid and sceptical about his promises.

A few minutes later, when Tahsin Pasha, his private secretary, was distracted for a moment and Abdülhamid thought no one was watching them, he had leant over to the two princes and whispered: "All I have done, I have done for the greater good of the Empire. Never believe for one moment that I did not love my brother."

These completely unexpected words had struck both princes speechless, and now, as Nihad waited for his aunts, he mulled them over in his mind. The Padishah was the man who had stolen his grandfather's throne and taken away his entire family's liberty, and Nihad had always hated him. Yet now that he had met him face to face, his feelings were less unambiguously negative than they had been before. Abdül-hamid, in contrast to his brother Murad, was without doubt a ruthless and Machiavellian man. Could it really be true, Nihad wondered, that he had usurped the throne not just because of his craving for power, but also because he had been convinced that only an authoritative and unyielding hand could save the Empire at a time when foreign powers were scheming to dismember it? Nihad considered the possibility that Abdülhamid may have been right to act as he did: perhaps, after all, it had been too early for the Empire to adopt Murad's ideal of a constitutional monarchy in which the Sultan governed alongside a democratically-elected parliament. Could it be that the Empire and her people had not been ready for such a radical step? There was confusion in his mind on this issue: part of him felt disloyal for even contemplating such a thing, but he could not deny to himself that he had begun to see Abdülhamid in a new light – not simply as an arbitrary tyrant, but as a man who was prepared to make use of any means possible to prevent the greatest Islamic Empire the world had ever seen from crumbling in the face of its devious and infinitely resourceful enemies.

Nihad could not help but admire the resilience and strength of will Abdülhamid had shown in carrying out his mission. His dedication to duty and enormous capacity for work were undeniable, as was his unmatched skill in the art of diplomacy; moreover, he deserved appreciation for bringing about some sound and far-reaching fiscal, administrative and educational reforms. Where Nihad found Abdülhamid wanting, however, was in his failure to accept that there was no longer any place for autocratic rule in the modern world. Nihad dearly wished that the Padishah would see this truth and, having met some of the ministers and government officials from the Sublime Porte that day, he felt inspired to push for the realisation of his grandfather's dream of parliamentary government.

While they had been waiting, the five young princesses had talked incessantly, telling each other how much they had enjoyed the performances by the dancers and the various other entertainers, how wonderful the music – and the food – had been, and above all how much they had enjoyed meeting so many of their cousins all at once. Behiye had spent most of her time talking to Münire, who since the death of her father Prince Kemaleddin had been living at Yıldız with her mother under Abdülhamid's protection. She had told Behiye how considerate and thoughtful the Sultan had been in his behaviour towards them, saying that she was as happy as she could possibly be in the absence of her father.

Rukiye, meanwhile, had been sitting between Naile and Ayşe, two of the Sultan's daughters, and had taken an instant liking to them both. When she had told them of her interest in the Sherlock Holmes novels, they had promised to tell their father about it, and to ask for a copy of 'The Return of Sherlock Holmes' to be sent to her. This latest publication was a selection of thirteen short stories that Rukiye was keen to read, so she very much hoped they would not forget. Adile and Safiye, for their part, had made a pact with Şadiye, one of Abdülhamid's younger daughters. As they were all very similar in age, they had decided to call themselves 'the triplets'! Atiye's companion had been Refia, Abdülhamid's youngest daughter; Refia was only a few months older than she was, and together they had spent their time looking after the Princesses Ulviye and Sabiha – Prince Vahideddin's two daughters.

Eventually Hadice, Fehime and Fatma appeared in the doorway of the Imperial Lodge. As they were making their way down to the waiting carriages, a strong gust of wind caught the folds of their *feraces*, so they paused to smooth down the soft silk of their robes. As Selahaddin watched his sisters glide down the marble steps looking noble and dignified, he searched their faces for an explanation as to what might have caused their delay, his eyes betraying anxiety. Before either Fehime or Fatma could speak, Hadice said: "Please forgive us, dear brother. Aunt Cemile asked us to join her for a private audience once the celebrations were over. She welcomed me back to Court most graciously, and also spoke kindly to Fatma on the occasion of her first visit to Yıldız. In fact," Hadice said with a brief smile in Fatma's direction, "she invited Fatma to visit her."

Fehime and Fatma exchanged glances, but Selahaddin was too tired to notice. He wondered for a moment if when they

418

got home, he should mention what the Sultan had whispered to him, but it took no more than a moment for him to decide that in this case, discretion was definitely required: knowing what strong emotions might be stirred up in them by this news, he thought it better to let his sisters wind down from the excitement of the ceremony before he shared this startling piece of information with them. Meanwhile, Nihad helped his aunts into their carriages; then both princes mounted their horses and rode out of the palace gates.

It had been an exhausting day for everyone, and the young princesses from Çırağan were eager to get home and tell Fuad all about their many cousins, whom they had found to be charming and friendly. He had had to remain in the nursery with Vâsıb, having been considered too young to accompany his father and his elder brother. Fuad had, of course, argued that now that he was ten and a half years of age – slightly more, in fact – he was manifestly old enough to join the men at Court!

CHAPTER TWENTY-ONE

An Optimistic Future

October 1905

Nᴀïᴍᴇ kept her promise to her aunt: one mild autumn day towards the end of October, just before the beginning of the holy month of Ramadan, she called on Hadice. As the *kalfas* showed her into her cousin's salon overlooking the Bosphorus, their eyes met for just so long as was necessary for Hadice to welcome her courteously. Naime gave a thin smile in return. Then, when the *kalfas* had been dismissed, they sat down opposite each other; both stared at the carpet for a while, listening to the crackling sounds coming from the hand-painted porcelain stove. Finally, when Hadice felt that the silence could not possibly be prolonged any further, she initiated an awkward conversation about the clement weather, extending it to cover a few other innocuous topics. Soon coffee arrived, and this brought a much-needed respite.

The two cousins had once been so fond of one another: they had spent many hours in each other's company reading romantic novels, poring over French fashion plates in search of new dress designs, and sharing secrets that now seemed inappropriately intimate and personal. Now, however, their conversation was limited to strained pleasantries – which both of them knew would soon be exhausted. Hadice did her best to catch Naime's eye, but to no avail: her cousin's firmly pursed lips and glazed expression did not bode well for what was to follow.

Hadice was the first to finish her coffee. Putting down her cup with a decisive gesture that signalled to Naime that the matter between them was about to be broached, she began: "I do not ask your forgiveness, dear cousin, for I am undeserving of it, but I do beg that you hear my sincere and most heartfelt apology."

Terrified lest she allow her resolve to be compromised, Naime at first did not look at Hadice directly. Instead, she stared down into the darkness of her steaming coffee as if it were some murky, clouded crystal ball that might show her the way out of her dilemma. Then she pretended to examine the delicate enamelled *zarf*, which she was holding tightly in her hand. Inset in the holder were rubies and emeralds that protruded outwards, and they pricked her long, elegant fingers as she clasped them even tighter, steeling herself to make her all-important first response.

"Of course I will listen to what you have to say, Princess Hadice. But to be clear, I do not think we can ever be reconciled." This curt reply gave her a moment of self-satisfaction; but then, as her glance fell on Aslan – who was lying asleep, curled up on a velvet cushion in front of the stove – she felt an immediate pang of regret. Now that her husband was no longer with her she was in need of company, and she missed her cousin's intimacy and friendship desperately. Before coming to call on Hadice she had been to see Zekiye, and her elder sister's words of advice were now going round and round in her head: "Remember, dearest Naime, forgiveness is the fragrance that flowers give off when they are crushed. Be strong and show compassion, for

421

you will not heal until you have forgiven." Struggling to hold back the tears that she could feel welling up, Naime held her head down – but nevertheless she listened.

Hadice spoke softly, almost in a whisper. She spoke of her wish to atone for the pain she had caused, vowing that after ruining her cousin's marriage and being the cause of Kemaleddin's separation from his family, she would never allow herself to enjoy true happiness. Naime, however, failed to show any response: she sat there biting her lip, unable to look up for fear that her tear-filled eyes would be noticed – so Hadice rose from her chair and fell to her knees before her cousin, weeping with remorse.

"You welcomed me as a sister when I first came to Court, yet I have repaid your kindness by betraying your trust in the most deplorable way," she said through her tears. "I am truly penitent, and my guilt and shame will never leave me. Please believe me, Naime, when I say that I am deeply sorry for all the pain I have caused you and your two children."

Naime had not been prepared for such an outpouring of emotion, and she had certainly not expected her usually rather haughty cousin to make such an unequivocal apology. Having anticipated a good deal of frost at their meeting, she had been met with fire – and it warmed her heart. Remembering her Aunt Cemile's words, and her sister Zekiye's advice, she instinctively put down her coffee cup and took Hadice's hands in her own.

"My heart is shattered, but *Inshallah* one day it will mend," she said, her voice breaking as she spoke. The two princesses looked into each other's eyes – the first time they had done so since news of the betrayal had been broken to Naime – and Hadice now saw the tears her cousin had been holding back. Naime sobbed gently for a little while; then Hadice was amazed to see a half-smile come over her face as she whispered: "Everyone tells me that it will. My father has even begun to suggest new suitors to me!"

That remark had been intended to lighten the atmosphere, but it wounded Hadice deeply: she put her hands over her face and let out a suppressed wail of agony. The two then sobbed together for a few moments. Naime was the first to recover.

"I know that Kemaleddin Pasha never loved me as he loves you," she began. "How could he? You are so much more beautiful than I am, and like him you are charming and passionate, clever and witty. You are like a brightly-coloured songbird that everyone admires, whereas I am a plain, dull garden sparrow that is barely noticed." Hadice began to say something in protest, but Naime waved her remark aside and continued: "I see now that when he looked at you, there was more love in that brief, stolen glance than was ever bestowed on me in all our years of marriage. I do believe that I deserve to be married to someone who loves me above all others – but Kemaleddin Pasha was never going to be that person. We were perhaps always unsuited."

She pulled her hands away from Hadice and smoothed down her skirts. Hadice stood and returned to her chair; as soon as she had sat down, her loyal dog Aslan, who had only been pretending to doze – as the two princesses would have discovered if they had been watching him closely – jumped into her lap, sensing that she needed his comfort. The ice had at last been broken.

At this point Hadice, mindful of her duties as hostess, offered her cousin some further refreshment – which was refused. Instead, Naime cleared her throat and addressed Hadice in a tone that evinced determination.

"Hadice, would you do me the courtesy of being completely truthful? We are alone in this room, so the things we speak of need go no further. There are just a few questions that I need to ask, for my own peace of mind." Pulling out a silk handkerchief from her beaded reticule, she handed it to Hadice so that she could wipe away her tears. Hadice accepted this olive branch, noticing as she did so the swirling monogrammed letter 'N', surmounted by a crown, that was embroidered in the corner in silver thread. She remembered how she had spent many happy winter evenings at Yıldız sitting before a roaring stove in one of the palace's many reception rooms with Naime and her sisters, chatting happily as they embroidered their linens together.

"Of course, Naime. You may ask me anything you like. I promise to tell you the absolute truth," Hadice replied, wiping away her tears.

For the next hour, they opened their hearts to one another. Naime wanted to know everything, and Hadice willingly obliged, answering all her cousin's questions in full – how long the affair had gone on, where they used to meet, what they had discussed, and what promises they had made to each other. She even wanted to see the few letters that Abdülhamid's spies had not been able to find. Although the conversation was awkward, it was also healing, and by the end of it they both felt relieved of at least part of the burden of pain that had oppressed them for so long. It gave Naime a great deal of consolation to learn that despite the obvious love and passion that had existed between Hadice and Kemaleddin, their relationship had never become physically intimate. Hadice, for her part, had the satisfaction of being able to reassure her cousin that the Court gossips had been mistaken in their claim that she had set out to take revenge on the Sultan for his unjust treatment of her father and her family by deliberately hurting his favourite daughter: the simple truth was that she had fallen in love.

Then Naime asked the final question – the one that mattered the most to her. As she did so, a note of hesitation bordering on anxiety entered her voice. "If my father ever grants you the annulment you seek, and if one day Kemaleddin Pasha is allowed to return from exile, will you … marry him?"

Hadice could see the pleading expression in the hazel-green eyes beneath her cousin's finely-shaped eyebrows. She gazed down at the little Yorkshire terrier lying in her lap and stroked him lovingly, thinking of the night when Kemaleddin had given him to her. She even remembered his words: "Do not be deceived by his diminutive size, for he is rather feisty, just like you, and like you he desires only love and affection." How bitterly ironic it was that the dog he had thought would keep her company between their meetings should have been so sorely needed – as a companion in his absence! And it was yet another irony – though this time Hadice was not aware of it – that it should be Aslan who now gave her the inner strength to make a promise.

"I vow to you that I will never marry him. I love Kemaleddin Pasha with all my heart – I cannot deny that – and my love for him has only grown in the time we have been apart. But, dear cousin, the punishment I will impose on myself for causing you pain and for bringing shame to our family is to live the rest of my life without the man I love."

Naime hung her head. She knew that her cousin was an ardent romantic who had dreamed of nothing but love during her long years of seclusion in the Çırağan Palace, and she also knew – probably better than anyone – what endless misery Hadice's marriage had caused her, having listened to her confidences on that subject often enough during their regular visits to one another. She could ask for no greater sacrifice. A wave of sympathy swept over her. "Then the matter shall lie in the past, as my father has decreed," she said. "I want … I want to be able to forgive you, Hadice. Truly I do. Just give me a little more time."

Naime now looked up, and Hadice, unable for the moment to absorb the words she had just uttered, gazed at her cousin in wonder: there was a genuine smile on her face. Her generous, kind-hearted nature had ensured that the houses of Muradiye and Hamidiye, so long at odds with each other, were reconciled.

❉ ❉ ❉ ❉ ❉

A New Kingdom: 19th November 1905

Fuad was in the garden, playing with the new brown leather football that Zülüflü Ağa had bought him during his latest visit to the bazaar. A few weeks previously Nihad had told Fuad that some students at Galatasaray School had established a football club, and that the following season they planned to be the first Turkish football team to take part in the İstanbul Sunday Football League. Fuad had resolved to practise his skills in the hope that when he was older he might be selected to play for this new club against the English and Greek teams who were already playing in the League. The fledgling League, which was only in its second season, consisted of four teams. The title-holders were HMS Imogene FC, a team made up of members of the crew of the English yacht that served as a special service vessel attached to the British Embassy. Fuad had often seen it sailing along the Bosphorus in front of the palace, and had greatly admired its elegant lines.

The thought of beating these English sailors was one that held great appeal for Fuad: it was his strongly-held belief that they ought not to possess an Ottoman shield of any kind,

426

even a football trophy. He was adamant that the İstanbul Football Shield must be won by Ottomans, not by foreigners, and that Galatasaray must endeavour to wrest the title from them. His tutor had explained the basic rules of the game to him after making discreet enquiries on the subject, being aware of the need to be careful not to let the young prince's interest in the game reach the Sultan's ears. Football had first been played in the Empire towards the end of the previous century, when games had taken place between groups of British and Greek merchants in İzmir. It was then taken up by the Greek community in İstanbul, and later still by other minority groups – Jews, Armenians, Frenchmen and Italians.

While the Palace tolerated the playing of the game by foreigners and non-Moslems, Abdülhamid had been per-suaded by his theological advisers to prevent his Moslem subjects from participating in the sport, which was fast gaining in popularity. They feared that it would keep young men from their studies and from the Quran, and the Sultan had endorsed this view in order to appease them. It was also believed by some that the game called to mind the terrible atrocities of the 'Karbala Event' in which Imam Hussein, the grandson of the Prophet Muhammed, had been beheaded and his head kicked around by his murderers as if it were a ball. These rather unconvincing arguments had not prevented the young men at Galatasaray from playing the game, however, and they would not dissuade Fuad from playing it, either. As a result, the young prince was spending endless hours dribbling the ball around trees as if they were opposition defenders before booting it between the two stone urns that marked out the goal.

"Fuad, what are you doing?" Nihad asked as he walked towards his brother. Looking down at his shoes, Fuad saw that they were covered in mud, and knew that he would be

427

in trouble with his mother for getting so dirty – not to mention for sneaking outside on such a bitterly cold day.

"I am playing football, Nihad. Would you like to play, too? It would be so much more fun if I had someone to play with – much better than playing by myself!"

"I will play once Ramadan is over. I promise!" Nihad answered. "Now, come inside before this ice-cold wind blowing in from the Balkans strikes you down with pneumonia!"

Reluctant to return to the boredom of the nursery, Fuad at first ignored his brother's request. But then Nihad added: "Come, I have a surprise for you."

Fuad was instantly persuaded: he loved surprises. He picked up his muddy ball and took his brother's hand; together they walked back into the warmth of Nihad's apartment in the harem building.

❀ ❀ ❀ ❀ ❀

Since the summer, Orville and Wilbur Wright had been testing their new flying machine over the vast American prairies, and Nihad, who was fascinated by all matters of technical innovation and design, had kept abreast of their progress. He had read in a French journal that in early October the Wright brothers had claimed that they had successfully flown their powered aircraft for nearly forty minutes, and had then landed it safely. The article was sceptical about the performance of the Wright brothers' flying machine, but Nihad believed that it would not be long before they, or perhaps one of the daring French aviators who were also trying out flying machines, made a dramatic breakthrough. The dream of flight was perhaps as old as mankind itself: ancient legends were full of stories of man's

428

attempts to take wing and conquer the skies. Now that this long-held ambition seemed within grasp, the likelihood that it would become a reality during his lifetime filled Nihad with a keen sense of excitement.

Nihad moved the armchairs nearer to the stove so that Fuad could warm his cold hands and feet. He then placed on the table between them a model he had just finished making.

"This is for you, Fuad," he said. "It is a model of 'Flyer III', a flying machine that has taken a man up into the air and kept him there for over half an hour, and then brought him safely back down to earth," he explained.

"Oh, Nihad, it is absolutely amazing!" Fuad exclaimed. Picking up the delicate model, he examined it carefully. Soon a puzzled look came over his face. "So … where does the driver sit?" he asked.

"I think the correct term is 'pilot', Fuad," Nihad replied with a smile. "Judging from the photographs I have seen, I would imagine that he lies on his front along this central part here, next to the engine. When he wants to change direction and height, he takes hold of these control sticks – they move the rudder and warp the wings during flight. It is all very clever, but also brilliantly simple."

Nihad then showed him the journal containing the photograph of Flyer III in flight – the one on which he had based his model – and pointed out all its important features. "The wooden frame of the original machine was built using timber from spruce trees, and the wings were made from a double layer of unbleached muslin. I have used the same materials, and have tried to copy every detail as accurately as I could – using both the photographs and my understanding of the technology," Nihad said modestly. It gave him satisfaction to know that his brother liked his present, but now that the model was finished his active mind had already begun to

429

speculate about what new diversion might occupy him during the final week of Ramadan. Perhaps a rocking horse for Vâsıb, or maybe a jewellery box for his mother?

"Well, I think you are brilliantly clever to have made a replica as good as this, Nihad. Thank you. I love it!" Fuad hugged his brother in delight. He studied the photograph for a few more moments, then added: "I think the flying machine looks rather like my giant box kite! Just imagine what it must feel like to go up in it!"

"You are right, Fuad. It does resemble a kite somewhat," Nihad replied. Then, in a more serious tone, he said: "I wonder, little brother, if your tutors have ever told you about a Turkish inventor called Hezârfen Ahmed Çelebi who lived in the seventeenth century, during the reign of our noble ancestor Sultan Murad IV?" Fuad shook his head. "It is important that you remember his name, for when the story of flight is recorded it will begin with him: he was the first man to successfully make a controlled and sustained unpowered flight – whereas the Wright brothers have become the first to achieve a controlled and sustained flight that was mechanically powered." Fuad's imagination had been captured, and he listened attentively to his brother's account of Hezârfen Ahmed Çelebi's achievement. "In 1638, this brave inventor flew his machine from Europe to Asia: taking off from the top of the Galata Tower, he crossed the Bosphorus and landed safely in Doğancılar Square in Üsküdar. In all, it was a distance of about three and a half kilometres. For those watching him, it must have been an incredible sight – it was witnessed not only by the Sultan and the people of the city, but also by the famous traveller Evliya Çelebi, who later described it in his *Book of Travels*."

"So the first man to fly was a Turk, then!" said Fuad. "That is really something to be proud of, and I am sure everyone will be impressed when they read about it in their history books." He gave a broad grin; then he asked: "May I play with the model? I promise to be careful." Nihad nodded.

Fuad immediately began racing round the salon with his new toy, pretending it was flying through the air like a swallow. He was making it dive between chairs and tables and circle around vases and lamps – much to Nihad's alarm – when an unexpected visitor was announced: it was Selahaddin. Fuad landed the plane on the patterned rug near the stove and went to greet his father, who had brought with him a bundle of newspapers: he was clearly hoping to have a discussion with Nihad about some articles that had caught his attention. This was something Selahaddin had done all his life with his father, and it now gave him great pleasure to do it with his elder son. It was undoubtedly their enforced isolation that had led all three princes to take an almost obsessive interest in world affairs; after all, what else was there for them to do other than debate the issues of the day?

"Look what Nihad has made for me!" Fuad said excitedly, pointing to the miniature flying machine. He ran over to pick it up, and showed it to his father. Selahaddin never failed to be impressed by the things his eldest son was able to create using only his hands, his tools and a few pieces of wood.

"That is marvellous!" he exclaimed. "However do you manage to make such intricately detailed things, Nihad?" he said. Instead of replying to the compliment, Nihad acknowledged it with a slight bow. Then Fuad embarked on a display of aerial acrobatics – and in the process nearly knocked over a priceless Qing Dynasty vase that stood precariously close to his flight path. Seeing what had just happened, Selahaddin admonished him; he could not prevent himself from smiling at his son's enthusiasm, however. Then he said: "You should go and show it to Vâsıb. I am sure he will take great delight

431

in it, but do take care not to let him break it." Fuad readily accepted this invitation to leave the senior princes alone to discuss politics and current affairs: to tell the truth, he was relieved that he had not been asked to stay and listen.

❁ ❁ ❁ ❁ ❁

For Selahaddin, the long days of fasting had been punctuated by sessions of prayer and contemplation; he had also spent countless hours recording his thoughts and observations in his journals. The holy month had begun with encouraging news for the monarchies of Europe and in the wider world: In an attempt to restore law and order in his empire, Tsar Nicholas had signed a document known as the 'October Manifesto' on the first day of Ramadan. This document had announced that an elected parliament, to be called the 'Duma', was to be established in Russia; at the same time, the Russian people were to be granted basic civil rights.

Selahaddin and Nihad greatly admired the Tsar for taking these first cautious steps towards the introduction of consti-tutional government: they believed this action would secure both his throne and the future of the Romanov Dynasty. At the same time, they were aware that these steps had been taken with reluctance, and only in response to the general strikes and widespread civil unrest that had paralysed Impe-rial Russia that year; it seemed, however – on the surface at least – that the once despotic Tsar had finally seen the impossibility of ignoring the changes that were taking place in the world order, and had understood that his autocratic system of government would have to be modified if the monarchy was to survive.

Some journals were of the opinion that these actions had come too late, and that only the complete eradication of the old order and the establishment of a new one would satisfy the Russian people. The Ottoman princes sincerely hoped they were wrong on that score: they had no wish to see similar revolutionary activities bring chaos and destruction to their empire and threaten their dynasty. In fact, they had prayed that the Padishah would follow the Tsar's example and – albeit tentatively – place his trust in democracy. Their fervent wish was that he choose this moment to renounce his autocratic powers and establish a constitutional monarchy. They believed it was imperative that he grant a constitution to his subjects of his own accord before he was forced to promulgate one against his will; much to their frustration, however, there was nothing they could do to influence him in this direction.

Selahaddin had come to his son's rooms that afternoon to share another piece of positive news with him. Sitting down in one of the armchairs next to the stove, he announced: "There is now one more kingdom in the world than there was last month."

Nihad came to sit next to him. Feigning surprise, he said: "Oh really, Father? And what do you mean by that?" Inwardly, however, he was smiling to himself: he knew his father was referring to the outcome of the Norwegian referendum, the results of which he had been eagerly awaiting.

"As you know, Norway recently gained her independence from Sweden," Selahaddin began. "The Norwegian government then decided to hold a referendum in which people were asked to choose whether they wanted the country to be a constitutional monarchy or a republic. A few days ago they voted overwhelmingly in favour of establishing a constitutional monarchy; now they have offered the throne to Prince Carl of Denmark, and he has accepted. He has a young son

433

who is the same age as Vâsıb, so the future of the new dynasty seems to have been secured. This Danish prince appears to be a considerate man, but also a shrewd one: he has already won the hearts of his new nation by adopting the name 'Haakon', which was that of many Norwegian kings of former times. He will henceforth be known as 'Haakon VII'." Selahaddin then went on to describe how encouraging it was that despite the growing popularity of socialist and Marxist ideas – which were rampaging through Europe and threatened to destroy the established order – a people known for their liberal principles had chosen of their own free will to be ruled by a hereditary monarchy. This confirmed his belief in the sanctity of the sultanate and reinforced his conviction that a constitutional monarchy needed to be established in the Empire before it was too late.

"I am sure Britain will be pleased to see Princess Maud crowned Queen of Norway as this will bring the Norse kingdom within the British sphere of influence," Nihad remarked. "I once read that Britain was becoming wary of increasing German influence over the strategically-important ports in the Baltic States, and I am sure that having the King of Norway married to the youngest daughter of Edward VII will go some way towards preserving the balance of power." Nihad was always very conscious of the complex power play that went on in politics, and was especially cynical about the British and their endless intrigues. "In fact," he went on, "it would not surprise me in the least to learn that the cunning and manipulative British government had actually had a hand in bringing about the constitutional crisis that led to the dissolution of the union between Sweden and Norway – and thus ultimately to Prince Carl's accession to the Norwegian throne. The British Foreign Office is a nest of serpents!"

Selahaddin, familiar with his son's distrust of the British, ignored the aspersion he had cast on them. "One of these articles says that Norway has not had a ruler of its own since 1387," he said. "So this must be a time of great celebration for this once proud nation of warrior Vikings. No doubt the Norwegians will be pleased at the prospect of not being ruled by a Swedish king of French ancestry, although the new occupant of their throne is a Danish prince of German descent. I cannot for the life of me understand why so many European nations are willing to accept foreign sovereigns. Surely an ancient noble Norse family would have been more appropriate in this case?" Aware that this was a purely rhetorical question, Nihad remained silent. There was much about the ways of Europeans that they did not understand.

For over four hundred years, Norway had been in a union with the Kingdom of Denmark before being ceded to Sweden as one of the spoils of war after the defeat of Napoleon and his allies in 1814. Four years before this Jean Baptiste Bernadotte, a Frenchman of humble birth who had risen to become one of the generals of 'la Grande Armée' and a Marshal of the French Empire had been unexpectedly elected heir-presumptive to the Swedish throne. Following Napoleon's fateful invasion of Russia, Bernadotte had brought Sweden into the alliance that opposed his former Emperor on the promise that Norway would be given to Sweden as a reward. Now his grandson, King Oscar II of Sweden, had graciously relinquished his right – and that of his descendants – to the throne of Norway. King Oscar had clearly chosen to accept the loss of territory in order to avoid war with his neighbour, and Selahaddin admired him for this prudent act of appeasement.

"The Norwegian people have certainly brought off a coup," he said. "They have obtained their independence without bloodshed, and without provoking hostility between themselves and their former suzerain. I think there is a lesson for us here. If we were to apply a policy of appeasement and conciliation in the Balkans, we might perhaps be able to forge valuable and reliable alliances with the nations of the Balkans that would serve us well in the future."

"Perhaps, Father, but I fear the Balkan nations will never be our allies, whatever policy we adopt towards them," was Nihad's gloomy reply.

"You are always the pessimist, Nihad," his father retorted. "However, I refuse to accept any such negative views. We must work hard to cultivate trust and mutual respect among our many and diverse subject peoples. It is not yet too late. Maybe, in fact, we should follow the example of Sweden and grant independence to our more troublesome and belligerent Arab and European provinces – or, like the British, create semi-independent dominions like the Canadian Confederation or the Commonwealth of Australia, both of which enjoy full autonomy while retaining the British monarch as their head of state. Another idea I have considered is that of establishing an 'Imperial Federation' as a means of uniting our Arab and European provinces under our rule. If we freely grant them independence but maintain some level of power and prestige in these regions, we will not lose our influence over them; indeed, we may find that in this way we have ensured their loyalty for generations to come. The alternative, as I see it, is the growth of hatred and distrust – and these will be a deadly tumour within our empire that will ultimately lead to its destruction."

Selahaddin's researches into history and philosophy had taught him that if subject peoples ardently desired their freedom, any attempt to keep them under subjection was futile; at the same time, however, he was searching for some way in which Ottoman interests in former territories could be maintained after they had been granted their freedom. In fact, he cherished the hope that if the occasion were to present itself, he would one day be able to make a case for a policy of this nature to the Padishah.

Nihad admired his father's irrepressible optimism. However, he did not share his belief that the Ottoman Empire might be able to retain its power – or even its influence – in the Balkans. That had been slipping away for far too long, and indeed had all but disappeared. He did believe, however, that if a policy of appeasement along the lines his father had suggested was immediately put into effect in the Holy Lands and in Mesopotamia, the Empire might perhaps be able to maintain its influence over its recalcitrant Arab subjects for generations to come. If only Abdülhamid would contemplate decentralisation, even though such a step would be a radical one!

Nihad looked out of the window with a wistful expression on his face. The sun was fast sinking towards the horizon, drawing a mauve-tinged hue across the darkening grey skies. Selahaddin, too, had noticed that the afternoon was drawing to a close. He stood up from his chair, gathered his pile of newspapers under one arm, and kissed his son on both cheeks. "I am afraid I must hurry," he said. "I promised your grandmother that I would have *iftar* with her this evening. So I will see you tomorrow, my dear boy!" And with that, he left the room.

❂ ❂ ❂ ❂ ❂

The Night of Power: 23rd November 1905

As autumn gave way to winter, the days were becoming noticeably shorter, but to Atiye it felt as if they were somehow becoming longer. This year, for the first time, she

437

had joined her family in observing the Fourth Pillar of Islam during the holy month of Ramadan. Now that she had entered puberty, she was fasting between the hours of sunrise and sunset – and she was finding it hard. Out of the entire household, only Fuad and Vâsıb now remained exempt: they were still too young. Selahaddin had insisted, however, that this year Fuad fast on the twenty-seventh day of Ramadan – the holy day following the 'Night of Power' – in preparation for the time when he too would reach adolescence.

That evening the 'Night of Power', the holiest night in the Islamic calendar, was to commence. It was celebrated as the occasion when the first revelations of the Quran had been made to the Prophet Muhammed; it was also a time when peace descended to earth and destinies for the forthcoming year were preordained. Selahaddin and his family had been joined – with the Sultan's permission – by Hadice and Fehime, and they had all gathered in the main dining room at the Çırağan Palace for *iftar*, the meal that was to break their fast. The food and drink remained untouched on the table until the firing of a cannon announced that the sun had set. Selahaddin, as head of the family, was to break his fast first; meanwhile, everyone waited patiently. When at last the loud report reverberated through the walls and windows, he said his prayers, then ate the first of the three sweet dates that lay on the small plate in front of him. It was believed that Muhammed had always eaten three dates to break his fast, and Selahaddin observed this custom. As for Atiye, as soon as she felt it appropriate to do so she reached for her glass of water and quenched her thirst. She had found the abstinence from food manageable; it was the denial of water that had been the real test of her self-discipline.

As always, the kitchens had produced a sumptuous feast in honour of this holy night. Among the generous array of mezes were stuffed dates and vine leaves, as well as crushed chickpeas mixed with pureed currants, pine nuts and cinnamon. A warm chestnut soup giving off a sweet aroma of apples was served, and this was followed by melon stuffed with minced lamb and veal – cooked in sweet melon juice with rice, almonds and rich spices. Finally, there was a sweet milk pudding flavoured with rosewater and sprinkled with pomegranate, and this was supplemented by a saffron rice pudding; these dishes were designed to ensure that everyone's craving for sugar was fully satisfied after the fast.

Once dinner was over, the family disappeared to perform their ablutions before gathering once again in the palace's prayer room. The princesses, Murad's consorts and Selahaddin's wives covered their heads with gauze veils; the three princes, meanwhile, wore white cotton prayer caps edged with cream satin. The direction of the *qibla* was indicated by a tiled *mihrab*; on the walls, looking down on the family, were prayers and the names of Allah, his Prophet Muhammed and the first four Caliphs, all done in elegant calligraphy and hung in simple walnut frames. Each member of the family knelt on their silk prayer rug in front of the walnut *rehal* that held their personal leather-bound copy of the Quran. The Quran rests, exquisitely inlaid with mother-of-pearl and ivory, displayed craftsmanship of the highest quality, and were thus fully worthy of holding the sacred books. Facing the direction of the Kaaba in Mecca, everyone began to follow Selahaddin in prayer.

The customary prayers were followed by recitations from the Quran. Everyone had chosen a verse or a *sura* – a chapter – to read aloud. The princes recited their passages first; they were followed by the princesses, and then the consorts and wives. Since Gabriel and all the angels were to descend to earth that night to bestow the peace and blessings of Allah on those who worshipped Him, Atiye had decided to read a

439

short verse about the guardian angels that was contained in the Thirteenth Sura.

When her turn eventually came, Atiye spoke from memory, reciting the verse slowly and clearly: *"For each person there are angels in succession, before and behind him: They guard him by command of Allah."* She felt pleased with her choice of verse, and was relieved that she had not ruined the beauty of these exalted words by stuttering or stammering. She also sensed that her own guardian angels were very much present, and her care over the recitation was her way of thanking them for protecting her on her journey through life.

Once the consorts and wives had also recited from the Quran, the family sat together in quiet contemplation to strengthen and renew the essence of Islam in their hearts and souls, praying and seeking guidance and forgiveness. It is written in the Quran that to pray on the 'Night of Power' is better than to offer worship for one thousand months, as every supplication is answered and every sin forgiven on that holiest of nights.

Hadice, for her part, recited the following words: *"Though my sins be as great as the ocean, Thy pardon is greater still, Allah."* Yet again she prayed fervently that Allah would forgive her for her sins towards Naime, and that He would give her the strength to live without Kemaleddin, the love of her life.

The ladies and Fuad retired to bed just after midnight, but Selahaddin and Nihad remained in the prayer room reciting from the Quran until the beating of drums in the street outside announced that it was time for *suhur*, the pre-dawn meal. They stayed awake all night, enjoying a feeling of oneness with their Creator. They would rest later.

CHAPTER TWENTY-TWO

The Trial

Winter 1905

THE newly-elected Norwegian royal family was met by a large cheering crowd when they stepped ashore near the imposing Akershus Fortress in Kristiania on November 25th. Haakon VII, holding his young heir in his arms, removed his hat before being greeted by his prime minister. The crown prince, wrapped in a light blue blanket to protect him from the heavy snow flurries, looked so angelic that he instantly won the hearts of all those present. There was a general feeling that an auspicious future lay ahead for the newly-restored Kingdom of Norway. On that very same day in İstanbul, meanwhile, the trial of those accused of plotting the assassination of Sultan Abdülhamid began. Except for one man – a Belgian anarchist by the name of Edouard Joris upon whose defiant and full confession much of the case had been built – the defendants were all Armenian. Contrary to the usual practice in political cases, the trial was held in open court, so Selahaddin had asked Asım Ağa to attend the proceedings each day so that every detail could be reported back to Çırağan.

During the investigation and the trial that followed, it became apparent that the assassination attempt was only part

441

of a much wider plot by the Armenian Revolutionary Federation that was designed to cause terror and bring disruption to the Ottoman Empire, plunging it into chaos. The aim of this nefarious organisation had been to involve the major European powers in Ottoman affairs in the hope that they would intervene in support of its cause. Selahaddin was incensed to learn that had the assassination of Abdülhamid been successful, a whole series of further explosions throughout the capital and in other major cities had been planned. Targets would have included government buildings, the Galata Bridge, the Ottoman Bank and a number of foreign embassies, the intention of these callous people being to provoke mass riots and large-scale unrest, and thereby destabilise the government.

The Armenian Revolutionary Federation was a nationalist revolutionary group with socialist leanings that had been founded by three Russian Armenians in 1890 with the aim of uniting all the Armenians in the Russian, Persian and Ottoman Empires, bringing about administrative and social reform, defending Armenian villages from attack, and ultimately establishing an independent Armenian state. Armenians had lived peacefully under Ottoman rule for centuries; they had been free to practise their religion and their own traditions, and had attained high positions both in government and at Court. They had even been referred to by the Ottomans as 'the loyal nation'; some, however, manipulated by unscrupulous agents of the Tsar and encouraged by meddling foreign missionaries, had begun to demand autonomy, or even full independence. In this they had been emboldened by the defeat of the Ottomans in the Russo-Turkish War, and – as was the case with many other nations – they found the temptations of nationalism hard to resist. The Armenians had believed the promises made to them by the Russians, and were seemingly oblivious of the fact that they were allowing themselves to be used as pawns in the Tsar's grand scheme to conquer İstanbul, resurrect Constantinople as an Orthodox stronghold and secure a sea route to the Mediterranean for his warships. In reality, the Tsar cared nothing for the Armenian cause: he simply wanted to create unrest in eastern Anatolia in order to give himself an excuse to invade Ottoman territory, ostensibly in the interests of protecting the Armenians. So everything had changed, and regrettably the 'loyal nation' was – still not entirely, but to an increasing extent – loyal no more.

Following the Russo-Turkish War, Abdülhamid had been determined to prevent any further loss of territory; as a result, he had dealt a good deal more ruthlessly with the threat to the integrity of his eastern provinces posed by the Armenians than his natural inclinations would otherwise have allowed. No previous Ottoman sultan had lost more territory during their reign than Abdülhamid, and he had resolved that dishonour and humiliation would have no part in his legacy. Consequently, in the mid-1890s he had unleashed his Hamidiye Cavalry Regiments on Armenian villages in order to root out the traitorous revolutionaries who were causing the unrest. The stated purpose of these regiments was to patrol and secure the Ottoman-Russian frontier and ensure that the Armenian villagers remained subjugated; in practice, however, their over-zealous methods were often unnecessarily cruel. Ottoman governors and military officers found it next to impossible to maintain control over these regiments, which were in fact no more than bands of fierce Kurdish irregulars, and as a result terrible deeds were committed in the name of the Sultan. At the time Murad and Selahaddin had been greatly saddened by these atrocities, and had prayed that Abdülhamid would find an alternative solution to the problem presented by the ever-mounting number of Armenian revolts and uprisings.

The attempt on Abdülhamid's life had therefore been an act of vengeance – the outcome of the Armenian nationalists' frustration at the failure of the uprisings they had repeatedly provoked; an additional cause was their desperation at the failure of the foreign powers to show an interest in their grievances and lend their assistance.

Necib Melhame Pasha had worked tirelessly to assemble the facts and prepare a watertight case to bring before the court. He knew that on the one hand the Padishah expected convictions, while on the other the eyes of the world would be focused on the Ottoman judicial system; therefore, there was no room for mistakes. The trial was to be held in nine public sessions, the order of the law was to be followed with the utmost stringency, and many foreigners – including members of the international press and representatives of the Belgian legation – were to be present.

In the event, neutral observers deemed the trial to have been conducted fairly, and its findings to have been fully justified by the evidence produced. Every detail of the proceedings was meticulously noted down for Selahaddin by Asım Ağa, as well as being reported in the press. The *Times* newspaper later referred to the plot as *'One of the greatest and most sensational political conspiracies of modern times'*. Every salon, every coffee house and every bazaar in the Empire was buzzing with talk of the trial, as indeed were rooms and corridors throughout the Çırağan Palace.

The conspirators had been clever, patient – and most of all, thorough in their planning. They had evaded the secret police and coerced unwitting accomplices; what was truly remarkable, however, was the ease with which they had penetrated to the very heart of Hamidian power. Only fate – or perhaps divine intervention – had prevented the assassination of one of the world's most autocratic and most powerful rulers, and the Ottoman State had been left reeling from the shock.

It emerged that Christapor Mikaelyan, one of the founders of the Armenian Revolutionary Federation, had been the main instigator of the plot. His initial plan had been to kill Abdülhamid by throwing a bomb into his lap as his carriage passed in front of the Ambassador's Terrace during his return to the palace after Friday prayers. In March, however, Mikaelyan and his associate Kendiryan had died in a remote Bulgarian village while testing the explosives they were planning to use. Other members of the Armenian revolutionary committees that were based in Geneva, the Caucasus and Bulgaria then assumed control of the plan. These people decided that owing to the strict surveillance in force at Yıldız Palace, Mikaelyan's scheme was too risky. Instead, a bomb would be placed in a carriage parked outside the mosque, and a timer would be set to detonate the device just as the Sultan was driving out through the gates. A method of this kind had never been employed before, but even so the plotters believed it would work. It was certain to result in a large number of casualties as many bystanders would be killed in addition to the Sultan himself, but this 'collateral damage' was considered acceptable in view of the fact that the risk of the conspirators being apprehended would be considerably reduced.

Necib Melhame had been able to discover the exact means used by the plotters thanks to one small and seemingly unimportant piece of evidence that could easily have been overlooked. Selahaddin was extremely impressed by this clever piece of detective work, which had enabled the dark and tangled web of conspiracy to be unravelled and the identity of the culprits to be brought to light. A carriage spring discovered amongst the wreckage had been found to be bent and twisted in such a way that according to artillery experts, it must have been positioned directly under the source of the explosion. During their search for further pieces of evidence, the police had unearthed a fragment of metal bearing the discernable marking *'Nesseldorfer, Wien, 11123'*. From this fragment, which must also have been in the epicentre of the explosion, Necib Melhame deduced that the bomb had been placed in a phaeton, and the discovery of the company's mark allowed him to trace the manufacturers of the particular Victoria carriage that had been used in the attack.

One discovery led to another, and before long the Investigation Commission also learnt from custom house records that the carriage had been imported by a man named Silvio Riccio in May. Further enquiries revealed that this man was in fact an Armenian named Vahan who had stolen the real Riccio's passport and papers and was using his identity. It also became evident that Vahan had received delivery of the bomb, which had been sent from Paris in separate parts; it had entered the Ottoman Empire via Athens and the Bulgarian port of Varna. Having contacted the carriage-makers in Vienna, the Investigation Commission established that certain modifications to the driver's box had been requested – the intention being to enable it to hold the large explosive device. Concrete evidence in the form of letters and telegrams was produced to prove that Vahan and the wife of Lipa Ripps had ordered the carriage, and that they had requested these modifications.

Lipa Ripps was one of the ringleaders, as was Konstantin

Kabilyan, who went by the assumed name 'Safo'. Ripps had hired Mehmed Ağa, a carriage driver from a local stables, to teach his groom Mıgırdıç all the back roads in the city – and the fastest route to and from the Hamidiye Mosque. It had been easy for the police to track down Mehmed Ağa: they had gone from one livery stables to another until they found the one where the plotters had stored their carriage. It was from this stables, too, that they had hired their horses. Mehmed Ağa, who had been completely unaware of his role in the plot, had been a very obliging witness: he had told the police how Mıgırdıç had visited the Russian Consulate, and had obtained from there the papers permitting him to attend the *Selamlık* ceremony. It became clear from the testimony of other witnesses that Mıgırdıç had carried out an extensive surveillance operation: he had tracked the Sultan's movements on thirteen separate occasions in order to establish his exact routine during Friday prayers and ascertain the timing of his departure from the mosque. During his interrogation, Mehmed Ağa had also spoken of the involvement in the plot of Edouard Joris and his wife, and this vital piece of information had led to the Belgian citizen's arrest, following which he had made a full confession. Joris had admitted to assembling the bomb once it had arrived, and to placing it in the driver's box. He had also admitted meeting Mikaelyan, Ripps and others on several occasions, having been introduced to them by Kendiryan, the person who had recruited Joris to the Armenian revolutionary cause.

On the day of the assassination attempt, Lipa Ripps and a certain Robina Fein, who appeared to be the daughter of Mikaelyan – who often used the alias 'Samuel Fein' – drove the carriage to the gates of the Hamidiye Mosque. The wheels of the phaeton had been covered in rubber to minimise vibration; a bomb weighing eighty kilogrammes, packed with twenty kilogrammes of iron pieces, lay hidden within an iron chest under the driver's seat. Once prayers were over and Abdülhamid appeared at the top of the steps, they had set the clockwork timer to detonate the bomb after one minute and forty-two seconds. This was the exact amount of time they had found it always took Abdülhamid to pass from the door of the mosque to the gates of the courtyard, where the carriage was parked. They had then calmly left the scene in another carriage driven by Mıgırdiç – just before the bomb went off. When it became known that the attempt on the Sultan's life had been unsuccessful, Lipa Ripps, Konstantin Kabilyan, Robina Fein, Vahan, Anna Joris and some others involved in the plot had fled the city, hoping to find safety in Europe. Only Edouard Joris and some of the less prominent conspirators had remained behind.

The trail of evidence that had begun with the finding of a small, inconspicuous piece of mangled ironwork from a carriage had taken Necib Melhame and his commission on an exhaustive search through the streets of İstanbul. They had interviewed hundreds of suspects – from porters, dockworkers, grooms and carriage drivers to telegraph operators, boarding house owners and hotel managers. Their investigations had led them from the port and customs house in Karaköy to livery stables in Şişli and the grand hotels of Pera. It had also caused enquiries to be made in Paris, Vienna, Geneva, Athens and Sofia – a process which had revealed the huge extent of international support for the Armenian revolutionary cause. Selahaddin was flabbergasted to learn that over 300,000 French francs had been raised to finance the attack on the Ottoman Sultan. The money had come primarily from Armenians living in America, Bulgaria and Russia who had willingly financed the cost of what was discovered to be a vast quantity of explosives, revolvers and

448

ammunition. The enormous scale of the plot sent shivers down Selahaddin's spine when he contemplated what might have happened if they had succeeded in their devilish plan.

☻ ☻ ☻ ☻ ☻

Passers-by glanced with curiosity at the tall, handsome Nubian eunuch walking briskly along the Grande Rue de Péra dressed in a thick black stambouline jacket and a warm woollen coat against the cold. Though the stares were unwelcome, he was accustomed to them: eunuchs from the Imperial households always attracted attention in the streets of İstanbul. His cherry-red fez was tilted slightly towards his left ear, and as he strode purposefully in the direction of Galatasaray, the black silk tassel that hung down to the nape of his neck swung gracefully to and fro like the pendulum of a grandfather clock.

In obedience to the instructions he had been given, he had taken the horse-drawn tram that plied between Ortaköy and Galata. Since it was such a beautiful day, he had decided to walk along the famous boulevard in the crisp winter sunshine: accordingly, he had got off a few stops earlier than he otherwise would have done. Fashionably-dressed ladies and gentlemen were making their way to the elegant hotels and restaurants or browsing in the windows of the expensive shops looking for something decadent to buy, and the sight of them gave him great pleasure. He walked past the towering iron gates of the Galatasaray Imperial High School, marvelling at the way the sun's rays danced off their ornate gilded decorations, then round a slight bend in the road and on past the Dutch Embassy. Now he took out the neatly-folded piece of paper on which he had written the address – surely it could not be much further. Shortly afterwards, he spotted the huge

449

gold letters spelling out the words 'Sébah & Joaillier' on the building that stood next to the Russian Embassy, which was easily identified by the double-headed eagle standing guard above the entrance. He slipped into the shadow cast by the red and white awning that veiled the shop's frontage, and disappeared inside.

✪ ✪ ✪ ✪ ✪

Selahaddin was in his study reading a pamphlet in which there was an interesting report on the events of the previous few days in Persia. He was astounded to read that the country seemed likely to be heading towards revolution. He had always believed that the Ottoman Empire would be the first Moslem state to introduce a constitution, but now he was beginning to feel that this might not be the case after all.

Russia was fast becoming Persia's largest trading partner; it was therefore hardly surprising that in the wake of the Russo-Japanese War, and as a result of the widespread strikes and violent unrest that had been crippling Russia since the beginning of the year, Persia should be experiencing a dramatic rise in inflation. Food prices in the country's bazaars had soared owing to a poor harvest and heavy snow, and in every city – from Tabriz to Tehran, and from Isfahan to Shiraz – there had been demonstrations to protest against the government's inept handling of the situation. The pamphlet stated that prominent mullahs, respected merchants, guild members and students had recently joined together to form a cohesive opposition movement that was intent on reforming the bankrupt, corrupt and militarily weak Qajar government, introducing constitutional monarchy and putting an end to foreign interference.

According to the article, the demonstrations had begun

peacefully, but the situation had deteriorated on 12th December, when the Governor of Tehran had ordered a number of merchants to be bastinadoed on a false charge of hoarding sugar, and thereby artificially raising its price. He had apparently ignored their plea that the high prices were due, purely and simply, to the situation in Russia. The public was incensed by the harshness of this unjust and humiliating sentence – especially in view of the fact that one of the merchants was a highly revered elderly man who had personally funded the repair of the Grand Bazaar and the restoration of three mosques. The following day, every shop, stall and workshop in the Grand Bazaar had closed, and seemed likely to remain closed indefinitely. Selahaddin was interested to read that an estimated two thousand people had taken *bast* – that is, taken sanctuary – in the courtyard of the Shah Mosque, the place near the Grand Bazaar where the beatings had taken place, and that they had presented a list of demands to the Shah and his ministers; these included the dismissal of the Governor of Tehran and the establishment of a parliamentary body that would be known as the 'House of Justice'.

"I wonder how Muzaffar al-din Shah Qajar will react to this!" Selahaddin said to himself, studying the photograph of the Persian Shah in the middle of the article. A short sentence below the picture indicated that it had been taken during his state visit to Belgium earlier that year. Selahaddin stared at the image, trying to imagine what sort of man he might be: he had the reputation of being a weak and apathetic ruler, but the man Selahaddin saw in the photograph was a frail individual, prematurely aged. Although obviously weighed down by ill-health and troubles, he had large, gentle eyes, and gave the impression of being fundamentally kind-hearted. The face was dominated by an outlandishly long and wiry moustache that nevertheless gave him a distinguished appearance; it reminded Selahaddin of a miniature he had once seen of the sixteenth-century Safavid ruler Shah Abbas the Great. Muzaffar al-din Shah Qajar was dressed in European-style military uniform, but was also wearing the black astrakhan hat associated with the Qajar tribe; on it, the white feathers of his jewel-encrusted aigrette were held in place by a large diamond brooch.

Selahaddin decided to keep the pamphlet. He would show it to Nihad and to his elder daughters after dinner: they would be interested to learn that the rumblings of revolution were being heard in yet another of the countries bordering the Empire. Now that Cevher Ağa was no longer carrying out random searches of his apartment, Selahaddin was less careful in the matter of hiding these illegal pamphlets than he had been, but old habits die hard! He folded the leaflet in half and slipped it under the cushion of his armchair to be retrieved later.

ⴲ ⴲ ⴲ ⴲ ⴲ

At that moment, he heard the excited voices of his daughters coming from outside his study door. Before they had had a chance to knock, he called out: "Come in! Come in, my beautiful girls."

He noticed that Behiye was not among them, and that the other four were dressed in fur-lined coats, hats and scarves. Atiye was the first to speak. "Baba, we have come to get you," she said, sounding more than a little breathless. It was clear that they had run down the stairs and along the corridors from their rooms – though they would surely have been scolded if they had been caught doing so. Atiye pulled her father towards the window, her eyes wide with excitement.

452

Outside, the first snow of winter had fallen. Snowflakes had settled in the corners of the glass panes and on the window-sills; the bare branches of the trees were bowed low beneath the weight of the freshly-fallen snow, and the whole garden was covered in a thick, white, feathery quilt. "It has just stopped snowing, so we thought we would go outside and build a snowman. Will you come and help us, Baba?" she pleaded. "Please, Baba! Before it gets dark and we have to come inside for dinner."

Selahaddin smiled at each of his daughters in turn. He loved them all equally: though they were all so different from one other, each was precious to him. "Well, then, who is going to help me find my coat and hat?" he replied jovially. That answer provoked high-pitched squeals of delight, and they all immediately volunteered – all, that is, except Adile, who smiled shyly at her beloved father: when Atiye had raced past her, desperate to find Selahaddin's black fur *kalpak* before he changed his mind, she had nearly been knocked off her feet.

Stage by stage, Selahaddin got ready for the expedition to the garden. First, he put on the heavy grey coat that Rukiye had fetched for him. Then he wrapped the soft green scarf that Naziknaz had knitted the previous year – and which Safiye had found – round his neck, and put on the hat, made from tightly-curled lamb's wool, that Atiye had triumphantly produced. Finally, Adile stepped forward holding out a pair of woollen socks to go over the ones he was wearing: knowing that her father's feet were prone to getting painfully cold, she had gone to find him a second pair. Selahaddin, grateful for this act of consideration, kissed her on the cheek and sat down in his armchair holding the socks in his hand. Addressing all his daughters, he said: "Now, I think we also need to find a hat and a scarf for our snowman, and perhaps a walking stick for him, too! What do you think, girls?" There were more excited noises from his daughters as they raced around the apartment looking for suitable items. Meanwhile, Selahaddin took advantage of the hiatus to commence putting his extra socks on: an expanding waistline was making it increasingly difficult for him to bend forward – something he found very frustrating. Once he had finally completed this task, huffing and puffing as he did so, he stoically brushed these feelings of irritation aside and lifted himself out of the armchair.

The rest of the afternoon was spent playing in the snow in the harem garden. Not long after Selahaddin and his daughters had ventured outside, Fuad ran out to join them, and Behiye followed behind holding on tightly to Vâsıb's small mittened hand as his little legs struggled to wade through the deep snow. Naziknaz, Jalefer and Safiru, who were watching from the warmth of one of the salons overlooking the garden, waved and smiled whenever Selahaddin or one of his children looked in their direction. Behiye had attempted to persuade Safiru to join them all in the garden – in fact, she often tried to include her sister-in-law in the family games – but Safiru's shyness, and her mistaken belief that Naziknaz might disapprove, had prevented her from doing so. However, as she watched Vâsıb playing in the snow, she immediately regretted her decision.

First Selahaddin supervised Fuad and Atiye as they made a large snowball; then he helped them roll it round and round the garden until they were satisfied that it would make a corpulent frame for the snowman. Rukiye searched for stones and twigs that she thought might be used to decorate it, while Adile and Safiye busied themselves making a smaller snowball that was soon ready to be lifted on top of the rotund belly. Behiye encouraged Vâsıb to collect handfuls of snow to pat into the portly snowman's tummy, and he took great delight in doing this – until his hands got wet and cold, and he began to cry. Behiye bent down, took off his damp mittens, blew onto his chubby pink hands and gave them a gentle rub to warm them. This seemed to work: he giggled as he watched Fuad place Selahaddin's old fez on top of the snowman's head and Atiye wrap one of her father's scarves around its neck. Rukiye pushed two stones into its face, giving it two large black eyes, and laid a row of smaller stones in a curved line to form a somewhat lop-sided smile. Adile and Safiye made spindly arms out of the sticks Rukiye had gathered, and rested their father's wooden walking stick against one of the plump figure's twiggy hands.

"I think our snowman is missing something," Selahaddin announced. So saying, he took a clay pipe out of his pocket and stuck the amber mouthpiece in the snowman's mouth. From another pocket he pulled out an old, broken pair of spectacles and placed it over the stony, vacant eyes. Everyone clapped and cheered.

"I think this is definitely the best snowman we have ever made," Fuad said proudly, and everyone agreed.

After the finishing touches had been added to the snow-man, Behiye decided to take Vâsıb inside straight away as he was beginning to shiver; his funny-shaped nose had turned red, and was streaming with mucus. Privately, she was thankful to have an excuse to miss the family snowball fight that always seemed to follow the building of a snowman. Vâsıb did not object: by now the novelty of playing in the snow had completely worn off – and besides, his fingers were starting to sting once again and his big toes had gone numb. Safiru met them in the entrance hall holding a thick, warm blanket; taking her little boy in her arms, she wrapped it around him and instinctively covered his face with kisses, ignoring his half-hearted remonstrances.

"Let me take my grandson," said Naziknaz, who had appeared at the bottom of the stairs. She held out her arms to receive Vâsıb, who at the first sound of his grandmother's voice had turned towards her and was now trying to wriggle out of his mother's embrace. "We must take him to my room and get him out of those wet clothes immediately!" Naziknaz added in a tone that signalled that she was in no mood to countenance any opposition. Bowing in deference to her mother-in-law, Safiru passed her son into her arms. "My beautiful boy, did you have fun in the snow?" Naziknaz asked, kissing Vâsıb's cold, pink cheek and wiping his nose with her silk handkerchief; he replied with his usual enthusiastic but unintelligible chatter.

Behiye placed a comforting hand on Safiru's arm and gave her a sympathetic smile. She knew that her mother could be overbearing at times, and understood very well how as a result, Safiru often felt excluded from the upbringing of her own child. Behiye had tried to encourage her timid sister-in-law to be a little more assertive – especially with regard to Vâsıb – but despite the fact that Safiru had been married to Nihad for nearly three years now, she still remained in awe of the family and felt undeserving of her position within it.

"If you will excuse me, I will go and prepare a cup of warm, sweetened milk for Vâsıb," Safiru said quietly. Naziknaz did not seem to hear her: she had already begun to walk determinedly along the corridor that led to the apartment she shared with Nihad and his young family, and called out to Behiye to follow her.

Outside in the harem garden, meanwhile, two opposing sides had established themselves; each had set up makeshift defences behind one of the clumps of trees, and was busy building up supplies of snowy ammunition. The once-pristine blanket of snow was now dotted with large patches of

456

uncovered grass and haphazardly-scattered footprints, giving it the appearance of a tattered patchwork quilt. Selahaddin had been voted the 'commander' of one of the sides by Adile and Safiye, his two 'captains', while 'General' Fuad had assumed command of the other. He had appointed Rukiye as his second-in-command, and this had instantly angered Atiye, who was not at all happy to have been relegated to the position of a mere sergeant! That had been the first argument. The second had been about tactics – Fuad had ordered his sisters to draw the enemy out into the open, where he would attack from above. He planned to climb one of the trees and rain down snowball bombs on his adversaries, undetected by them. Rukiye had said this was too dangerous – a remark that was not well received by Fuad, who retorted that she obviously did not understand that war was in any case a dangerous business. He had then felt obliged to remind her that a junior officer should never contradict the orders of her superior, especially on the field of battle; however, she had ignored him and told him not to be silly.

Battle was now joined. Despite feeling somewhat disheartened by this untimely mutiny, Fuad modified his tactics, leading a death-defying head-on charge into the clump of trees that his father was defending together with the 'twins'. Snowballs flew in all directions, bursting open on impact; for the most part their trajectories ended on the ground or against tree trunks, but a few did indeed find their target. As ordered, Rukiye and Atiye concentrated their attack on their father, and he soon surrendered in fits of laughter. Fuad's missiles hit Safiye first on the leg, then on the chest. She raised both hands above her head in a gesture of surrender, not wanting to be hit again – which meant that only Adile now remained to be forced into submission. By this time Fuad was running low on ammunition, but seeing his sister crouching behind a tree he took aim and lobbed a particularly compact snowball straight at her. It hit her hard in the face, and she burst into tears. This had not, of course, been his intention, and he rushed over to apologise, but all the same the incident brought the game to an abrupt end.

Before long everyone was sitting huddled around the roaring stove in Selahaddin's salon, warming their hands and drinking hot apple tea. Jalefer had joined them, and after reprimanding Fuad for being so ferociously determined to win the snowball fight she went over to comfort Adile, who had a badly bruised nose. Fuad was desperately upset. He had not meant to hit his sister in the face: the only thought in his mind had been to capture the enemy's position and win the day. However, he had – as happened all too often – got a little carried away. This was, he thought sadly to himself, the problem with playing with girls: they just cannot enter into the spirit of the thing. It made him wish more than ever that he had playmates of his own age with whom he could enjoy the rough and tumble of war games, football and wrestling, none of which seemed to appeal to his sisters. He loved them all, but if he had to choose a favourite it would be Adile because she was the gentlest – and that, of course, made him feel even worse about having hurt her. He sat quietly beside her feeling guilty and ashamed, meanwhile asking himself what had possessed him to throw that snowball so hard. It had been a stupid thing to do, and he could not forgive himself.

"I am so sorry, Adile," he said for what was probably the twentieth time. "I swear to you that I was not aiming at your face, and did not mean to hurt you. Poor Adile! I promise I will never hurt you again."

"I know, Fuad," she said with a brave smile. "Really, it does not matter at all." She leant over to her brother and gave him a kiss on the cheek. In doing so, her nose brushed against his skin, causing sharp ripples of pain to spread across her face; seeing that it had immediately made him feel better, however, she told herself that it had been worth it.

CHAPTER TWENTY-THREE

The Verdict

December 1905

As Fehime sat in the elegant drawing room of her *yalı* on a sunny afternoon in mid-December, the topic of her conversation with her sister Hadice was not the ongoing trial, nor was it the situation in Persia: rather, it was the visitor whose arrival both ladies were awaiting. After months of hesitation and procrastination, Fehime had finally mustered the courage to invite the acclaimed photographer Jean Pascal Sébah to her home in Ortaköy, where he was to take photographic portraits of the two ladies. Sébah was of Armenian descent; however, he came from a family who – in common with so many other families belonging to the Empire's minorities – remained loyal to the Ottoman State despite all the propaganda that had recently been directed towards them. Fehime, in turn, was happy to reward this loyalty with her patronage.

She had originally invited Fatma to join them in this escapade, but Fatma had politely and tactfully declined the invitation, giving no hint of the horror and consternation that the idea aroused in her – while privately feeling genuine admiration for her sisters' daring. In order to avoid any awkward confrontations with Ali Galib Pasha, her husband,

460

and spare him embarrassment, Fehime had prudently chosen a day when he was away visiting his family and was not expected home until late evening.

After lunch, Fehime had given instructions for her carriage to be sent to the Grande Rue de Péra to collect the young photographer from his studio and bring him secretly to her *yalı*. She did not want him arriving in a hired carriage as she was only too aware that if he did, rumours would spread through the city faster than any of the fires that so often rampaged through its narrow streets. Her family had suffered quite enough recently from gossip and rumour, and she had no intention of being the cause of yet another conflagration of that nature. Thinking that the fewer people who knew about the sitting the better, she had also requested that Jean Pascal Sébah come without his assistant – a condition to which he had willingly agreed.

All the necessary negotiations with the photographer had been conducted the previous week by Fehime's trusted eunuch – who, used to her unconventional ways, had not voiced any of his misgivings: it was certainly not his place to question his mistress, nor would he ever dare to do so. Now, at a quarter past two on the prearranged afternoon, he was standing guard in the main salon together with Zeynel Ağa, Hadice's eunuch. His hands were clasped in front of his chest; meanwhile, the index finger of his right hand played with the emerald ring he wore on his left. Both men watched with obvious interest as the photographer methodically went through the process of setting up his complicated-looking equipment. First, the rolling tripod stand was opened out; then the central column was raised by winding the rack and pinion slowly until it reached the required height, whereupon it was firmly locked into place. Next, the camera box was secured on the mounting plate, which was lined with

461

dark green felt, and the tapered bellows of the focus box, which were made of plum-coloured leather, were part-extended in readiness. Following this, the contraption was carefully attached to the tripod head, and the shiny brass screw of the mounting bracket tightened. Opening a small, round wooden box, Jean Pascal now reverently lifted out a camera lens and screwed it slowly into place. Nodding in the direction of the eunuchs to indicate that he was ready, he could not help but admire their smooth complexions, their high cheekbones, their long, proud noses and their full, fleshy lips; the moment he had set eyes on them, it had occurred to him what wonderful subjects they would be to photograph.

Hadice and Fehime, meanwhile, were waiting anxiously in the drawing room; both were feeling uncertain as to whether they had picked the right dresses to wear, and whether or not their hair was dressed in the most flattering style. Jean Pascal had arrived a little earlier than expected, and ever since they had been informed of this fact they had been in a fluster. In fact, now that he was actually present in the *yalı* and the long-awaited moment had arrived, their nerve – to varying degrees – was beginning to desert them.

"It is not too late to change our minds, you know," said Hadice, her cheeks flushed as pink as pomegranate seeds. "I know your original intention was to give Father these portraits as a reminder of our love for him, but now that that is no longer possible, perhaps it will be best if we thank Monsieur Sébah for the trouble he has taken in coming here and inform him that we will no longer be requiring his services."

"But my dear Hadice, now that we have come this far, we really must see it through," Fehime replied, trying to conceal her exasperation at her sister's volte-face. "Imagine what it will be like to have our images captured for eternity! Whether we like it or not, our youth is fading, and this is our opportunity to preserve it in some way before it is lost forever. Don't you agree?" Hadice did not reply; instead, she looked away and pursed her lips. Fehime had thought this line of argument would appeal to her sister, but frustratingly, it did not seem to have had the hoped-for effect. After that, they sat in tense silence until they were disturbed by a gentle knock on the door: Sıdıka Kalfa, the most devoted and most discreet of Fehime's servants, had come to announce that the photographer was ready to begin.

Fehime rose and smoothed down the skirts of her gown; then, approaching her sister, she took her hand and began to address her. "It is not my vanity that is speaking now, Hadice," she said. "The person standing before you is not 'Kelebek Sultan', the supposedly frivolous 'Butterly Princess', but the real me – the all-too-headstrong and rebellious Fehime, who is begging you to do this with me, for I cannot do it alone." Hadice was taken aback by the imploring tone of her sister's words. Then Fehime continued: "This is something I feel I really must do, Hadice. I have a voice, and I need to use it. I see having these portraits made as a way of expressing my innermost self, of making a strong statement; it will allow me to speak directly to those who *Inshallah* will come after us. It may not be Allah's will that we should have children" – here, Hadice looked at her sister intently and marvelled at the courage of these words – "but we are already blessed with nephews and nieces who – *Inshallah* – will have descendants. How wonderful it will be for them to see, perhaps in later life, that we were not bound by the conventions of our times and the restrictions of our position – that we were independent, free-thinking women who had the courage to rebel against the monotony and what some might see as the meaninglessness of our lives, even if only

463

in small ways! If we do this, we will be remembered, Hadice – remembered not simply as names on our family tree, but as we really were, as people. Don't you see? Thanks to these portraits, when our descendants look into our eyes, our souls will be laid bare to them, and they will accept us as human beings. That is why we must do it."

Hadice gazed at her sister in astonishment, seeing her in a new light. "Oh my, Fehime, what eloquence! Father would be so proud of you for daring to challenge the suffocating conventions that restrict us! You are quite right, of course. I see that now." Her sister's outburst had restored to her some of the old spirit that had been so badly crushed and beaten down by the scandal. "After all, we cannot have future generations assuming us to have been boring old fuddy-duddies, can we?" she said with a twinkle in her eye. The sisters grinned at one another, pinned their translucent silk veils in place and walked out of the drawing room with their heads held high, holding hands.

❁ ❁ ❁ ❁ ❁

Jean Pascal Sébah had naturally been extremely nervous about accepting this prestigious yet delicate Imperial commission, and it vexed him that his hands had not stopped trembling for one moment since he had stepped into the luxurious carriage that had come for him. He wondered whether the two statuesque Nubian eunuchs had noticed this as they watched him assemble the camera, fumbling hopelessly as he did so. Their large, almond-shaped eyes, completely devoid of expression, had given no clue as to what they were thinking, but he certainly hoped his failure to maintain his sangfroid had escaped their attention! As soon as Hadice and Fehime entered the salon and introduced

464

themselves, however, the two princesses immediately began to describe their ideas for the photographs to him, and this made him feel much more relaxed: it was clear that they had given the composition of their portraits a great deal of thought. Moreover, their kind, considerate manner immediately put him at his ease, allowing his experience and professionalism to come to the fore and giving him the confidence to try his best to dispel any inhibitions the sisters may still have had. It did not take him long to realise that these sittings might well produce some captivating pictures, and he was filled with eagerness to get under way.

Being the elder of the two, Hadice was the first to have her photograph taken. She was adamant that she wanted Aslan, her beloved pet terrier, to be in it, and Fehime – despite thinking this was rather silly as he would probably move and spoil the image – knew better than to argue. Hadice was equally adamant that the photograph should be taken of her in a standing position as she felt that this would show off her slim waist to the best advantage: she did not wish the discomfort of a tightly-laced corset that she had stoically borne for the last few hours to have been undergone for nothing.

Jean Pascal Bey now sought and received the permission of both princesses to set about creating a suitable photographic composition with the props available to him. First, he lifted the finely-gilded tête-à-tête chair that stood by the window and placed it against a wall at an angle so that one end projected into the room; then he unrolled the small Hereke carpet that he had brought with him and laid it under the back legs of the chair, ensuring that the fringe was arranged in a way that looked haphazard and informal. He was glad that he had decided to bring this carpet: he had been right in thinking that the opulent *yalı* would not have such a

465

small rug to hand. After that, he picked up a three-legged pedestal table that he had previously spotted in a corner of the room and put it on the opposite side of the rug from the tête-à-tête chair, placing on it a vase full of heavy-headed blooms. Standing back to contemplate the scene, he rubbed his chin, moved forward to remove two or three of the flowers from the vase, and laid them on the table. During the entire process, the princesses had been watching him work with great interest. After a few final tweaks, he appeared to be satisfied with the scene he had created, and turned to address Hadice.

"If your Imperial Highness would be so kind," he said, "I would ask you to please stand between the seat and the table, and place your right hand on the curved back of the seat … Oh, and maybe your left hand might be placed behind your back." Hadice did exactly as she was bidden. "Hmm … there is something missing. I wonder …" he mused, scratching his head just above the right ear and making the hair stick out beneath his fez. "A fan! Princess Hadice, do you have a fan? I think it would complete the portrait most satisfactorily if you were to hold a closed fan in your right hand as it rests on the back of the seat." This was an item that it had not occurred to Hadice to bring with her: she looked across the room at her sister, who opened a narrow rectangular box that was lying on a nearby table – it bore her initials in swirling gold letters – and took out an ivory fan with a beautifully-carved ebony handle. Fehime then handed it triumphantly to her sister, who smiled at her in gratitude. "Perfect!" exclaimed Jean Pascal. "Now we are ready for Aslan Bey." He placed a richly-embroidered cushion on the seat of the tête-à-tête chair, which was upholstered in red velvet, and Hadice called Aslan to her. The dog obediently jumped up onto the seat and sat on the cushion facing the photographer just as if he knew precisely what was expected of him. Everyone laughed, and this served to lighten the atmosphere in the room even further.

Hadice looked magnificent. Her thick dark hair framed her face in a loose pompadour bun; the simple cream dress she was wearing had a high neck and ruffled sleeves that fell to the top of her white gloves, while its sweeping train lay pooled in front of her. She had decided not to wear much jewellery as she wanted the Imperial Order that hung around her neck, and the Mecidiye Order pinned to her left breast, to stand out. Fehime thought she had never seen her sister looking more lovely or more dignified.

Jean Pascal wheeled his camera forward on the small wheels attached to the tripod legs; noticing how badly they creaked, he made a mental note to have them oiled as soon as he returned to the studio. He then made a slight adjustment to the camera's angle, tilted the lens, and disappeared for a moment beneath the dark cloth draped over the camera box in order to view the inverted image. He brought the image into focus by adjusting the distance between the lens and the film plate, moving the folding leather bellows as though he was playing an accordion. When he reappeared, he was utterly dumbfounded to see that Hadice was unveiled: during the few seconds it had taken him to re-emerge from under the dark cloth, she had unpinned her *yashmak* and allowed it to float to the floor. Zeynel Ağa moved forward to pick up the discarded veil, his smooth, finely-chiselled face betraying nothing of what he might be thinking. Jean Pascal, meanwhile, looked thunderstruck, having been thrown completely off guard. Unlike the old eunuch, he was incapable of hiding his mental confusion.

"Jean Pascal Bey, I think you will need to hurry before Aslan tires of the pose," Hadice said. Fehime giggled behind

467

her hand. How she loved her sister, and how she admired her ready wit!

Jean Pascal now disappeared under the dark cloth for a second time – more to settle his nerves than to double-check the focus. Then, standing to attention beside his camera box, he squeezed the small air-pump ball that operated the shutter system and took the photograph. Neither Hadice nor Aslan had moved even a millimetre. He knew instantly that he had captured a perfect image.

❁ ❁ ❁ ❁ ❁

After taking three more photographs of Hadice, each one with a slightly different composition, Jean Pascal carefully put away the glass plate negatives in their case, feeling relieved that his hands had at last stopped trembling. Hadice thanked him for his patience; then, more out of a sense of obligation than a sudden access of modesty, she put on her *yashmak* once more.

Something in her had irrevocably changed as a result of the two recent upsets in her life – the scandal over her affair with Mehmed Kemaleddin Pasha and the death of her father. She was no longer the lively, over-confident narcissist, always on the look-out for an opportunity to shock, that she had been before. Instead, she lived out each day under a heavy burden of guilt and shame, believing that she was to blame for Murad's sudden relapse into illness and his subsequent death. It had greatly distressed Fehime to see her sister continue to torture herself in this way, in spite of the fact that she had told her innumerable times that no one in the family held her responsible for what had happened; perhaps all Hadice needed was just a little more time to come to realise this herself.

Just then Müyesser Kalfa, Fehime's pretty young maid, appeared carrying a silver tray on which were a jug of mandarin sherbet, three crystal goblets and a bowl of warm *saray lokması*. She poured the iced drink into the glasses and offered them first to the princesses, then to the photographer, before bowing out of the room. By now everyone was thirsty, and this timely refreshment was gratefully received. Fehime refilled everyone's glass once it was empty, and offered the bowl containing the honey-soaked sweetmeats, generously sprinkled with cinnamon, to her sister and then to Jean Pascal; both were unable to resist.

It was now her turn to have her photograph taken. This was the moment for which she had been waiting for so long, and she could barely conceal her excitement. Inspired by her sister's act of courage, she removed her *yashmak* and turned confidently to face the photographer. By now Sébah had come to the realisation that these two Muradiye princesses were far more modern and liberal in outlook than any of the Court ladies he had previously encountered, so this time he was better prepared.

"I would like to be photographed playing my piano," Fehime announced. This was something Jean Pascal had never done before, but he was always keen to try something new. Hadice, for her part, was not at all surprised by the request: she knew that music was her sister's greatest love. Fehime had been introduced to music by her father, and had soon discovered that she had inherited his gift for it: over the years, she had turned herself into an accomplished pianist and composer.

"Of course, Your Highness," he replied. "But if I may make a suggestion, perhaps we could first take a portrait of you standing beside the piano. After that, we can take a more informal one of you seated at it."

"As you prefer," she answered happily. Fehime walked across the salon – passing the two eunuchs, who remained on guard on either side of the door – and stood in a rather awkward pose next to the highly-polished piano. She was wearing a pale pistachio-green silk dress with a richly-embroidered bodice and a delicate chiffon sash trimmed with tassles, and it contrasted beautifully with the rich dark brown wood – in which the gleaming chestnut shine of her hair was reflected. Her loose pompadour chignon, adorned with a diamond crescent hair comb, fell forward onto her forehead, and a pair of diamond drop earrings hung from her petite ear lobes. The only other piece of jewellery Fehime had chosen to wear was a single string of luminescent pearls.

"Princess Fehime, perhaps you might like to consider opening the cover to expose the keys," Jean Pascal suggested. "And I feel it might enhance the composition if a sheet of music were to be placed on the stand – if one is readily available, of course," he added.

"Certainly," Fehime replied. "An excellent idea!" She opened the lid and playfully tinkled the keys. Then she opened the boulle box, decorated in red tortoiseshell and gilded brass, that sat on a nearby table. This box contained all her favourite sheet music, and she rummaged through the leaves of manuscript paper for a few seconds before finding what she was looking for; then she placed on the music stand the handwritten score of her father's composition 'Waltz in E Major'.

Jean Pascal's expert eye was now satisfied that everything was in readiness. A sumptuous carpet already lay on the floor, and an upholstered chair and a large fern in a porcelain planter formed the background, giving depth to the composition. He wheeled his camera into position – ignoring the squeaks; then he altered the angle of the mounting plate, adjusted the key knobs that held the lens in place and fiddled with the aperture adjustment ring. Meanwhile, Hadice looked on with interest, admiring the way the young man's artistic flair was allowing him to create the ideal setting for her sister's portrait photograph. Helping herself to some more of the *saray lokması*, she smiled with pure happiness, feeling pleased that she had allowed Fehime to persuade her to participate in this risqué exploit. She was having fun – an experience that had been denied to her for a very long time.

"Your Highness, would you perhaps like to move a little closer to the piano, and maybe rest your right hand on that sheet of music? And may I also suggest that you let your left hand fall onto the tails of your sash?" To tell the truth, he could see – although he did not say so openly – that the pose Fehime had adopted was a rather stiff one, and he wanted to find some way of helping her to appear more natural. She did as she was asked, and Hadice was impressed by how greatly these small adjustments improved the pose. Jean Pascal now disappeared beneath the dark cloth, just as he had done when photographing his previous subject. He adjusted the length of the pleated camera bellows until he was satisfied that the image was in focus; then he set the shutter, inserted the film, pulled the dark slide part way out and pressed the air-pump ball firmly between his fingers. Like her sister had done, Fehime remained as still as a Grecian statue, and Jean Pascal had the satisfaction of knowing that the portrait would come out crisp and unblurred. He was a little concerned that he might have slightly over-exposed the image as the light coming in from the window had suddenly changed, and he resolved to increase the shutter speed for the next photograph. He then took three more shots of Fehime, including one that he was especially excited about: this showed the princess sitting straight-backed at the piano facing away from the camera in a serene pose, her head turned towards the window so that her gentle yet regal profile was captured to perfection; meanwhile, her long, elegant fingers appeared poised to begin playing a sonata.

His work at the *yalı* now over, Sébah was eager to get back to the studio in Pera so that he could develop the film plate of that special image: he wanted to see if it would turn out as well as he hoped, and indeed fully expected. As he folded his camera back into its box and locked the case, the thought occurred to him that he might even produce a coloured print of this picture, which he believed might well be one of the finest he had ever taken.

As the young photographer took his leave, Hadice and Fehime thanked him with genuine sincerity, and were delighted to hear that they would not have long to wait before their portraits were ready for collection. They told him that they would send one of their eunuchs to collect them rather than have them delivered, as this would be more discreet. They also insisted that in view of the sensitive nature of the images, the negatives should be given to them along with the printed portraits. Jean Pascal readily assented to all these requests, assuring them once again of his absolute discretion. "I will always be at Your Highnesses' service," he said with a bow. Then the princesses left him to pack up the remainder of his equipment under the watchful eyes of their trusted eunuchs, and retired to Fehime's drawing room; there, they drank coffee, indulged themselves with a tray of sweetmeats and congratulated each other on their audacity.

☙ ☙ ☙ ☙ ☙

18ᵗʰ December 1905

It was the day on which the verdict was to be announced. Nihad had hoped to be allowed to attend Court for this occasion, but Abdülhamid had withheld his permission, as indeed he had done in the case of all the other Imperial princes who wanted to see the verdict pronounced, and justice done. That meant that Nihad would not be able to learn the plotters' fate until Asım Ağa returned to the palace. It was now getting dark outside, and the wind was rattling the windows as if it were desperate to come inside to escape the cold. Nihad was eager for news, but playing backgammon with his father in Selahaddin's study was providing him with distraction of a kind.

Nezihe Kalfa entered the room, drew the heavy brocade winter curtains that served as a second barrier against the persistent northerly wind, and stoked the stove. Before withdrawing, she lingered in the doorway for a moment in the hope that Nihad might look her way for just a second – so that she could meet his gaze with her flirtatious eyes, and perhaps ignite a spark of interest in him with one of her spuriously bashful smiles. She had turned fifteen earlier that year, and ever since then her idle moments had been filled with little else but the thought of Nihad's strong hands on her pale, untouched skin; much to her chagrin, however, the handsome prince remained oblivious to her eager attentions and impervious to her charms. Today was no exception, and it was with a pang of disappointment and frustration that she closed the door behind her, wondering – not for the first time – how Safiru, who was patently so plain and dull, had succeeded in capturing the heart of this most dashing of princes.

Murad had bequeathed his backgammon board to his youngest grandson Fuad to keep alive in him the memory of the many pleasurable hours they had shared while playing the game. It was kept on a shelf in Selahaddin's study for safe-keeping, and was used not just by Fuad but by everyone else in the family. As Nihad and his father rolled the dice and moved the pieces round the board, they discussed the recent passing of a law in France that had made the French Republic a secular state; rather than being a completely new departure, this step was in fact no more than the outcome of the secularist policies that had been carried out by successive governments since the French Revolution. The two princes, for their part, found the idea of state secularism an interesting, albeit contentious, one.

Selahaddin was in two minds as to the merits of such a policy. As a philosopher, he respected the arguments put forward by thinkers of the French Enlightenment such as Voltaire, Diderot and Montesquieu who believed that religion was inherently divisive and suppressive. They had argued that the firm and fixed doctrines of the Catholic Church kept the people in a perpetual state of ignorance – with the result that it prevented them from questioning religious teachings, and therefore also from giving consideration to new scientific discoveries. They saw religion as a form of coercion, and felt that only freedom of conscience, freedom of thought and freedom of worship could ensure true liberty and equality. In the opinion of these men, the place of religion was not in the public domain, but in the private spiritual life of the individual. Selahaddin, however, was a man of devout religious beliefs, and as such he espoused the view that the principle of secularism was not one that could easily be put into practice in Islamic states, the reason being that it seemed to him to contradict some of the basic tenets of Islam. In the Moslem worldview, religion and politics were fused together in the Quran and the other holy texts of Islam – and this led him to doubt whether secularism would be a viable system if any attempt were to be made to apply it to the Ottoman Empire.

The law of 1905, which reflected the ideas of the philosophers of the Enlightenment, had brought an end to the long-standing conflict between the Republic of France and the Catholic Church. With its passing, the principle of *laïcité* had been enshrined in the statute books; the neutrality of the state in religious affairs had thus been guaranteed, freedom of religious expression and practice assured, and the power and influence of the Church over the people and over public institutions restricted.

"My understanding is that this law is absolutely not intended to encourage the people of France to become atheist, or even to encourage them to become less religious," Nihad remarked. "Its sole purpose is to bring about a change in the relationship between religion and the state, and in the role that religion plays in society. If anything, I see it as more anti-Rome and anti-ecclesiastical than anti-religious." Selahaddin sat back in his chair with a pensive look on his face; he was listening to his son with full attention. "For centuries," Nihad went on, "Christian monarchs have resented the power and authority of the Pope and his army of scheming cardinals, interfering bishops and meddlesome priests – who have never abandoned their attempts to influence European politics from within the Vatican. Here, however, we have never encountered a problem of this nature: since the head of our religion is also our head of state, we cannot fully comprehend the need for such a separation."

Selahaddin was silent for a while, mulling over what his son had said. "You are right, Nihad, and it is because of this that I do not believe we need consider adopting a secularist policy," he replied at last. "As you know, England is believed by everyone to be a modern, democratic state, yet it is not a secular one. The current king is both head of state and head of the Church of England; this surely demonstrates that secularism is not a prerequisite for the taking of a liberal attitude. What we need is not secularism but the enforcement of a strict policy of religious toleration towards all our subjects. A heterogeneous, multi-religious society such as ours requires nothing less than this."

"Yes, Father, I agree with you completely," Nihad continued. "In fact, one could argue that secularism is actually a suppressive policy rather than a liberal one." Selahaddin appeared a little confused by this statement, so Nihad went on to explain what he had meant. "The reason I say this is that in some respects, it actually curtails rights and freedoms by setting out to censor, and in some cases actually silence, religious institutions through legal means." Selahaddin reflected with satisfaction that as usual, his son had been very astute: he had fully grasped the implications of the new French law, and had understood the various ways in which it could be interpreted.

After a short pause, Nihad continued to expound his views; he always found a discussion on the subject of religion stimulating. "I would also argue that since in Islam we do not have a religious hierarchy such as the one that exists in Roman Catholicism, our situation is very different," he said. "Our Caliph has no college of cardinals or synod of bishops to whom he must defer, and does not depend on the votes of any such body for his power. Instead, his authority is derived solely from Allah; meanwhile, his position as the most powerful leader in the Islamic world enables him to protect the faithful and defend the holy cities. The source of this political and military power is the Ottoman State, and the political role of the sultan – the head of that state – cannot be separated from his religious duties as Caliph since both roles are embodied in the same man. In consequence of this arrangement, the Empire can never become secular so long as the Sultanate and the Caliphate are combined." At this point Selahaddin nodded, seeing the logic of his son's argument. "That does not mean, however, that it cannot become a progressive modern state – indeed, there is nothing to prevent it from becoming just that!" Nihad added.

"Hmm," said Selahaddin, impressed yet again by his son's perspicacity. "You certainly seem to have given the matter some thought!"

Nihad leaned forward in his chair, and with a shake of the hand and a flick of the wrist he ejected the die from the leather shaker. He had rolled another double six! He picked up four ivory checkers and retrieved his die from the board. Selahaddin smiled wryly at his son's good fortune – it had been a close game, but once again he had lost! Graciously admitting defeat, he began to set up his pieces, stained cochineal red, for another game. Just as he was moving them into position, however, he heard the familiar sound of Asım Ağa's cane on the wooden floorboards in the corridor outside. The next game would have to wait: obviously, the verdict had been delivered.

�☻ ☻ ☻ ☻ ☻

The old scribe stood before the two princes and began recounting to them the findings of the İstanbul Criminal Court. He had taken detailed notes during the proceedings, and referred to them as he spoke. Selahaddin and Nihad listened attentively, hoping to hear that the perpetrators of the horrific atrocity at Yıldız were to be punished as severely as the law permitted. Everyone who had been present at the mosque that day bore scars that they would carry with them for the rest of their life; some were physical and thus in plain sight, while others – like Nihad's – were emotional, and so much less visible from the outside.

As they listened, they learned that the court had acquitted a number of the accused. Some had been found to be completely innocent of any crime; others were people who had given aid to the plotters without being aware that they were involved in a deadly conspiracy. Members of the revolutionary committee who had helped smuggle the carriage into the country and hide it, or who had acted as messengers between the main conspirators, had been sentenced to fifteen years penal servitude; those guilty of the more serious offence of concealing weapons, bombs and explosives, meanwhile, had received life sentences. The court had condemned fourteen of the conspirators to death, but of these only four were actually in custody – a situation that was highly frustrating for Necib Melhame Pasha. The rest, who were all foreigners, had either fled the Empire immediately after the failure of the assassination attempt, and had thus been tried and sentenced in absentia, or had died while it was still in the planning stage, and so had been tried posthumously; in the first group were Konstantin Kabilyan, Lipa Ripps, Robina Fein and Anna Joris, while in the second were Mikaelyan and Kendiryan.

Asım Ağa explained that the four men who were currently in prison under sentence of death were three Armenians known to have strong connections with the Armenian Revolutionary Federation plus the Belgian anarchist Edouard Joris, who had pledged himself to their cause after meeting Kendiryan at the Singer factory, where they both worked, and being persuaded by his arguments. All four had freely admitted their guilt, stating that they had acted in retaliation for the oppression suffered by the Armenian people. Of the three Armenians, Manouk Oumidyan – who worked as a porter at 'Maison Jones' – was understood to have been the most active member of the İstanbul Revolutionary Committee. The second, Nichau Ohanessyan, a former waiter at the Grand Hotel Kroecker, had concealed fifteen bombs in the basement of this famous hotel, while Arakel Nahanetyan, a porter at the Austrian Hospital, had concealed large quantities of dynamite and ammunition in the storerooms there. Asım Ağa concluded his account by informing the princes that the conspirators who had been convicted and sentenced earlier that day had been led away to loud cheers of "Long live the Padishah!" from the public galleries.

Selahaddin thanked his loyal servant for his diligence in observing and reporting on all that had occurred during the course of the trial, and for bringing news of the verdict back to Çırağan so swiftly. He then dismissed Asım Ağa, sat back in his chair and looked intently at Nihad. They had waited nearly five months to learn exactly what had led up to the events that took place at Yıldız on that fateful day, and to hear the court's pronouncements. Now that the trial was over, perhaps there would be an end to the nightmares that had been triggered by that deeply wounding experience.

"It seems to me that justice has been done, and that our police and our judiciary have discharged their duties honourably and with great efficiency," Selahaddin said after a few moments of reflection. "However, I sense that trouble lies ahead for us. Once the Court of Cassation has confirmed the rulings, I fear that a protracted diplomatic and legal dispute between the Sublime Porte and the Belgian government will arise." Selahaddin was referring to the fact that while the Belgian Legation had been cooperating fully with the Ministry of Justice until the day before, they were now challenging the legality of the trial, and were demanding that Joris be given into their custody under the terms of an old treaty that

479

was now obsolete. The Porte had rejected this outlandish demand, pointing out that the treaty to which they were referring had been superseded by numerous more recent precedents, as well as by later modifications to the original agreement. There had been many occasions on which Belgian citizens had been tried in Ottoman courts without the Belgian authorities raising any objection; consequently, the Porte argued that the right of the Ottoman judiciary to do this had already been accorded tacit acceptance. In addition, ever since Joris's arrest Necib Melhame had been scrupulously careful to ensure that every form of legal procedure was observed, and a dragoman from the Belgian Legation had been present both at all Joris's interrogations and during the trial. Thus there were no possible grounds on which the Belgian government could base an objection; moreover, the fact that the European Powers remained silent on the matter implied endorsement of the position taken up by the Porte.

The United States alone had voiced sympathy for the Belgian government's point of view, but this dissident voice would be ignored by an indignant Ottoman administration. The Porte had not yet forgiven the Americans for intervening the previous summer on behalf of two Armenians who had murdered a respectable Armenian merchant in cold blood for refusing to contribute to the revolutionaries' funds, and this latest action on the Americans' part would only worsen an already troubled relationship. However, since the United States of America had no ambassadorial representation in İstanbul, the Porte would pay little heed to their objections, and no change to this situation was expected until such time as the Sultan approved the elevation of the American Legation to the status of an embassy.

"I am quite sure Hamid will not succumb to pressure from a fledgling state like Belgium – one that has not yet reached adolescence, let alone adulthood! Who does this inexperienced nation think it is to make demands on us?" Nihad expostulated, making no attempt to hide his anger. "The Kingdom of Belgium has not yet celebrated its first seventy-five years of existence, whereas the Ottoman Empire has played a leading role in world affairs for over six hundred years. Being dictated to from time to time by the British and the French is humiliating enough, but to be treated like this by a country as inconsequential as Belgium is utterly intolerable! And how, in all conscience, can King Leopold and his ministers come out in support of an acknowledged anarchist who has pleaded guilty to attempted regicide, and is undeniably responsible for the deaths of a large number of innocent people? The whole thing is preposterous!"

Selahaddin smiled sadly at his son. "My dear Nihad, I understand you completely, but do not expect justice from these people! Do not forget that we are described by them as 'the Sick Man of Europe', and unless we reform and modernise ourselves as a matter of urgency, we will continue to be dictated to by everyone – including the Belgians!" Adopting a more serious tone, he went on: "The problem is that by stubbornly refusing to introduce constitutional government, Hamid has driven us into an impasse. The Europeans view our Sultan as an archaic oriental despot: his authoritarian rule is repugnant to them. Liberals everywhere see us as uncouth, backward people completely devoid of humane values, and are lobbying their governments in the hope of persuading them to intervene in our affairs. They do not understand the reasons behind the policies Hamid is following in the eastern regions of our empire, they have no knowledge of the complexities involved in governing a multi-racial and multi-religious society that is further divided by tribal conflicts, and they certainly do not comprehend the

481

pressures under which we are forced to live as a result of our monstrously heavy foreign debt. And I am afraid that is not all: Europe is inherently Islamophobic and Turcophobic, and has been since the fall of Byzantium. They have never accepted us as their equals, and have always resented our power and influence on the European continent and in the Holy Land. Now that we are weaker than we used to be, they are waiting to pounce on us like hungry jackals."

Selahaddin went on to explain that the reason the Belgian government had acted in this manner could only be that it wished to appease its own people, who had been organising public rallies and petitions in support of Joris ever since the previous summer. He added that King Leopold would no doubt be nervous of the militant anarchism that was sweeping across Europe: knowing that his country was young and therefore vulnerable, he had very likely chosen to give way to public opinion rather than risk his throne. "The actions of King Leopold's government are those of a weak and insecure bunch of people," he concluded. "After all, what kingdom could ever condone attempted regicide?"

Nihad had calmed down a little since his earlier outburst. "It is very sad, but of course I have to admit that you are right," he said, looking dejected. "Perhaps the Belgian king has little option but to bow to the will of his people during turbulent times like these."

"This is not the first time Belgium has shown leniency towards an anarchist who had attempted to assassinate a member of a royal family," Selahaddin said, clasping his hands together and resting his elbows on the arms of his chair. "You may not recollect the episode I am about to relate as it happened in the spring of 1900, but I remember reading about it in a French journal. My father was deeply shocked by it at the time, so we followed developments day

482

by day in the foreign press." Nihad's interest was aroused, and he listened with rapt attention. "A young man by the name of Jean-Baptiste Sipido made an attempt on the life of the current British king when he was still Prince of Wales," his father went on. "The assailant jumped onto the footboard of the royal carriage as it stood on the platform of Brussels-Noord Railway Station and fired two shots through the window; fortunately for Prince Edward, Sipido was an appalling shot, and he missed his target. The reason why he tried to kill the Prince was that he considered him guilty of complicity in the massacre of thousands of people during the Boer War. Much to the anger of the British government, however, the Belgian court acquitted him – in the same way as they doubtless want us to do now in the case of Joris."

Nihad was astounded. "Really? How appalling!" he said. "I knew nothing at all of this affair. I am amazed that the British government did not intervene to insist that justice be done in a case involving a direct threat to the life of the heir to the throne. How rapidly, and how drastically our world is changing! It seems that with every passing day fewer people have respect for the way things have always been, and it pains me deeply – we appear to be teetering on the edge of an abyss. It is my firm belief that there is no better form of government than constitutional monarchy. Naturally, having a democratically-elected government is the best way of ensuring that the people are represented and their voice is heard, but an hereditary head of state – a sultan, an emperor, a tsar or a king – can unite his people in a way that no elected leader ever could. A world without sovereign rulers would indeed be a dark and chaotic one," he said with a shudder. "So what do you think Hamid will do now that the verdict has been pronounced?" he asked his father. "Will he relent and release Joris, or will he endorse the sentence and order the execution of the Belgian and the three Armenians?"

"I do not know, Nihad," Selahaddin replied. "But my guess is that in conformity with his usual practice, he will procrastinate for a time; then he will exercise his prerogative and commute all four death sentences to life imprisonment. My uncle has always preferred to exile or imprison convicted criminals rather than sanction their execution – even in the case of his most dangerous enemies. I would guess that in this instance, the condemned men will be left to languish in jail for the rest of their days, forgotten by the world. Such a course would have the added benefit of circumventing the awkward legal dilemma that has arisen by reason of the fact that Belgium has abolished capital punishment, which of course renders her unable to carry out Joris's sentence – although according to the Capitulations, it is her right to do so."

"Well, you may be right, I suppose," Nihad said. "But I think Hamid ought to make a show of strength and act with resolution now that the sentences have been passed. If he shows clemency, the people will be angry and disappointed: they will not believe that these traitors deserve his mercy considering the fact that they tried to murder our Sultan and Caliph, and in addition killed so many innocent people – and horses." Nihad's face betrayed his anguish as he went back in his mind to that dreadful day in July. "It is imperative that Hamid show the world that the Ottoman Empire is determined to deal ruthlessly with any assassin, conspirator or traitor – otherwise, every foreign anarchist and revolutionary fanatic will be encouraged to mount attacks on our Padishah and our state."

"There is always reason to show mercy, Nihad," Selahaddin replied. "However, the important thing is to find a way of preventing foreigners from interfering in our affairs and inciting our Christian subjects to revolt. We have all lived together in harmony for centuries, and must continue to do so." Selahaddin could see that his son had become incensed, and wished to restore him to a calmer and more rational frame of mind; he had no intention, however, of failing to acknowledge the facts of the case. "The trial has revealed that the entire conspiracy was planned, financed and carried out by foreigners," he continued. "The plot was devised by Russian Armenians, and its execution financed by Armenians living abroad. The conspirators corresponded with each other through our city's network of foreign post offices; they were able to carry out their surveillance of the *Selamlık* ceremonies thanks to the recommendations they had obtained from foreign embassies, and they stored their weapons and explosives – which had, of course, been bought with foreign money – in foreign-owned buildings. It seems that the Levantine quarter of Pera has become a den of iniquity where loyal Christian subjects are constantly exposed to seditious publications and are subjected to relentless intimidation. Hamid must address this problem with the greatest urgency before we lose the loyalty of everyone who lives there."

Just then the study door flew open with great force, knocking into the side of the ormolu mahogany bookcase that contained Selahaddin's personal journals – and in ran Fuad. Seeing the open backgammon board on the table, he asked: "Can we play together, Baba?" Selahaddin well understood that there would be no dissuading Fuad: the discussion with Nihad could continue tomorrow.

"Yes, my dear boy," he said, "but do you really have to barge in like that? You nearly cracked the door."

"Sorry, Father," Fuad replied, sitting down at the table. Nihad asked to be excused; getting up, he ruffled his brother's hair affectionately and walked towards the door. Once in the corridor, he almost bumped into Nezihe Kalfa. "She always seems to be loitering around here. How odd!" he thought to himself. Then he made his way to his apartment; entering the salon, he barely noticed his wife as she smiled lovingly up at him. Safiru knew it was wiser to leave him alone when he appeared distracted like this, so she stopped what she was doing, put the half-finished jumper she was knitting for Vâsıb back in her work-bag and slipped out of the room to put her little boy to bed, intending to go on with her work in her boudoir once he had fallen asleep.

Nihad sat down at his grandfather's piano, running his fingers over the keys absent-mindedly as he contemplated the many complex problems facing the Empire. Would it survive, or were there just too many enemies intent on bringing about its destruction? Was there still time for it to introduce the changes that were so desperately needed if it was to survive? In any case, how long could a multi-racial empire survive in this strange new century? Was it inevitable that the increasingly strong currents of nationalism, aided and abetted by foreign interference, would one day sweep it away? How he longed to be given a meaningful role that would allow him to work to address the dangers that threatened the state! How he hated being confined to Çırağan – that gilded cage where his time was taken up with trivial diversions when there was so much more he could be doing! Nihad feared that the frustration he felt would prove to be yet another prison – this time an invisible one – in which he would remain trapped for the rest of his life, in the same way as his grandfather had been forced to bear his burden to the end of his days. Perhaps this was his fate – perhaps, indeed, it was the fate of all princes of the Muradiye line. But of far more concern to him at the moment was the question of what would become of the Ottoman

Empire and the Caliphate. Would they, too, bleed their life away as his grandfather had done?

Just at that moment, Vâsıb toddled into the room, sleepily rubbing his eyes. His mother must have left him in his grandmother's care after settling him down to sleep in the room they shared, and after that Naziknaz must have dozed off herself – something she was increasingly prone to doing. Nihad took the child on his knee. Never having seen the piano from this angle before, he seemed fascinated by the keys. Nihad kissed him on the top of the head; then he instinctively took Vâsıb's right hand in his and placed it on the keyboard so that his thumb was on middle C. It was time for his son's very first piano lesson.

Author's Note

As a History graduate, I very much appreciate the importance of remaining faithful to historical fact, and that is something I have endeavoured to do throughout this book. All the members of the Ottoman family who are mentioned in it were real people, and the same is true, in most cases, of the servants at Çırağan Palace, the officials at Yıldız Palace and the government ministers. A small number of characters have been invented in order to make the story more lifelike, but all of these are based on what is known of real people who were alive at the time – the main examples of such 'invented' characters being Hayriye Hanım, the midwife, and Fevzi, the young farmer who works the lands of the Muradiye Estate.

I regard first-hand accounts as of particular value and importance, and so I have relied for much of my information on my grandfather's memoirs and on those of others. During my childhood, I was lucky enough to be told numerous stories regarding bygone times by my paternal grandparents and my great-aunts and uncles, and I tried to commit all of these to memory; they gave me a precious insight into what life was like for the people who lived in the Ottoman palaces at the turn of the twentieth century. These stories fostered in me a great sense of pride in my family's history, and laid the foundations for my resolve to discover more about the forgotten world of the Imperial Ottoman Court. My father's recollections and those of others have also made an invaluable contribution to the story; any gaps in it, meanwhile, have been filled by my imagination with the help of some intuited assumptions – and, of course, a little informed guesswork!

489

Key to the Pronunciation
of Turkish Words

Letters of the Turkish Alphabet

Most letters of the Turkish alphabet are the same as those of the English alphabet and are pronounced in a similar way. There are, however, the following exceptions:

- 'a' is longer than in English – half way between the 'a' sounds in *hat* and *hard;*
- 'c' is pronounced as a 'j', as in *jam;*
- 'i' is longer than in English – half way between the 'i' sounds in *bin* and *been;*
- 'j' is pronounced like a French 'j', as in *je;* below, we will show this sound as 'zh';
- 'u' is longer than in English – half way between the 'u' sounds in *put* and *rule.*

The Turkish alphabet does not have *q, w* or *x.*

These letters of the Turkish alphabet do not exist in the English alphabet: ı, İ, ö, ü, ç, ğ, ş. The following is a guide to the pronunciation of these extra letters:

- 'ı' is pronounced with the tip of the tongue touching the gums at the back of the lower teeth and the upper lip pushed up and curled back slightly; in rapid speech, this letter is pronounced like a 'schwa' – the first vowel sound in '**a**rrange'. Below, we will show this sound as 'ə'.
- 'İ', a dotted capital 'I', is pronounced in the same way as small 'i';
- 'ö' is pronounced in a similar way to the French 'eu' sound, as in *deux;*
- 'ü' is pronounced in a similar way to the French 'u' sound, as in *tu;*

490

- 'ç' is pronounced as a 'ch', as in 'chair';
- 'ğ' ('soft g') can be pronounced in two different ways:
    (i) after a 'front vowel' ('e', 'i', 'ö' or 'ü'), it is pronounced as a 'y';
    (ii) after a 'back vowel' ('a', 'ı', 'o' or 'u'), it just lengthens the vowel that precedes it.
- 'ş' is pronounced as a 'sh', as in 'shop'.

Some Examples of Pronunciation

In these examples, the syllable in bold type is the one that is stressed:

Hadice – **Ha**-dee-jé	Gözde – **Göz**-dé
Fehime – **Fe**-hee-mé	Nihad – Nee-**had**
Behiye – **Be**-hee-yé	Fuad – Foo-**ad**
Rukiye – **Roo**-kee-yé	Hanım – **Ha**-nəm
Adile – **Aa**-dee-lé	ağa – **aa**-a
Şayan – Shy-**aan**	Çırağan – Chə-**raa**-an
Ayşe – **Eye**-shé	tuğra – **too**-ra
Gülnev – **Gül**-nev	loğusa – low-**oo**-sa

Accents on Letters of the Turkish Alphabet

A circumflex accent on a vowel – for instance, 'â' as in 'Vâsıb' – usually means that the vowel concerned is to be lengthened in pronunciation.

Pronouncing Turkish Words

Spelling in Turkish is phonetic: there are no silent letters, and every letter is given its full value. A double letter is extended in pronunciation. For instance, *anne* ('mother') is pronounced '**ann**-né', and 'Selahaddin' is pronounced 'Sé-la-**had**-deen'.

491

The Turkish Letter 'R'

In British English, an 'r' at the end of a word is usually not pronounced – though it is, of course, in American English. Also, the 'r' sound is produced at the back of the mouth.

In Turkish, an 'r' is produced at the front of the mouth, and an 'r' at the end of a word is *always* pronounced. In a Turkish 'r', the tip of the tongue briefly touches the gums above the top teeth; there is a slight 'hiss' as a puff of breath is released – it is almost like a lisping 's'. Below, we will show this sound as 'rh'. Some examples:

suhur – soo-**hoorh**   Jalefer – Zhaa-lé-**fairh**
Cevher – Jev-**hairh**   Dürrünab – Dürh-rü-**nab**
Aynifer – Eye-nee-**fairh**   Ertuğrul – **Erh**-too-rool

Place Names for Pronunciation Practice

Now, here are some places names for you to practise:

Şişli – **Sheesh**-li   Ortaköy – **Orh**-ta-köy
Yıldız – **Yəl**-dəz   Beyoğlu – **Bey**-oh-loo
Topkapı – **Top**-ka-pə   Doğancılar – Doe-**an**-jə-larh
Üsküdar – Üs-kü-**darh**   Yeni Cami – **Yé**-nee **Jaa**-mee
Eminönü – **É**-mee-nö-nü   Keşiş Dağı – **Ké**-sheesh **Daa**-ə
Kadıköy – **Ka**-də-köy   Söğüt – **Sö**-yüt

492

Glossary

abla – elder sister

Ağa – an honorific that was bestowed on some male servants of the Ottoman State, especially the eunuchs who served in the Ottoman Imperial palaces

Alhamdulillah! – "Praise be to Allah!"

Allahu Akbar! – "God is [most] Great!"

anne – mother, 'Mummy'

aslan – lion

baba – father, 'Daddy'

bağlama – a traditional Ottoman stringed instrument, similar to a lute

bast – sanctuary or asylum in a holy place

Bey – an honorific that can be translated as 'Mr'; the customary way of addressing a man politely is to use 'Bey' after his given name(s)

birader – brother

Bismillah – "In the name of Allah"

caïque – an elegant, narrow rowing boat that was used on waterways such as the Bosphorus during the Ottoman period; this word is an anglicised version of the Turkish word *'kayık'*

Caliph – the spiritual head of all Sunni Moslems; from 1517 onwards, the Caliph was the Ottoman Sultan

cami – a mosque

Çelebi – an honorific that can be translated as 'Gentleman'; it followed the given name(s) of a person of distinction (usually a scholar, writer or poet)

Damad – literally means 'bridegroom', but is also used as the title of husbands of Imperial princesses

dede – an informal word meaning 'grandpa'

Efendi – an honorific that can be translated as 'Sir'; it can be used after the given name(s) of a man of distinction, or after the given name(s) of an Imperial prince when addressing him informally *fatwa* – a ruling on a point of Islamic law that is given by a recognised authority

ferace – a long, loose-fitting cloak worn by Ottoman women when outside the home

firman – an Ottoman Imperial edict

Gözde – literally means 'in the eye' (i.e., has caught someone's eye); the title given to a woman who was the favourite of the Sultan

Grand Vizier – the most senior minister in the Ottoman government, a position equivalent to that of prime minister

hadji – a person who has performed the hajj (see below)

hajj – the pilgrimage to Mecca carried out during the twelfth month of the Islamic calendar; making this pilgrimage is the Fifth Pillar of Islam, and all able-bodied Moslems are required to perform it at least once during their lifetime

Hamidiye – connected with or belonging to Sultan Abdülhamid

hammam – a Turkish bath

Hanım – an honorific that can be translated as 'Mrs'; the customary way of addressing a woman politely is to use 'Hanım' after her given name(s)

Hanımefendi – a combination of the honorifics 'Hanım' and 'Efendi'; 'Hanımefendi' can be placed after the given name(s) of any woman to indicate special respect; this word is also part of the respectful form of address for the wife of an Imperial prince

harem – the living quarters in a traditional Moslem home, reserved for women and their immediate male relatives

High Hazinedar – the most senior female administrator in an Ottoman palace, who also acted as palace treasurer; 'High Hazinedar' may be translated as 'Senior Lady Steward'

hodja – a teacher

hotoz – a traditional Ottoman headdress

iftar – the meal taken to break the fast after the sun has set during the holy month of Ramadan

imam – a Moslem prayer leader; his duties and responsibilities are similar to those of a priest or vicar

Inshallah – "God willing"

İkbal – literally means 'luck' (i.e., 'fortunate one'); the title given to a woman who had been elevated from the position of *Gözde* ('Favourite') to that of *İkbal* ('Junior Consort') after her marriage to the Sultan; a *Başikbal* or 'First Junior Consort' was the most senior of the junior consorts

Kaaba – the building surrounding the sacred black stone in the courtyard of the Great Mosque in Mecca; this place is the holiest shrine in Islam

Kadınefendi – a combination of the word *'kadın'* (which means 'woman') and the honorific 'Efendi'; *Kadınefendi* was the title of the first four consorts of an Ottoman sultan

kafes – literally means 'cage'; the word can also be used to refer to the Ottoman tradition whereby Imperial princes were kept under house arrest, or at least strict surveillance, to prevent them from attempting to usurp the throne

kalfa – a housemaid or female attendant in an Ottoman palace; when addressing or referring to such a woman, 'Kalfa' was placed after her given name

kalpak – a traditional item of headwear for Turkic males; it is usually made from felt or lamb's fur

kaplan – a tiger

kaymak – rich clotted cream

Khan – a title bestowed on a Turkic or Mongolian ruler

Khedive – a title bestowed on the hereditary ruler of Egypt by Sultan Abdülaziz in 1867; the Khedive of Egypt was a vassal of the Ottoman Sultan, although after the British invasion of Egypt in 1882 the Sultan's suzerainty over Egypt was only nominal

kismet – literally means 'fate, destiny'

konak – a large mansion or town house, usually built of wood

köfte – a lamb meatball

köşk – a large house, usually built of wood and often outside the city centre; this word is the origin of the English word 'kiosk'

loğusa – a new mother who has given birth during the past forty days *lokum* – Turkish Delight

Mashallah – "It is the will of Allah"; used to express joy, gratitude and praise

meze – a selection of small dishes, similar to Spanish tapas, that is eaten before a main meal

mihrab – the niche in the wall of a mosque that indicates the qibla (see below)

minbar – the pulpit in a mosque, from which the imam addresses the congregation

muqarnas – a form of decoration in Islamic architecture, usually seen in a vaulted ceiling or alcove; in visual effect, it resembles a honeycomb

Muradiye – connected with or belonging to Sultan Murad

nalın – a type of wooden clog worn when taking a bath in a hammam

narguile – a water pipe used for smoking flavoured tobacco

Padishah – 'sovereign ruler'; a word sometimes used for the Ottoman Sultan

Pasha – a title bestowed on high-ranking government officials and military commanders in the Ottoman Empire; although 'Pasha' was not a hereditary title, the word may be translated as 'Lord'

qalamdan – a pen box

qibla – the direction of the Kaaba; Moslems face this direction when praying

Quran – the holy book of Islam, dictated to the Prophet Muhammed by the Angel Gabriel

rakı – a Turkish alcoholic drink, usually flavoured with aniseed and similar in taste to pastis or ouzo

Ramadan – the ninth month of the Islamic calendar; during this month, Moslems traditionally fast between the hours of sunrise and sunset

rehal – a folding wooden book-rest used to hold the Quran

revani – a type of soft semolina cake soaked in syrup

sanjak – an administrative region of the Ottoman Empire, being a subdivision of a vilayet

saray lokması – literally means 'palace morsel'; a dainty round sweet, similar to a very small doughnut soaked in syrup

Selam aleyküm – a form of greeting meaning 'Peace be upon you'; the reply is *"Aleyküm selam"*, meaning 'May peace be upon you, too'

Selamlık – the weekly procession of the Sultan to one of the mosques in İstanbul for Friday prayers

selamlık – the living quarters for men in a traditional Ottoman home

Shahada – the Islamic profession of faith, worded as follows: "I bear witness that I will worship no god but Allah, and that Muhammed is His Messenger"

Sheikh ul-Islam – the religious official in the Ottoman Empire who held the highest rank below that of Caliph; he was appointed by the Sultan, who after 1517 was also the Caliph; the Sheikh ul-Islam was responsible for making pronouncements on Islamic law and maintaining all Islamic institutions

sherbet – a sweet drink made from fruit or flower petals and served chilled

simit – a piece of bread baked in the shape of a ring and covered with sesame seeds

stambouline – a type of frock coat worn by men in the Ottoman Empire

Subhan'Allah! – "Glory be to Allah!"

Sublime Porte – the compound, just outside the gates of Topkapı Palace, that housed the offices of the Ottoman central government

suhur – the meal taken before sunrise during the holy month of Ramadan

Sultan – (1) when placed *before* the given name of a *man*, a title meaning 'sovereign ruler'; (2) when placed *after* the given name(s) of a *woman*, a title meaning 'Imperial princess' (i.e., the daughter of a sultan or Imperial prince)

sura – a chapter of the Quran

süt kardeş – literally means 'milk brother' or 'milk sibling'; the phrase refers either to the child of a wetnurse, or to another woman's child who is being breastfed by that wetnurse; in Ottoman society, the bond between 'milk siblings' was important and binding

Tanzimat – literally means 'reorganisations'; this term is used to describe the reforming edicts promulgated in 1839, during the reign of Sultan Abdülmecid; the 'Tanzimat period' was that between 1839 and 1876, the year in which the first Ottoman constitution was promulgated

temenna – a form of greeting showing a high degree of deference and formality; it involves performing a deep bow and touching one's right hand first to one's lips, then to one's forehead

tuğra – an emblem containing the name of a sultan written in stylised calligraphic script; the *tuğra* was the Sultan's official signature

ulema – the body of Moslem scholars who interpret Islamic canon law and the doctrines of Islam

Usta – an honorific bestowed on high-ranking female servants in the Ottoman Imperial palace; 'Usta' follows a word defining the person's role – for example, the *'Kahveci Usta'* was the 'Mistress of the Coffee Service', and the *'Külhane Usta'* the 'Mistress of the Baths'

valide – a formal word meaning 'mother'; *'validem'* means 'my mother'

Valide Sultan – a title meaning 'Mother of a Sultan'

vilayet – a province in the Ottoman Empire, administered by a governor *(vali)* and made up of *sanjaks*

yalı – a waterfront mansion, usually on the shores of the Bosphorus

yashmak – a Turkish-style veil worn by women during the Ottoman period

zarf – an ornamental metal holder, usually for delicate porcelain coffee cups

zill – a brass finger cymbal

Select Bibliography

Doing the research for this project has been a great pleasure; I have spent many happy hours in the company of these (and many more) fascinating and informative books:

Alloul, Houssine (ed.); Eldem, Edhem (ed.); de Smaele, Henk (ed.). *To Kill a Sultan: A Transnational History of the Attempt on Abdülhamid II (1905)*, 2017

Brookes, Douglas Scott (translator). *The Concubine, the Princess, and the Teacher: Voices from the Ottoman Harem*, 2008

Croutier, Alev Lytle. *Harem: The World Behind the Veil*, 1989

Davis, Fanny. *The Ottoman Lady: A Social History from 1718 to 1918*, 1986

Djemaleddin Bey. *Sultan Murad V: The Turkish Dynastic Mystery, 1876-1895*, 1895

Ellison, Grace; Melek Hanım. *Abdul Hamid's Daughter: The Tragedy of an Ottoman Princess*, 1913

Findley, Carter Vaughn. *Bureaucratic Reform in the Ottoman Empire: The Sublime Porte, 1789-1922*, 2012

Goodwin, Godfrey. *The Private World of Ottoman Women*, 2006

Hanioğlu, M. Şükrü. *The Young Turks in Opposition*, 1995

Haslip, Joan. *The Sultan: The Life of Adbul Hamid II (1842-1918)*, 1973

Işın, Mary. *Sherbet and Spice: The Complete Story of Turkish Sweets and Desserts*, 2013

Kia, Mehrdad. *Daily Life in the Ottoman Empire*, 2011

Osmanoğlu, Osman; Adra, Jamil; Eldem, Edhem. *Genealogy of the Imperial Ottoman Family*, 2011

Öztuna, Yılmaz. *Devletler ve Hanedanlar*, 1989

Riedler, Florian. *Opposition and Legitimacy in the Ottoman Empire: Conspiracies and Political Cultures*, 2011

Sancar, Aslı. *Ottoman Women: Myth and Reality*, 2007

Saz, Leyla. *The Imperial Harem of the Sultans: Daily Life at the Çırağan Palace During the 19th Century: Memoirs of Leyla (Saz) Hanımefendi*, 1994

Shaw, Stanford J.; Shaw, Ezel Kural. *History of the Ottoman Empire and Modern Turkey, Volume II: Reform, Revolution, and Republic: The Rise of Modern Turkey, 1808-1975*, 2002

Vâsıb, Ali. *Memoirs of an Ottoman Prince*, 2017

Wharton, Alyson. *The Architects of Ottoman Constantinople: The Balyan Family and the History of Ottoman Architecture*, 2015

Woods, Henry F. *Spunyarn: From the Strands of a Sailor's Life Afloat and Ashore: Forty-Seven Years Under the Ensigns of Great Britain and Turkey*, 1924

ꙮ ꙮ ꙮ ꙮ ꙮ

In order to gather further information, I made use of a large number of websites – far too many to list or remember; however, the ones I kept returning to are the following:

Turkish Cultural Foundation: www.turkishculture.org

Wikipedia: www.wikipedia.org

ꙮ ꙮ ꙮ ꙮ ꙮ

In addition, I read numerous contemporary newspaper articles that had been published in the archives of the following sites:

The National Library of Australia: https://trove.nla.gov.au

The New York Times: https://archive.nytimes.com

The Times: www.thetimes.co.uk/archive

ꙮ ꙮ ꙮ ꙮ ꙮ

The websites of current Turkish newspapers often publish excellent articles on a wide variety of topics by highly respected historians such as Professor Ekrem Ekinci. I stumbled across many that were useful on the following sites:

www.dailysabah.com
www.hurriyetdailynews.com

❀ ❀ ❀ ❀ ❀

Finally, I had the good fortune to come across and read two very well-researched theses that helped me greatly with a couple of the chapters:

Yanatma, Servet. *The Deaths and Funeral Ceremonies of Ottoman Sultans (From Sultan Mahmud II to Sultan Mehmed VI Vahideddin)*, 2007

Yaşar, Murat. *The Russian Revolution of 1905 in the Ottoman Empire*, 2003

If you have enjoyed my story and would like to find out more about me, my book or would just like to connect on social media, then please visit:

My website:
www.ayseosmanoglu.com

My Facebook page:
www.facebook.com/ayseosmanogluauthor/

My Instagram account:
https://www.instagram.com/ayseosmanoglu2020

Or my Twitter account:
https://twitter.com/AyseGulnev

To see photographs of the characters, and many other pictures from which I took my inspiration for the novel, please look on my pinterest board 'The Gilded Cage on the Bosphorus' at:
www.pinterest.co.uk/aysegulnev/

Printed in Great Britain
by Amazon

43884860R00314